april/50

THE BIG EYE

MAX EHRLICH

THE BIG EYE

GARDEN CITY, NEW YORK

DOUBLEDAY & COMPANY, INC.

The characters and the incidents in this book
are entirely the product
of the author's imagination
and have no relation
to any person or event in real life.

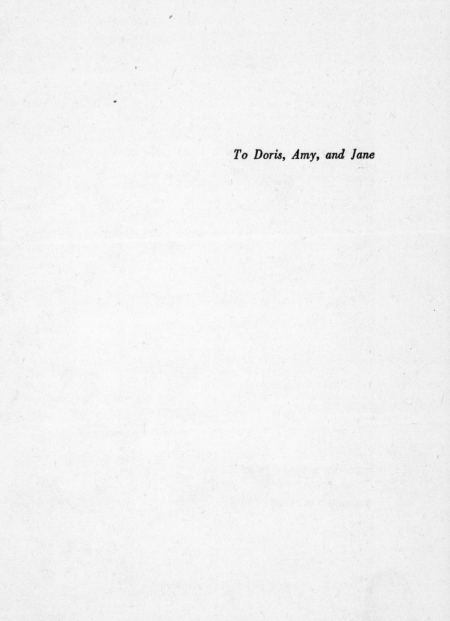

To Doris, Amy, and Jane

THE BIG EYE

1. It was eleven o'clock at night, in the month of November, in the year 1960.

The great stratocruiser, eastbound from California, slowly began to lose altitude. David Hughes shivered a little as he stared at the empty seats yawning ahead of him along the lower deck. His shiver was one of relief as much as anything else. Outside of the stewardess, he was the only passenger in the huge, luxurious belly of the plane, built to accommodate seventy. It had been an eerie experience to ride alone that way for almost three thousand miles.

In a few minutes the plane would dip and settle into a long glide for Idlewild Airport. And then he would be in New York—and with Carol again.

New York.

People spoke of the city in hushed tones these days. David remembered the startled look on the reservation clerk's face, back at Lindbergh Field in San Diego, some five hours ago.

"New York?"

The man had echoed the word, as if in a dream, as though he couldn't believe what he heard. When David turned toward the ramp leading through the gate, he had felt the man's curious eyes on his back. And when he had entered the plane, even the stewardess, a pert little redhead, had stared at him as though he were a little mad.

She had not expected any passengers. Not on the non-stop flight to New York. Not these days.

He had almost felt impelled to explain: "Look, I'm not out of my mind. I didn't expect to be on this plane myself a few hours ago. No one in his right mind would. But it's orders. Something big."

He clutched the bulging brief case close to him and thought of Carol. This was his chance. This was his chance to get her out of New York before it was too late.

The trouble was that it might be too late almost any hour now.

But all that was back on the Coast, five hours ago. Now he pressed his face against the window and looked down at the earth sliding by below. It was drowned in darkness, but this time it wasn't an ordinary kind of darkness. It was blacker, more suffocating. It was a darkness of Fear, of agonizing suspense, of anxious waiting for God knew what.

This was November, in the year 1960.

The stratocruiser's motors changed pitch, became a little louder. David glanced at his wrist watch—the watch his father had given him just before he had entered Harvard University for his Ph.D. in astronomy.

Eleven-three.

That would be eight-three, Coast time. And just about now, back home on the flat top of isolated Palomar Mountain, six thousand feet above the Pacific, things would be humming. The curved observatory dome would be down, and the great electric driving clock motors would be droning as they set the Big Eye and pointed it up into the thin, clear California air.

The Big Eye was the 200-inch reflector telescope, the biggest in the world, a gigantic marvel of steel and glass, encased in a building fifteen stories high. Working with it was part of David's nightly routine, and he was the envy of every other young research astronomer in the country. Yet he could never get used to the Big Eye; he could never get over his awe of it. Its great mirror alone weighed twenty tons. It could trap and hold the light of a candle sixteen thousand miles away in space. It was a million times sharper than the human eye, and ten thousand times more powerful that the little lens with which Galileo Galilei discovered the moons of Jupiter back in the seventeenth century. It reached twice as far into the hungry vault of the universe as its nearest competitor, far beyond the sun and the planets, into the outer boundaries of space itself.

This was the Big Eye, and it took a big man to run it.

David could almost see Dr. Dawson now, standing on the aerial platform, a pygmy on a dizzy flight, moving upward and outward on curving rails toward the mouth of the giant telescope.

Or perhaps he had already gone down the pipe-rail ladder leading into the top of the yawning tube and was not at his instrument desk in the cisternlike observer's cage. Huddled in his fur coat, heavy gloves, and pull-over wool hat, he would look like some futuristic gnome crouched at the tiny revolving desk up in the top of the Big Eye. It was cold up there in the dome when the roof was down, and the sharp night air blasted downward and in.

David could almost hear the Old Man's gentle, detached voice over the telephone coming to him as he stood at the control switchboards on the lower tier.

"All right, David. All short settings tonight. Give me the first star."

This was his boss, the man who had taken him out of the Harvard Observatory three years ago and brought him to Palomar. This was the man they called the Wizard of Palomar, a world-famous celebrity in his own right, whose personal arena stretched two billion light years into the outer limits of the universe. This was Dr. Charles Dawson, the astronomers' astronomer, who spoke the language of Einstein, Eddington, Bohr, Thompson, Chadwick, Zwicky, and De Broglie; who did magic tricks with the mathematics of quantum mechanics; whose contributions to the theory of the expanding universe had won recognition and backing in the great observatories of the world.

Most people thought the Old Man never took the trouble to step off his airy eyrie at the top of the telescope and survey his own planet. They believed that to him the earth was a kind of globular platform, conveniently located so that, like an acrobat, he could plant his feet upon it and swing in an arc through space and stare at the heavens. The newspapers played him up as a cold fish, an ascetic with a special and remote kingdom of his own, a kind of sky giant to whom the interplay of earthy peoples seemed to be a disorderly and rather messy Lilliputian game.

But, reflected David, they didn't know the Old Man as he did.

In the past month something had happened to Dr. Dawson. He'd been absorbed about something he had caught in the Big Eye, something big, spending every night at the telescope and locking himself in his study almost every day. He hadn't told David what his research line was, but he would, all in good time. It was characteristic of the Old Man never to break anything, no matter how important it was, till he had it all down on photoplates and charts, signed, sealed, and delivered.

But there was no doubt about it. Something was in the wind back at Palomar—something big.

"Better fasten your safety belt, sir. We're coming in."

The voice of the stewardess, coming from the shadow in the rear of the cabin, startled him, pulled him abruptly out of his reverie. As if in response to her voice, the sign over the pilot's compartment flashed red: "Fasten Safety Belts—No Smoking." He fumbled with the clasp and felt the belt draw tight just as the stratocruiser hung in space for a moment and then dipped for the descent.

He looked down at the city of New York and drew in his breath at what he saw. He suddenly felt cold; a kind of dread possessed him. No wonder he hadn't been aware that they had reached their destination.

It was unbelievable, unbelievable. . . .

New York, at night, had always been a brilliant sight, man's best imitation of the galaxy of stars. It had always been a bejeweled riot, like a reclining dowager wearing a million diamond tiaras.

Now it was a great eerie blanket of darkness, with only a few illuminated islands breaking through the forbidding expanse.

Mechanically David picked out the islands. The Telecast Building way downtown, a hundred and twenty stories high and the biggest of them all, was still a cluster of light. So was Radio City. But the Empire State Building had only a red cylindrical glow on its top-mast to identify it. Some of the main thoroughfares were dimly lit, crisscrossing through the darkness like chains of old gold. As for the rest of the city, there was a solitary light here, another there, and the occasional flicker of automobile headlights crawling along.

That was all.

The stewardess came down from the lounge on the upper deck and moved forward up the aisle. She watched her only passenger covertly as she did so, trying to figure him out. She was a woman, and curious, and she was wondering why he was going to New York now, of all times. She had tried to draw him out in the rather desultory conversation they had exchanged on the way in, but he had been very vague. Perhaps it was something in the brief case he guarded so jealously. She had offered to take it from him when he had boarded the plane back in Dago. But he had refused to let go of it, despite the fact that there were no other passengers.

Something Very Important, she decided.

Still, he didn't look important. The name on his baggage tag had read simply: "David Hughes. Palomar Observatory." If he *was* an astronomer, he certainly didn't look it, not the way she'd pictured the type. He was young, for one thing, about thirty, and good-looking in a quiet sort of way. There was nothing tweedy about him, he didn't wear a Vandyke beard, he didn't need a haircut, and he didn't wear glasses, as you might expect of a scientist. Or at least what you had been taught to expect from the television screen or the movies. He was tall, with a pair of good, broad shoulders, and his clothes were as well cut as those of any of the young men of Hollywood-to-New-York-and-return, who used to ride her flight.

Now the stewardess leaned over and looked out of the window in front of him and said: "The lights get fewer every trip."

"Many people left in the city, Stewardess?"

"Very few, outside of the soldiers. Most New Yorkers, especially those with somewhere to go out in the country, have left. They really started to evacuate about a month ago." She straightened, and now David Hughes saw that there was a flicker of fear in her eyes. "We're canceling all New York-bound flights in a couple of weeks. I hope nothing happens—before then."

He stared back through the window again. "Funny. About the lights, I mean. They used to warn you that you were coming into the city long before you got there. Now—it just jumps right up at you all of a sudden. This is worse than the brownout."

"Brownout?"

"Oh." He glanced at the stewardess. "You wouldn't remember. It was during the last war. I was just a kid then, and my dad and I flew to Chicago from the old field—La Guardia. They had the curtains drawn, and we weren't supposed to look out, but, well—being a youngster, I peeked. They'd dimmed the lights—afraid of air raids—and the city looked pretty dull. But this?"

Idlewild Airport came up suddenly, a huge white wash of light directly ahead and below. A minute or two later, David, unable to find a porter, was carrying his bag up the wind-swept ramp and into the terminal.

Coming out of the night and into the building was like walking into a frightened beehive. The place was jammed with an excited, nervous crowd. Nobody seemed to be sitting down; everyone was milling about. People were crowded around the reservation counters, their faces strained and eager, trying to get passage out of the city. And always the refrain of the weary ticket clerks:

"I'm sorry. . . . We're sold out solid. . . . Every flight booked. . . . All booked up. . . . I'm sorry, I know you've got a priority, but we won't be able to accommodate you for weeks. . . . Yes, sir, if we get a cancellation we'll try to call you. . . . I'm sorry, madam, we're all booked up. . . ."

The voices of the crowd were taut and tense and shrill. They rose and fell in a frightened, unnatural babel. They were urgent, they demanded, they wouldn't take no for an answer.

But the answer was always no.

No one was in the terminal to meet a plane. The airliners coming in from the North, the West, and South were all empty. Only those that were leaving the city were gorged with human freight. The Fear was upon the city and the people of the city. Every face in the terminal was stamped with it, branded with it, so that each was a carbon copy of every other face. The Fear was a kind of Personality, omnipotent, overshadowing all other personalities, making them neutral. It was written in the eyes of the people there, it quavered in their voices, it motivated their restless and agitated movements. It walked with them, stood with them, sat with them, like their own shadows.

It wasn't just a state of mind. It was a Presence. You could almost smell the Fear. It had feel and texture, like a stifling shroud. It had movement, too, like a slow, creeping paralysis, reaching clammy fingers into every nook and crevice of the building, permeating the place.

It was there, and it was inescapable. David felt it seep into his flesh and bones. His skin prickled a little; his mouth suddenly felt dry. He carried his bag to a phone booth and dialed a number.

"David! DAVID!"

It was good, hearing her voice again. He felt a surge of quick hunger. It had been lonely at the observatory, damned lonely. Three months straight, working nights and sleeping days, without a woman. Three months straight—without Carol.

"Where are you?" She was breathless, almost incoherent. "David, what on earth are you doing in New York? Where are you?"

"At Idlewild Airport. Just got off the plane. I was afraid you'd be down at the studios, broadcasting."

"I just got in, darling. This very minute. The phone rang—and there *you* were. But what are you doing in New York, of all places, *now?*"

David hesitated. His free hand tightened on his brief case in a kind of muscular reflex brought about by Carol's question. He couldn't tell her, he couldn't tell anyone. He had strict orders. Security. He was there for a reason, a reason so big that it fright-

ened him when he even thought about it. He evaded Carol's
question. But she was insistent.

"Darling, what are you so mysterious about?"

"I can't tell you."

There was a pause at the other end of the wire. "Oh," she said
finally. "It's hush-hush."

"Something like that. But that's only one reason I'm in town. The
other is you, Carol. I've been writing and writing you to come to
the Coast. Now I'm going to take you back with me."

"But, David, I told you why I can't go. You know why I've got to
stay——"

"Yes, I know," he interrupted. "But enough's enough. When I
fly back I'm taking you with me, and that's final!"

She was silent for a moment. Then: "We'll talk about it when
you get here, darling. And, David, David, don't stop anywhere, for
anything. Come right up to the apartment."

"Okay. But what about a hotel?"

"I'll make reservations for you at the Rutherford. You can check
in there later."

"The Rutherford? Never heard of it."

"It's a small hotel—one of the few still open in town. All the big
ones are closed and boarded up—the Waldorf, the Park Central, the
Ambassador. They've been closing in droves for the last month,
ever since the trouble began. And, David——"

"Yes?"

"Try to get a cab up here. There's no other way to get around,
unless you walk. The subways and busses stopped running a week
ago. And oh—you'll have to walk up ten flights."

"I will? Why?"

"Our elevator man quit on Wednesday. He's visiting a second
cousin somewhere out in Kansas." She tried hard to be light.
"Everybody's digging up distant relatives out in the country these
days."

He laughed and said he was only thirty and he thought he could make the ten flights in slow stages, and hung up. Then he walked through the terminal and out of the gate. A big black air-line limousine waited for him, to take him to the Forty-second Street terminal. The other limousines, coming from the city, were loaded with passengers. But he was the only passenger in his car, headed for New York.

The driver, a big, beefy, red-faced man, raised the telephone receiver on the dashboard and spoke briefly to the terminal in town. Then he swung the big black car onto the Van Wyck Expressway and gave it the gas. Theirs was the only car in the right-hand lane, and they raced along at high speed. But the other lane, moving away from the city, was clogged with cars, bumper to bumper. Horns honked continuously, and the drivers cut in and out of traffic.

They're all going in the same direction, away from town, thought David, and they're all in a hell of a hurry.

He stared at the long line of headlights hugging the curves of the parkway like a great illuminated snake.

"They've been heading out on Long Island like this for days," said the driver. "Anywhere, so long as it's away from the city. Babylon, Sayville, Southampton, Montauk Point—the further, the better. You'll find the same kind of traffic moving into Jersey, up into New England and New York State. And I don't blame 'em."

"Still, you seem to be sticking it out," said David.

"Yeah." The driver lit a cigarette, and his fingers trembled a little. "But don't get me wrong, mister. I'm just as scared as they are. The company's giving me triple pay for staying on the job, and they flew my wife and three kids out of town, but I'm going to quit in a couple of days anyway. I don't like money enough to stick my neck out like this."

David glanced at the driver's face. It had that same taut, tense look, the same haunted look he had seen at the airport. He felt a little queasy. He knew that the same look had settled on his own face now, like a cold gray mask.

You couldn't be here and not be afraid. Not now. . . .

He tried hard to be casual. "Where are they going to find room for all these people?"

The driver shrugged. "I don't know. You take the island here now, mister. It's jammed with extra people, all from the city. Must be half a million of 'em anyway. They're living in shacks, out in the open, anywhere. It's sure a hell of a situation. They declared martial law out here yesterday."

"That bad, eh?"

"Yeah. And worse in the city. They've got a couple of Army divisions in there now. Just to keep order. But as soon as everybody's out, I figure they'll move the soldiers out. As it is, they're sitting ducks right now." The driver shook his head. "You know about all the rumors flying around these days, the funny things happening that nobody can explain. You know who's behind it as well as I do, and what they're leading up to."

Yes, thought David, I know. That's why I'm here now. And that's why I won't be here tomorrow morning. His fingers seemed to perspire damply on the leather of his brief case as he caught the eye of the driver in the reflector mirror.

If you knew what I knew, driver, you'd turn this big black limousine around and follow those other cars to wherever they were going, away from the city.

The man at the wheel continued to talk. He was almost garrulous; he seemed grateful for someone to talk to. It was easy to guess that he had driven an empty car back to the main terminal time after time, that David's presence was a surprise.

"You take those GIs now," he said sympathetically. "Those poor bastards up ahead in town. A lot of 'em couldn't take it—went over the hill—deserted. They shot a couple of 'em last night." He shook his head. "I don't blame 'em for cracking up. It's the waiting that drives you nuts. It's beginning to get me too."

They continued down Van Wyck Expressway and into Queens Boulevard, racing by the slowly moving line of traffic on their left. David stared at the residential sections of Queens on each side of the main artery. They presented an eerie sight, a kind of macabre fantasy. They were like vast stone-and-wooden graveyards, dark and empty.

But the houses were not really empty. The Fear was there, living in every one of them. The only sign of movement was on the highway itself, the solid line of cars crawling along, bumper to bumper, impatient of delay, heading east—east and away.

The limousine sped across the Fifty-ninth Street bridge, into the silent and dark and dying city, and swung over to East River Drive. David looked hard at the black buildings and towers etched against the moon-washed sky. The few illuminated windows he could see were isolated, far apart, conspicuous in their loneliness.

And the Fear was the only tenant in these darkened office buildings too.

And then, at last, they passed the great area between Forty-eighth and Forty-second streets—the permanent headquarters of the United Nations.

With a kind of morbid fascination, David watched it slip by. There it was, the great international city within a city, the terraces, the auxiliary buildings and apartments, and finally, the main UN skyscraper itself.

The building towered there now, dark and empty and silent, a great massive mausoleum. It seemed to glower at them balefully as they went by. David fancied that the grass on the terraces now grew rank, and the hedges and foliage, once trim and clipped, would now be ragged and unkempt.

It was a symbol of failure now, a great empty House of the Dead, a house of shattered hopes, of the blighted dreams of mankind.

Back in 1946, when David had been a boy of sixteen, the delegates of the nations had first met on the site of the World's Fair and at Lake Success to bring about the salvation of humanity and the security of the world. There the giants of a decade and a half ago, Molotov, Byrnes, and Bevin, as well as the Greats and the near Greats of the other countries, had met to resolve what hitherto had been considered insoluble problems.

They had begun with fine words, and noble phrases, and good

intentions. But Byrnes and Molotov and Bevin had haggled and fought to begin with, and so had their successors, down through the years, here in this magnificent new setting on East River Drive. Marshall and Acheson, Stalin and Vishinsky, Truman, and now the President and *his* aides and advisers. They had all seen a vision in the beginning, but as time went on the vision had grown blurred and finally died, and at last it was gone. The cold war had grown colder with every passing day, and now it was ready to burst through the bottom of the thermometer.

And finally, a month ago, they had closed the magnificent buildings. The delegates had broken, pointing fingers at each other in recrimination, accusing each other of greed, of imperialism, of stubbornness, of bad faith. And they had broken irrevocably, and for good. The representatives had melted away and gone home, and they had closed the buildings and bolted the doors, and taken down the flags of the nations which had once flown proudly in the great courtyard, and abandoned it.

Now the UN stood there, a series of stone ghosts on East River Drive, seedy and unkempt, the symbol of a Great Failure.

And it had been the Great Failure that had brought about the Great Fear.

Now—*everyone* had the bomb.

Yes, thought David, *they* have it, and *we* have it. And where do we go from here? What now?

The driver turned and saw David staring back at the buildings. "Yeah, look at the joint," he said. "Many's the time I hauled these striped-pants diplomats from Idlewild to the UN. Big shots from all over the world. And where are they now? Hiding in caves, maybe, I dunno. All I know is we've got millions of dollars' worth of real estate back there, but it's not worth a nickel now."

"Maybe they'll open it again some day," suggested David hopefully. "Maybe they'll still be able to get together."

"You mean that conference the Secretary of State's having over in Russia right now?"

"Yes."

"Nuts," the driver snorted. "Not a chance. It's too late. People have gone crazy. They're set on blowing themselves up, and nobody's going to stop them. It's like watching a car without brakes rolling down a hill toward a cliff. Everybody's standing around, hollering 'Stop, stop,' but nobody's doing anything to stop it. The only question is, who's going to blow up who?" The beefy man lowered his voice. "And between you and me, mister, the Russians have already started it. They've already started to give us the business right now."

"What do you mean?"

"You know what I mean. The stories that are going around. The Reds are supposed to have something extra, something that we haven't been able to figure out yet, and they're using it right now. Look at all the funny things that are happening all of a sudden. The earthquake in Dallas and another in Montreal. The way the television and radio has been blacking out all of a sudden."

David was silent for a moment. "And you think the Russians are responsible?"

"Who else?" The driver looked at him, a little incredulous. "Things like this don't happen all of a sudden, out of left field. The Reds have got something bigger, maybe better, than the bomb. That's what everybody is saying. What about that atom bomb that went off down in Texas? Blew three towns right off the map. You can't tell me that was any accident, mister. The Russians are jabbing at us now, trying to panic us and throw us off balance. And they'll be winding up for their Sunday punch any minute now."

David listened, fascinated. This air-line driver didn't know it, but he was putting his finger on the reason why he, David Hughes, was in New York right now with a locked and bulging brief case.

"And that ain't all, mister," said the man, leaning toward David confidentially. "I'll tell you something else, and it's straight from the horse's mouth. The Reds have found a way to stop our rockets and jets the minute they're airborne."

David stared at him. "That's just rumor."

"Yeah." The driver almost snarled at him. "Listen, mister. I'll let you in on a little secret. I drive this car for the air line. And naturally, once in a while, I drive pilots and some of the crews in to town. I've heard 'em talking in the back seat, and what they've said is enough to make a guy's hair stand on end."

"What do you mean?"

"I mean that the instruments on the stratocruisers have been going haywire, crazy. The radar, too. Some of the boys have had to navigate as blind as a bat. You think those crashes you've been reading about just *happened?* Nuts! The Reds *made* 'em happen. They've got some kind of magnetic gimmick in the air, and they've been turning it on and off. What do you think's going to happen to our jets and rockets if we let 'em go? They're all operated by instruments, aren't they? If we let a few go and the Russians use this gimmick, our stuff'll land in Siberia instead of in Moscow. Hell, maybe the Reds can make 'em turn right around and come back!"

David listened, stunned by what he heard. His face was impassive, but his mind was racing furiously. This air-line employee *knew.* He didn't realize how *much* he knew. David hadn't known it himself until early that evening. He had heard it from a source on a much higher level, and he would hear more about it tomorrow morning, at a meeting place he did not yet know.

He shuddered to think of the reaction, the panic, that would sweep the country if the information volunteered by the garrulous driver suddenly became widespread and public knowledge.

The man wheeled his limousine west, up Forty-second Street, and finally brought the car to a stop in front of the air-line terminal. And as he opened the door he growled:

"Those goddamn fools back there. Those diplomats. They should have kept trying. They should have sat down on their striped pants and *made* it work! The goddamn stupid fools!"

David left the car and went into the terminal to check his return reservations. One look was enough to discourage him. What he saw was a repeat performance of the terminal at Idlewild. The same milling crowd, the same weary clerks, the same babel of frightened voices:

"But I've got to get out! I've got to! You've got to get me a reservation, clerk!"

"I've got Priority One. Right here. Doesn't that mean something?"

"Try the trains? What trains? Look through the window, clerk. They've closed the gates across the street at Grand Central and shut down the ticket windows!"

"Look, I've been down here two days, waiting for a cancellation. You can't tell me no cancellation has come through! One must have come through!"

"Listen, clerk, I've got a wife and daughter. I've got to get them out, I've got to! I'll take three seats on any plane, going anywhere, as long as it's out of town!"

Yes, thought David, I've seen it before, heard it before.

The same voices, the same people with the same pale and frightened faces, surging forward toward the counters until they were checked and pushed back by grim, white-helmeted military police.

This was where the Fear was the most paralyzing, its hand the clammiest, its clutch the tightest.

This was the city.

David hung onto his bag and brief case, elbowed his way through the crowd, and rode down the escalator. He pushed the glass doors open and stepped out into the dark, wind-blown night.

For a moment he stood irresolute and stared west, up Forty-second Street. His skin prickled at what he saw. It was a sight that no man could ever forget, a memory that could never really fade.

The towering buildings rose on either side, their dark windows, like sightless eyes, looking down at the dimly lit canyon below. It was quiet here—strangely quiet—a place brooding, barely whispering with life, waiting to die. Not a vehicle was in sight, and the only sign of movement in the street itself was a few old newspapers which the wind had snatched from the gutter and propelled along the road. David could hear them rustle as they drifted along.

Finally one or two civilians and soldiers came along, huddled deep into their coats against the wind. The sharp click-clack of their heels on the sidewalk echoed and re-echoed dismally.

David turned up his own coat collar and walked west, toward Times Square.

He passed the darkened Fifth Avenue Library and suddenly became conscious that on his left there was a single dull red light hanging high in the sky, like a displaced moon. It was the glowing top of the Empire State Building. Finally, between Sixth and Broadway, he began to see signs of life. A taxicab and then two Army cars, their headlights slashing through the darkness. A few more people, a bar and grill open, a restaurant. They were dimly illuminated inside, and what patrons there were within seemed to be soldiers. Outside, the neon and electric signs, the great spectaculars, were dark—dead.

It's the biggest and the weirdest graveyard in the world, thought David.

David turned right at Times Square and walked up Broadway. He looked for a cab but saw none. Carol lived up on Cathedral Parkway, West 110th Street. And, as she had said, not even the subways were running.

There was nothing to do but walk.

This was the theater district. He could make out some of the darkened marquee signs—the hits that had been playing here not much longer than a month ago. *Stepping Along*—the big musical down the street on one side of the deserted Astor Hotel. *F.D.R.*— the biographical drama of a President whom many people still remembered and whose great dream had now gone up in smoke. There was a bit of grim irony, too, in a huge theater ad that said: *"The Narrow Alley* . . . A Great Tragedy . . . Coming Soon . . ."

"A Great Tragedy . . . Coming Soon . . ."

And then suddenly Times Square became suffused in an eerie glow—a bluish-white wash of light. Startled, David turned to look at the source.

It was a huge television screen, high up on the side of one of the buildings. One of the networks operated it as an advertisement, bringing the Broadway crowds athletic events, news, dramas, and political speeches. It had been an instant and tremendous success. David remembered reading, back in Palomar, that they had been forced to rope off the entire Times Square area while two hundred thousand people jammed the streets to watch the last world's heavyweight championship fight.

He blinked at the blinding light, and another memory stirred in him. The television screen was located on the exact spot where the big Camel cigarette sign once stood. As a boy he had been fascinated by the old sign. There had been a smiling man blowing smoke rings across Broadway. When the air was calm, the rings floated across like huge white doughnuts. But when it was windy, the man in the sign kept smiling, but all he could blow out were wispy puffs of smoke.

A small knot of pedestrians and soldiers stopped on a corner to stare at the screen, and David paused with them. For a moment he wondered why the television screen was working, since there were so few spectators. Then he realized that the same images would be seen on a network system, on millions of television sets from coast to coast, and that operating the sign would make little difference in the over-all cost. His mind slipped back to the observatory at Palomar for a moment. Francis, the steward, who had been with the Old Man for twenty years, would no doubt be taking in whatever this show was going to be on the set in the reception room on the main floor. Francis was a great video and radio fan.

The glare softened into a dull silver background, and then a title in red letters appeared:

NEWS OF THE WORLD

The background dissolved into a scene showing a green-colored globe of the world spinning on its axis. Then came the voice of an invisible announcer:

"News of the world! A five-minute documentary summary brought to you every night at this time by the GENERAL TEXTILE CORPORATION, makers of DOWNYSOFT blankets and DOWNYSOFT towels.

"And now, here is your telecaster—Arthur Morrow!"

The spinning globe segued into a scene of a paneled study lined with bookshelves. A gray-haired man sat at a desk. He smiled at David and the others. Then the smile disappeared, and he looked professionally grim. He stared straight into the eyes of his watchers and then spoke.

"Good evening. This is Arthur Morrow. Tonight the world waits and wonders. The tension grows, becomes almost unbearable. And on the end of everyone's tongue is the same terrible question: 'Will it come? Will it really come at last?'"

The man on the screen leaned back in his leather chair, shook his head.

"No one knows. We can only hope and pray that in this last desperate moment Man will come to his senses. Even now, at this very moment, Mr. William Allison, our Secretary of State and special envoy of the President, is on his way to the Kremlin to meet in extraordinary session with Mr. Bakhanov, the Foreign Minister of the Soviet Union. In a moment we hope to telecast this historic event for you direct from the new Kremlin at Kirensk, in Asiatic Russia. Permission for this strange raising of the censorship curtain comes from the Soviet government. It is their claim that they are doing this to illustrate to us, and to the world, that it, too, is willing to compromise. At any rate, they are making much of it in their propaganda line. . . ."

Someone in the knot of spectators spoke up. It was a young soldier.

"So Allison's meeting Bakhanov. Geez, I hope they work out something!"

"I doubt it," said an older man. "Talk, talk, talk. Nothing but talk. That's all we've heard for years. The way it's going to end up, we'll talk ourselves into six feet under."

"Well, anyway," said the soldier, "nothing's gonna happen while they're sitting around a table."

"Oh no?" The older man laughed harshly. "Listen, sonny, ever hear of a man named Hull?"

"Hull?"

"Yeah. I guess you wouldn't remember, sonny. You were still pretty wet behind the ears. But Hull was our Secretary of State then. Back in '41, it was. He was sitting around a table with two Jap diplomats, and no one thought anything would happen. Not right then, anyway. Then all of a sudden—wham! Right in the middle of everything, the Japs let us have it at Pearl Harbor."

David listened and remembered. He'd been only eleven then. But he remembered his father, white-faced and shaking in anger, turning off the radio. He remembered the bewilderment, the surprise, the disbelief. The Stab in the Back, they had called it then.

David shivered a little as the gray-haired man on the screen went on:

> *"It seems incredible that the peoples of the earth stand on the brink of holocaust tonight, that the lights have gone out in the great cities of the world. Tonight, like a great colossus, the Soviet Union stands astride Europe and Asia, while we have declared our defense responsibility through the whole of the Western Hemisphere, from Canada, through South America. Tonight the Soviet Union, as well as ourselves, has the bomb. And tonight the world waits for the zero hour—the hour that no one wants to come but everyone expects to come. . . ."*

A soldier on David's left muttered, "Yeah, it's the waiting. It's the waiting that's tough. It's the waiting that's driving everybody crazy."

"What I want to know is, Frank, what are *we* waiting for?" His companion was emphatic. "Why don't we throw it first, before they do? Somebody's going to throw it first, and it better be us. Or else . . . !"

"You can say that again." A sergeant was talking now. "Listen, you guys, I heard something, and it ain't from the latrine either. The Reds are supposed to have an atom cocktail planted in one of these here buildings, or down in the subway somewhere. I dunno, there may be ten of 'em, or a hundred, for all I know. They've got some kind of gadget where they can set 'em off from Moscow without getting off their fannies."

There was silence for a moment. The faces of the men looked white and set and unreal in the glare of the television screen. Then someone in the rear said:

"Maybe they're touching off a few rockets right now, headed F.O.B. New York. How the hell do *we* know? Why take a chance? Let's give it to 'em and get it over with!"

That was the popular opinion. Everyone said that when the pay-off came—not *if* it came, but *when* it came—New York would get it first.

It was the biggest city in the world, the prime target. It would make the loudest noise, illustrate the power of the enemy in the most potent manner, create the most dramatic devastation. Aside from Washington, which was now a ghost capital by orders of the Army, the big city had completed a state of evacuation much farther along than any other. It was possible that the Soviet *might* pick Detroit, or Chicago, or St. Louis, or Los Angeles, if they threw the first punch.

But everyone said, everyone whispered, New York. That was the one, the big one; that was where it would come first.

The telecaster up in the illuminated screen was saying:

"In retrospect, the catastrophe that faces us now was not a matter of science, of atomic fission, of research or manufacturing techniques. It was a matter of the human mind, its ability to adjust itself to the fact that it had unleashed a terrible and

destructive power, and that men must either live with it, or be destroyed by it. But two decades were a pitifully short time to wipe away the accumulated mental debris, the accumulated prejudices and suspicions which had been bred in men for centuries. And we failed. For a while we thought we had succeeded. There was the United Nations, the various conferences of the Foreign Ministers at Washington, London, Paris, and Moscow. And after that the international control commissions and the nations' agreement to disarm. But then came the arguments over the veto power—the differences over the extent of inspection beyond national boundaries—the finger-pointing, the accusations of bad faith and subterfuge. And finally, the great blow—the dissolution of the United Nations—and separation.

"We might have succeeded, we could have succeeded with sincerity and mutual trust, and an awareness of how much we had to succeed.

"But we failed. And now, the world faces the consequences."

A phone rang on the telecaster's desk. He picked up the receiver, listened a moment, nodded, and hung up.

Then he looked directly at David and the other men on the Broadway street corner and said simply:

"We take you now to the new Kremlin in Kirensk, Russia."

The television screen crackled, sputtered a little, faded, and finally blacked out. The darkness smothered David and the others huddled with him in an eerie, impenetrable blanket. They waited silently, shivering a little, listening to the sharp wind whining up the deserted side streets.

And then the glow came to the screen again and a voice with a Russian accent said:

"This is Kirensk, capital of the Union of Socialist Soviet Republics."

The screen showed a street in the Soviet capital in bright daylight. A crowd of people lined the curb, waiting impassively. They seemed quiet and well disciplined, not surging forward like American crowds. But perhaps the line of Red soldiers guarding the approach had something to do with their good behavior.

The invisible telecaster spoke briefly again:

> *"The crowd outside the new Kremlin awaits the coming of the American envoy, Mr. Allison, to confer with the Soviet Foreign Minister, Bakhanov."*

"Well, I'll be damned," commented the soldier named Frank. "Look at the people in that crowd. They look just like we do." He giggled nervously. "I swear to Christ, that big guy on the left with the fur hat looks just like my uncle Phil out in Detroit."

"Sure they look the same as we do," said the sergeant acidly. "What'd you expect 'em to have—horns?" He proffered a word of wisdom. "Hell, what's so tough about them? We can take 'em any time we want to, if you ask me. They put their legs in their pants legs one at a time just like we do, don't they?"

"Geez," a civilian said. "Look at their faces. What do you know? They're just as scared as *we* are!"

The voice of the Russian telecaster came again:

> *"Now the American envoy is arriving."*

An armored car came into view, bristling with Red Army men. It was followed by a huge black limousine, and another armored car followed the limousine. The camera moved with the procession. It stopped at a big gate in front of a building set back behind a wall. Soldiers pushed the onlookers away. A gray-faced man got out of the limousine, carrying a brief case. The gate opened, and he walked between two lines of grim Russian soldiers standing at attention. The gate closed behind him.

The Russian telecaster concluded:

> *"Thus the envoys of two great powers meet to confer in this great crisis. We of the Soviet Union want no war, and neither*

does America, nor any of the other countries of the world. Let us hope that the envoy of your great country and mine come to an understanding on this historic occasion."

That was the trouble, thought David. Everyone hoped the same thing, but nobody did anything about it. The grim game of waiting, the tension, could not go on forever. The fear of men for each other had been like a progressive madness, a subtle and cumulative poison seeping into the blood stream, and there was a limit to how much the patient could take, a limit to human endurance.

The scene shifted back to the United States, back into the paneled study again.

The gray-haired telecaster was at his desk, staring down at Times Square. He began to speak again, when a young man came from the left of the television screen and gave the man at the desk a note. He glanced at it briefly and then looked grimly at the men on the street corner:

"I have a special bulletin here. Professor Albert Whaley, world-famous authority on atomic fission, and one of the scientists who aided in the preparation of the original Hiroshima bomb, committed suicide tonight. He was seventy years old."

The telecaster paused for a moment. Then he nodded and smiled —a wooden, professional smile. You could see that his heart wasn't in it, that the smile was merely a signature, a way of signing off.

"This is your telecaster, Arthur Morrow, speaking for the Downysoft Corporation and bidding you all—good night!"

The paneled study swung around on a turntable and disappeared, and the commercial came onto the screen in colors. First there was a household scene. A motherly-looking woman opened the door of a linen closet and took a blue blanket from the top shelf. She examined the label and as she did, the camera panned down to the label—DOWNYSOFT! The woman nodded, smiled, and shut the door.

An announcer crowed:

"*Yes—it's DOWNYSOFT—DOWNYSOFT blankets!*"

The camera followed the woman into a nursery. Tenderly she placed the blanket on a tousle-haired child sleeping in a crib. Then she caressed the blanket and smiled again.

The announcer said in an unctuous voice:

"*For that soft and intimate touch—it's DOWNYSOFT. DOWNYSOFT blankets and DOWNYSOFT towels!*"

The first scene whirled out of sight on the turntable, and a new scene whirled in. This time it was the interior of an orchid-colored bathroom. A tall, lissome blonde who looked like the third from the left in a chorus line was standing in front of a glass-enclosed stall shower. She was dressed in a bright orange silk robe, and from the way it clung to her curvaceous body it was plain that she wore nothing else underneath. She turned to a small towel shelf and took out two towels. She hung them carefully on a rack, caressed them with her fingers, and smiled. The camera panned down to a close-up of the labels again.

Then the blonde began to take off her robe in a kind of televised strip tease. First there was a view of a smooth back, with the curved suggestion of the girl's reasts barely showing. Then, just as she dropped her robe, she opened the door of the stall shower and stepped behind it. She stood there for a moment in a side view, every feature of her body etched sharply in silhouette behind the translucent glass. Then she reached up and turned on the shower.

The announcer crowed again:

"*Yes! For that soft and intimate touch—it's always— DOWNYSOFT! DOWNYSOFT blankets and DOWNYSOFT towels!*"

The man on David's right spoke softly. "Soft and intimate touch is right. Oh, brother!"

"Geez!" said his companion. "Geez, Joe! That blonde! How would you like to have *that* little number?"

David felt a little sick in his stomach. He turned up his coat collar and started to walk up Broadway, his feet echoing dismally on the empty pavement, past the dull marquees, the empty boarded-up stores, the dead neon signs. The wind whistled down the darkened canyon, and its cold breath, too, smelled of the Fear.

2. At Columbus Circle, the traffic lights, blinking sentinels on the dark-shrouded, desolate streets, continued to operate stubbornly. As they went red, green, red, green, the click of their mechanism as they changed sounded abnormally loud in the brooding silence.

David Hughes watched the lights break into a long illuminated V, one arm of lights extending up Central Park West, another up Broadway. They changed in a kind of staggered beat and cadence, red and green, red and green, winking glassily in a ghostly and grotesque stone-and-steel fairyland.

It seemed fantastic to David that he was here now, in the city of New York, a lone pedestrian walking through a wind-swept graveyard, committed to the most dangerous and most important mission of his life.

Ten hours ago his day had started like any other day.

A rough hand shook David.

"Wake up, Dave."

Dave tried to push the hand away and draw the covers back over him. But the shaking persisted, and finally he opened his eyes to look sleepily at the grinning, freckled face of his roommate, Joe Morgan.

"Rise and shine, Reverend," said Morgan. "Time the priest was preparing for the pulpit."

Morgan, a long string bean of a man with a constant grin under his sandy hair, was the spectrograph expert at Palomar. He had worked with David at the Harvard Observatory, later served a term at Yerkes, then at Mount Wilson, and finally hooked onto the Big Eye under the Old Man. Like David, he was a bachelor, and the two of them lived in the dormitory, an ascetic, monklike place of soundproofed walls and doors and black curtains, for men who slept all day and worked all night. They called the place the "Monastery" and each other "priests."

As for Morgan's reference to the "pulpit," that was David's special province. It was the nickname for the telescope control board, where David flicked switches or pushed buttons to turn the dome, open it, and swing the Big Eye onto a star, at the whim and direction of the Old Man up in the capsule at the top of the tube.

"Just came back from the observatory," said Morgan as David began to shave. "And the Old Man's acting mighty strange. Dave, what the hell is going on, anyway?"

"I don't know."

"You're his assistant," said Morgan. "You ought to know."

David turned to Morgan. "I'm just as much in the dark as you are. He hasn't told me a thing, and his own wife doesn't even know what he's up to. He's found something, Joe, I'm sure he has. But you know the Old Man, you know how he's acted about these things before. Until he gets it on the line, photographs, calculations, and theory, with a solid conclusion to go with it, everyone on the observatory staff can just keep on whistling."

Morgan lit a cigarette and flung the match into the wastebasket. "Maybe. But I think this is something big, Dave, much bigger than anything that's happened before. I've never seen the Old Man act like this. Working all night and all day, skipping meals, taking an hour or two of sleep when he's almost dead of exhaustion. You can almost see his cheekbones popping out from under his skin." He paused and threw away his cigarette. "You know what happened to me a little while ago at the observatory?"

"What?"

"I'm supposed to be the spectrograph man here. But I tried to get into the spectrograph room in the telescope girder, and it was locked. Had some plates there I wanted to see. The Old Man was in there, and he told me to go away. Go away, mind you! He sounded a little wild, like a jealous kid guarding a toy. I don't know, I've never heard him talk like that before."

David was thoughtful. "It could be the times, Joe. The trouble with Russia, everything. Everybody's snapping at each other these days. You couldn't find a calmer, more even-tempered man than Dr. Dawson. But the generals have been hounding him, running him ragged, for months."

"Yes, I know." Morgan spoke soberly now. "They've been taking the Old Man off his mountain every now and then, and he doesn't like it. That trip to New Mexico on the rocket-projectile thing— that Maryland job. He's kicked like a steer each time, but he's had to go. And those security guards they've got posted around the place. You'd think the Russians were going to drop paratroopers right through the dome."

David adjusted his tie. "Hear anything new on the saber-rattling up at the observatory, Joe?" He spoke casually, almost too casually.

Morgan shook his head. "Same old stuff. The fuse is lying right out there in the open, inviting somebody to light it. Francis had the radio on, and to hear the commentators tell about it, this little two-bit planet is scheduled to blow up any minute now." He grinned a little sickly. "It's funny."

"*What's* funny?"

"I don't know. Up here, on this nice, remote, clinically clean mountain, it's hard to get excited about this cold war. But I was down in San Diego last night—and it's different. The place is like a morgue, most of the lights are out. And that suits me fine!"

David stared at him, and Morgan grinned. "Professionally, I mean. Or, to repeat the old saying, it's an ill wind that blows no good. And I'll show you why." He reached into a box he had brought from the observatory and took out a number of photographic plates. "Here. Take a look at these, Dave. Developed 'em a couple of days ago."

David picked up a plate, looked at it. It didn't look like much, a few faint smudges of silver granules on a film of gelatin. "You haven't got it labeled, Joe. What is it?"

"Messier 31. One of our more skittish island universes, way about beyond the suburbs of our own star system. You see how clear it is?"

David nodded, and Morgan picked up another plate, gave it to him. "Here's the same thing, taken months ago, before the lights went out in Dago."

This spectrograph plate was fogged. "Mostly the scattered blue light of mercury," explained Morgan. "From the advertising signs in San Diego. It's been ruining our plates. Remember the last mess with the 100-inch eye at Mount Wilson? Los Angeles was growing too fast for the observatory there. The lights began to creep way out in the suburbs, making a nebula of their own and cluttering up the sky. That white, acrid haze they called smog climbed right over Mount Wilson, dimming the sky nebulae." David returned the plate to Morgan, and he restored it to the box. "And now we've got the same thing, Dave. San Diego's grown almost as big as Los Angeles in the last ten years, and conditions have been getting worse every day because of those damned lights."

"I know," said David. "I went down into Dago with the Old Man when he delivered a speech before the San Diego-California Club, complaining about the new neon and electric signs they were putting up. Asked them for an ordinance to stop it."

"And what did they say?"

"Oh, they were very polite about it. But they said the Old Man was asking too much, he was trying to stop progress."

"And what did the Old Man say?" asked Morgan.

David grinned. "You should have been there, Joe. It was wonderful. The Old Man really laid into 'em. Told them that if they were more interested in advertising sausages and soap and the latest movie epic than in finding out the secrets of the universe, then they could have it. If *that* was progress, he told them, he was going back to his mountain, where the air was clean, and never step off it again. Then he walked out."

"Well," said Morgan thoughtfully, "the Old Man got his wish about the lights. They've gone out here, and everywhere else, and God knows if anyone'll ever get a chance to turn 'em on again. And if *that's* progress," he added a little bitterly, "we'd better start retreating backward, damned quick!"

The phone rang, and David answered. It was Francis, the steward, calling from the observatory.

"Dr. Dawson wants you in his office right away, Dr. Hughes."

David frowned. It was only eleven-thirty in the morning, an unusual hour to get a call from the Old Man.

"What's up, Francis?"

"I don't know, sir." The steward sounded excited. "General Hawthorne is due here at any moment. He's flown in from the East, and it's some kind of extraordinary conference. I've never seen Dr. Dawson so agitated."

"And you're sure he wants me there?"

"Yes, Dr. Hughes. At once!"

Francis hung up, and David, puzzled, told his roommate briefly what had happened.

Morgan was impressed. "Sounds like big stuff, Dave. Hawthorne's head of military intelligence and the key figure in this whole cold war setup right now. If he says the Russians are about to let us have it, then we'll try to beat them to the punch. One word from him, one opinion, and the dynamite goes off, all hell breaks loose. And he wouldn't be traveling to Palomar, right in the middle of this witch's brew, just to pass the time of day."

David agreed soberly. "But this is high-echelon stuff. Why does the Old Man want *me* there?"

Morgan shrugged. "You're his first assistant—number one boy. And the Old Man must have his reasons. All I'm sure of is that this meeting isn't going to be a love feast. You know how the Old Man feels about Hawthorne and the rest of the brass. And that goes, vice versa."

A half-hour later David was closeted with the general and Dr. Dawson in the Old Man's study.

The general was a big, hulking man with the face and look of a bulldog. His ice-blue eyes were set deep in his square face, and they snapped whenever he spoke. He had made his reputation as a young colonel in G-2 during the last World War, the one they called World War II, back in the forties. In 1955, under the growing tension of the cold war, Congress had broken up the Civilian Commission for the Control of Atomic Energy, originally headed by David Lilienthal, and turned it over to the military.

It was then that Matt Hawthorne had been given four stars, and with it control not only of the whole atomic program, but of every scientist connected with it. In the next five years, because of the obvious integration of this function with the intelligence branch of the military, he had been authorized to mobilize and use, at his own discretion, the scientific brains of the United States in every field of endeavor.

David sat there, fascinated, and watched the two men, General Hawthorne and Dr. Dawson. The Old Man was sitting back in his chair behind the desk, watching the general clamp a cigar in his teeth as he paced up and down the room. Dr. Dawson looked small and almost frail behind the big desk, a man of sixty-five with a finely chiseled face cast almost in an ascetic mold and topped by a shock of tousled white hair. Now, in the light of the hooded lamp on the desk, David saw how gaunt the Old Man's face had become, how deep the shadows under his eyes, and how sharply etched the lines around his mouth. He's tired, thought David; he's got the look of a man almost unbearably weary, a man stretched taut and close to the breaking point. Only his eyes seemed to be very much alive against the pallor of his face. They were unnaturally bright, almost feverish and crackling in their intensity, and as they followed the general they were wary and hostile.

They're a couple of heavyweights, thought David, champions in their line, the best in the business. And they had already squared off; the very air in that quiet room was electric with their hostility. They had clashed brusquely, from the moment the general strode into Dr. Dawson's study, over the question of David's presence there.

"I told you over the phone that this was to be a private meeting over an extremely confidential matter," the general had snapped, glancing at David. "I don't think we want any third party present."

"Dr. Hughes is my assistant," Dr. Dawson said quietly. "He is here at my request, he knows the details of my work for the military, and he has my entire confidence. I think you can count on his discretion, General."

The general started to say something in protest. Then, with an impatient wave of the hand, he forfeited the point. It was plain that he had some larger matter of argument on his mind.

"Dr. Dawson," he began, "we have just established a new defense headquarters at an underground location not far from New York City. At eleven o'clock tomorrow morning there will be an extraordinary meeting of the General Staff and a select group of scientists. This meeting will be of the highest importance, and I want you to be there."

The Old Man stiffened. "May I ask what this meeting will be about, General?"

The general stopped his pacing. He flicked the ashes from his cigar, very deliberately, into an ash tray. Then he turned to the Old Man and looked him squarely in the eyes.

"We shall make a rather important decision," he said. "By noon we shall decide whether we will strike at the Soviet Union immediately, with every weapon in our arsenal—*or* wait for a few more days."

The room was quiet. David sat there, stunned, watching the Old Man sitting immobile behind his desk, the general staring at him. Suddenly David heard the grandfather clock in the corner of the study. It seemed to grow louder as he listened. Now it was abnormally loud; it seemed to tick faster and faster, with an accelerated metronomic beat. David resisted a crazy impulse to rise, to smash the glass face of the clock, to rip the hands off, to stop that loud and obscene beat, the thing it was saying, war or peace, war or peace, war or peace.

War or peace. They or we. Strike or wait. War or peace.

The Old Man stirred. Finally he spoke, quietly, almost inaudibly.

"General Hawthorne, why are *we* forcing this decision? Our policy is, and has been, not to strike in an undeclared war without moral justification. The President himself, the State Department, has promised the people that——"

"Bunk!" The general swung around the desk, leaned down, stared belligerently at the Old Man. "Moral justification! Ethics! Do you think the Soviets care a damn about nonsense like that?" He stopped, and then said slowly and deliberately, "Besides, we have plenty of moral justification—self-defense. What would you say if I told you the Russians have already attacked us?"

The general paused dramatically. But if he expected a reaction from the Old Man, he was disappointed. As for David, he had half risen from his chair, fascinated with horror, watching General Hawthorne.

"I have heard no evidence of any attack," the Old Man said.

"No," snapped the general. "No, you wouldn't. Not up here on this mountaintop, maybe. But down in the cities, my dear Doctor, down where people live, it's different. They're going crazy with rumors, and some of these rumors are true. We're holding them together by discipline, in some areas by martial law, and faced by the threat of a national panic if the people really find out the truth."

"*What* truth, General?"

"I'll give it to you straight, Dr. Dawson. The fact is that the Soviets have a secret weapon, some kind of new super weapon. We don't know what it is, we have no countermeasures against it, all we know is that they're throwing it against us in controlled doses and have been doing so for the past month. They're using it as a technique of cold war, trying to smash our morale, to demoralize

us and break us down, so that we'll listen to a deal—*their* deal!"
The general spat out the word. "But they may be in for a little
surprise. After we finish this East Coast meeting tomorrow, the
whole thing may boomerang back into their damned Red faces.
We've learned a few tricks of our own!"

He's good, thought David, watching the general. He's hard, and
he's ruthless, and he doesn't scare easily, and he knows his way
around. The Soviet propaganda had built up the Red soldier to
scarehead proportions, a man of physical might with a fanatic contempt of death. But watching General Hawthorne, under the circumstances, was strangely comforting. If there had to be a final
holocaust, thought David, it was the Hawthornes who would save
the country, or die trying, and the United States was lucky to have
them.

Dr. Dawson stuck to his point. "How do you know there *is* a new
Soviet weapon, General?" he said, almost dryly, as though he were
posing a question to some student in a lecture class. "What facts do
you have, what evidence?"

The general started to pace the floor again. "Dr. Dawson, in the
past month we have undergone a series of phenomena—unexplained phenomena, without any scientific rhyme or reason—freak
disasters. The earthquakes in various sections of the United States
where no tremors have ever been experienced before. The tidal
wave that rose out of the sea without warning, swamping Havana.

"These erratic changes in the internal pressures of the earth's
surface suggested something possibly astronomical, or cosmic, in
nature. We know that the top men in the Soviet, scientists like
Kavenoff and Malvik, have been working on this type of grand-
scale weapon for some time. They've drawn on the best brains of
their satellites, in addition—Ferenz of Hungary, Dubois of France,
Migliore of Italy, Peterson of Sweden, and Dietz of Germany."
General Hawthorne paused, looked steadily at the Old Man, and
then said with gentle irony: "And as you know, Doctor, we have
been conducting the same line of cosmic research ourselves, with
your own enthusiastic participation."

David glanced quickly at Dr. Dawson and remembered. First, the New Mexico job, and later, Maryland. Over the Old Man's violent protests they had dragged him off Palomar Mountain and bludgeoned him into the top post with the Ballistics Research Laboratory where his knowledge of measuring the speeds of galaxies had been applied to measuring the speeds of projectiles. David had gone along on both trips. He had participated in all details, and he knew how much the Old Man hated the whole setup.

But Dr. Dawson ignored the general's thrust and asked:

"About these phenomena, General. Do you know whether similar ones have taken place in the Soviet Union?"

The general grunted. "If they have, I haven't heard anything about it. Neither have our agents. Anyway, a field mouse couldn't get through the Iron Curtain these days. But aside from that, my dear Doctor, the question is academic. Why should these disasters happen in Russia? If the Russians have this new weapon, they obviously wouldn't be using it on themselves."

"Obviously not, assuming that your arbitrary assumption is correct, assuming that they *do* have some kind of weapon."

General Hawthorne exploded. "There's no doubt about it! You can indulge in the luxury of scientific skepticism all you want, Doctor, but I'm a realist, and I know what I'm talking about. And the last two weeks have proved me right."

The general's jaw set in a hard block as he went on: "In the last two weeks, Doctor, the Reds have stepped up their damned offensive. They've begun to hit us in the belly, where it hurts, in ways that the public doesn't know about yet, thank God. Last Monday a flight of long-range jets set out for a routine flight over the North Pole. Their instruments suddenly went out, they lost communication with their base, and we never heard from them again."

The Old Man leaned forward now. He became tense, interested in what General Hawthorne had to say; he seemed to hang on every word.

"This weapon of theirs, we have discovered, can deflect and sabotage magnetic instruments," continued the general. "We've noted fluctuations in our own magnetic equipment from time to time. Our air navigators and pilots have been losing their directional beams, they've been going far off their course, their radar has ceased to function." The general paused. "You can see what effect that would have on our A-projectiles, my dear Doctor, on our rockets, on our air force. Apparently the Reds have found a way to deflect them at will."

The Old Man was silent, but his bright eyes betrayed his interest. Finally he said:

"And this meeting on the East Coast tomorrow morning, General?"

"We're going to pool our brains and try to figure out just what the Russians have. If you and the other scientists there can't figure it out, can't put it down to any naturalistic phenomena, then we have only one conclusion. The Reds have got something, and we've got to beat them to the punch." The general's face grew brick red, and he flung his cigar in the wastebasket. "If it was up to the General Staff and myself, we'd be throwing everything we have at the Soviet right now. But no! The President doesn't want to make any overt move. Neither does State. For the record," General Hawthorne snarled. "For the record. What the hell good is any record going to be in a couple of more days?"

David watched the Old Man as he rose from the desk. He seemed perplexed, as though trying to come to some inner decision. The general picked up his hat.

"That's all, Dr. Dawson. When you reach New York City tomorrow morning, phone military headquarters, R-Section. They'll pick you up and drive you to the meeting place."

The Old Man turned and then said slowly, "I'm sorry, General, but I'm not going."

"You're not *what?*"

"I'm not going," Dr. Dawson said levelly. "In the first place, I cannot morally be a party to any arrangement that may set off a world war. And in the second place, I am in the midst of a tremendously important piece of research here at Palomar——"

"Research be damned!" blazed the general. He slammed his hat down on the table. "Look here, Dawson, I've had enough of this nonsense from you and from those other fools you call your colleagues. You've sabotaged me every step of the way, like a pack of Reds."

The Old Man suddenly blazed back. "You know what I think of the Soviet system of government, General. You know how I despise it, what it's done to its men of science, how it's bent them to the will of the state. I hate anything that smacks of a totalitarian society. I am still technically a free citizen in a free democracy and not yet a member of the military. And I resent your inference that my colleagues and I——"

"Listen, Doctor, I'm not going to argue with you," Hawthorne interrupted. He pounded the table with his fist. "You're going to stop your stargazing for a few days, and you're going to get back down to earth and fly East and be at that meeting tomorrow morning. And those are orders!"

"I'm sorry, General," said the Old Man stubbornly. "I am willing to compromise and send my assistant, Dr. Hughes, here, in my place, provided he is willing to go. But I repeat, I cannot go myself —not now."

The general saw there was no moving the Old Man and changed his approach. His voice was suddenly very quiet.

"I warn you, Doctor this is treason."

"A matter of definition, General. It's *your* concept of treason."

"Suppose I told you that under the present military law it is conceivable that you could be shot for this."

"It would not change my mind, I assure you," the Old Man said calmly.

For a long time they stared at each other. Then finally General Hawthorne turned his cold blue eyes on David.

"We'll expect you at that meeting tomorrow morning, Hughes," he said curtly.

He put on his hat, turned, and walked from the room without looking back at the Old Man.

At Sixty-fifth Street a taxi swerved around the corner.

David hailed it, and it came to a stop with brakes squealing.

"One Hundred and Tenth Street, between Broadway and the Drive," he said, settling back. The driver made no attempt to operate his meter.

"That'll cost you ten bucks."

The man behind the wheel caught David's incredulous look through the reflector and turned.

"Ain't you heard, buddy? There's a war on. Now, is it a deal or ain't it?"

David nodded.

They drove through the darkened streets toward the place where Carol lived.

3. He rang the bell, and Carol opened the door.

"David!"

Then she was in his arms. He could feel her body taut against his for a moment, then begin to tremble violently. Her nails bit into the back of his neck as he kissed her.

"David, David . . ."

Her body relaxed and blended into his now. He could feel the soft warmth of her; her lips inflamed him as she half cried, half laughed his name against his ear. After all, it had been three months since he'd last been East, since he'd last seen her.

He lifted her up, carried her into the room, and kissed her again.

Finally he set her down, and she said breathlessly: "Darling, darling, give me your coat and hat." She put them on a chair and turned back to him. "I'm not even going to bother hanging them up. Not now. Sit here, David, by the fireplace. Wait a minute, here's an ottoman for your legs; you have such long, long legs and you always like to lean them on something." She was excited now, nervous, all quick movement. "You've left the door open and your bag's still standing out in the hall. No, darling, don't move, I'll get it. Just sit here by the fire and don't go away. I've got scotch and soda ready in the kitchen—I know you never drink anything else."

He started to say something, but she put a finger on his lips and shook her head.

"No, David. Don't say anything. Not now. Not until I bring in the drinks and we can really sit down together. Not until I have a chance to really look at you again. Then we'll talk. . . ."

He watched her go into the tiny kitchenette, and he thought, She's coming back to Palomar with me. Tomorrow, right after that meeting, she's leaving this deathtrap and going back with me, if I have to beat her over the head and drag her with me.

He had written, wired, and telephoned her frantically to leave New York and come to the Coast. But Carol had refused, she had stayed on, she had business in New York. A talented and successful radio and television actress, she was making half-hour film television transcriptions for shipment to isolated military outposts. But more important, with her fluent knowledge of French and German, she was broadcasting short-wave to Occupied Europe.

The Department of Information was responsible for Carol's being in New York. The department, a super-streamlined agency, and a long cry from the old Office of War Information of World War II, had finally managed to tear itself away from the State Department. Now it stood on its own feet, its Secretary occupied a seat in the Cabinet, its power over all media was far-flung and virtually authoritative. It did not order an editorial line—not yet. It merely "suggested." But there was hard steel in the suggestions. And every day, in the temporary capital somewhere in the Middle West, the Secretary of Information lunched with the Secretary of National Defense.

"Information" had "suggested" that Carol and others like her volunteer for the hazardous New York post. It would be only temporary, the Secretary had pointed out. In another week the networks would complete the transfer of their entire New York radio and television operation to a new and emergency Radio City in Kansas.

David leaned back on the couch and listened to the clink of ice in glasses in the kitchenette. It was a relief to be here, in this warm and comfortable room, away from the graveyard outside. He looked about the room, noted that the furniture had been changed since he had last been in town three months ago. It was the new plastic and non-inflammable furniture—the kind they called "Modern Translucent." It was, he decided, a little too modern for his taste.

But then, he thought, he might have become a little stuffy, fallen behind the times, in his roost at Palomar. He could never quite understand how a lovely and talented girl like Carol could have fallen for a rather prosaic person like himself. True, he had a certain amount of prestige in his own field; he was first assistant to the Old Man himself.

But you couldn't eat prestige. And the fact that Carol made four or five times as much money as he did sometimes nagged him.

"David!" She spoke suddenly from the kitchenette. "I know you said you wouldn't tell me, but I just can't stand it. Why are you in New York *now?*"

"Military secret," he said lightly.

"Something in that brief case you brought in with you?"

"Yes."

"And you can't even tell your own wife?"

"You're not my wife yet." He grinned. "But that reminds me—there's something I *can* tell you." Then he paused dramatically. "I've found a place for us to live."

"David!" she cried out in delight. "No!"

"Yes! Right in the observatory colony. A cottage—fieldstone and white shingles, *and* two bathrooms. Wait'll you see it!"

"But, David, how on earth——?"

"Just one of those lucky breaks. That is, lucky for us—unlucky for someone else. The place belonged to one of our research associates—the man who ran the Schmidt camera. Anyway, he and his wife broke up, and they moved. He went to Lick Observatory, and she took the children and went back to her mother's. Anyway, there it is, all furnished and everything, waiting for our new name plate. We'll send out a hundred invitations for our housewarming."

She sounded surprised at that. "A hundred? Are there *that* many people at Palomar?"

"Sure. On the staff alone we've got four research associates, twenty-one research workers, and twelve computers. Not to mention their wives and children. And then there's all the other personnel—the cook, and steward, and chauffeurs, and engineers, and telescope mechanics." He listened to cupboards slamming and the pop of a soda bottle from the kitchenette. "But never mind that. What's taking you so long?"

"I'll be right in." A pause, and then: "David, did you *really* miss me?"

"Hurry up and come back in here," he said. "And I'll show you how much!"

She laughed. "Why, darling, you sound positively dangerous."

Maybe I do, he thought. He was one of the few bachelors at the observatory colony, and for him it was rather a lonely life. Palomar was a graduated society, in the manner of a small and isolated Army post, and its social life was restrained and somewhat clannish. Couples naturally entertained couples, and he was always the extra man.

As such, he was an irritant to the staff wives in the colony, and they had tried their hardest to marry him off, at least in the beginning. They had invited "friends" up from Los Angeles or elsewhere for week ends and thrown them into David's company.

Even Emily Dawson, the Old Man's wife, had made a special effort to marry David off. The Dawsons were childless, and when she learned that both David's parents were dead she had taken him under a motherly wing. She had a niece in San Francisco, and she'd brought the girl to Palomar just to meet him.

But the experiment had failed, and finally she had told David almost reproachfully:

"I had hopes for you and Ann, David. It would have done my old heart good to have you in the family. Why, I was even dreaming of a big wedding right here in my own house." Then she had shaken her patrician head and sighed. "I'm afraid you'll just have to bring this young lady, Carol, back to Palomar here, before we all burst a collective blood vessel!"

Now that he thought of it, he had spent most of his time with Dr. and Mrs. Dawson. It had been monastic, almost like living in a lighthouse without a woman. But there was blood running in his veins, good red blood, and sometimes, just before dawn, when the domed roof finally closed over the Big Eye like a great halved eyelid, his need of Carol had become a gnawing hunger.

Carol came in carrying a tray on which there was a bottle of scotch, soda, and glasses filled with cylindrical tubes of ice. David looked at the frozen cylinders curiously, then remembered seeing them advertised in magazines. They were a feature of the latest refrigerators—individual frozen ice tubes instead of the old and clumsy cubes. You merely pressed an ejector button in the refrigerator, and the ice tubes popped out, one by one. They fitted into a glass very neatly, one to a drink.

They think of something new every minute, thought David a little cynically.

Carol sat down beside him, gave him his drink. "How's His Eminence?"

"Who?"

"Dr. Dawson."

"Oh," grinned David. "Working his head off—on something big."

"What is it?"

He shrugged. "I don't know. The Old Man's keeping *this* one close to his chest."

"Poof!" She laughed at him. "I thought Dr. Dawson told you *everything!*"

He grinned back at her. "He usually does. But this time he hasn't seen fit to consult me and get the benefit of my vast experience. He never does till the job's all over." He put down his glass suddenly and looked at her. "But never mind the Old Man. It's been a long time, Carol. Come here."

They were in each other's arms again, and as David held her he thought, The hell with it all, the cold war, and the dark city outside, everything. It was bound to come; they could conceivably be blown up tomorrow, or now, tonight, at this moment, when he held Carol close. The world outside was complicated; you could worry yourself crazy just thinking about it, living in it.

This was the stuff, this was the idea, the way to live while living was good. A warm and comfortable room, the feel of a woman against your chest, and in your arms, and on your mouth, the touch of warm, throbbing, living flesh under the thin dress, the scent of her hair against your face, the sound of her tiny moans in your ear, the leaping, exciting hope that tonight, maybe tonight . . .

The phone rang.

It jangled with a kind of obscene insistence. It was an intruder there, unwelcome, coarse, inconsiderate. They did not stir, but it would not go away.

It rang again, and again, and again.

"David," whispered Carol. "David, let me go."

He released her finally, and she arose a little unsteadily. She smoothed her dress and walked toward the phone, and as she did, David thought shakily, She's lovely, she's wonderful. Everything about her—the way she walked, the way she talked with that low, husky voice of hers, the pale skin, the oval face, the way her jet-black hair was brushed up and back over her head, and her mouth, luscious and full.

Carol lifted the receiver, said: "Hello." She listened for a moment, and then:

"Dr. Hughes? Yes, he's here." She held the phone toward David. "It's long distance. Palomar calling."

"Palomar?"

He rose from the couch, suddenly worried. What had happened at the observatory? Why did they want him now? As he came to the phone Carol asked:

"How did they know you'd be here?"

"I told the steward he could locate me at your apartment, and if I wasn't here you'd know where to find me." He took the phone and said:

"This is David Hughes."

The operator told him to wait a moment. He heard a crisscross of vague filtered voices. Someone was trying to locate someone else in New York; someone wanted a St. Louis number. The voices were remote and mysterious; they began and were cut off abruptly, like disembodied wraiths.

David waited a full minute, then jiggled the receiver.

"Operator! Operator!"

The operator's voice came on again, told him to wait again, and he hung on impatiently. He glanced at his watch. One o'clock. That would be ten on the Coast. If it was clear, if the sky and seeing were good, the Old Man should be taking settings now, with Bill Forrester at the pulpit. . . .

The operator came on suddenly:

"Here's your party."

It was Francis, the steward. His voice sounded shaky, agitated; it was trembling.

"Dr. Hughes, Dr. Hughes!"

"Yes, Francis? This is Hughes. What——"

"Come back to Palomar at once. On the next plane. Dr. Dawson——"

Francis's voice was suddenly snapped off abruptly. There was a buzz, and the phone went dead. David swore, jiggled the receiver. The instrument buzzed again and then cleared; the phone was alive again for just an instant.

An operator spoke somewhere, very faint and very far away.

"Rio is ready for you, Palomar. Rio is waiting. We'll hold the Amsterdam circuit until——"

The operator's voice cut off. The phone went dead again.

What in hell was going on? thought David. Why were they calling Rio, Amsterdam, and God knows where, all of a sudden?

And why did Francis tell him to come back? Before his voice had been snatched off the circuit he had said something to David about the Old Man. But the Old Man had sent him on this mission; the Old Man knew he had to be at that meeting tomorrow morning, or else!

He got the New York operator, asked her to try Palomar. He told Carol briefly what Francis had said, and then he began to worry.

"I don't like it, Carol," he said. "Francis sounded like a scared rabbit. Maybe something's happened to the Old Man. His heart isn't any too good—angina—carries around nitroglycerin pills. Mrs. Dawson packs a vial of pills in every suit he's got, in his desk, and there's even a vial of the stuff up in the observer's cage at the top of the Eye. But the Old Man's pretty absent-minded; he's left 'em home more than once. And when he needs one of those pills under his tongue, he needs it fast!" He shook his head. "I don't know, Carol. He's been working his head off lately, and the generals have been running him ragged, and maybe his heart—maybe he's had a collapse. Otherwise, why would Francis sound the way he did?"

"David, you mustn't fret like that." Carol came over and twined her arm into his. "Perhaps it isn't Dr. Dawson at all. Those calls to Rio and Amsterdam you just told me about—maybe they mean something."

David jiggled the receiver, called for the operator. "This god-damned phone," he raged. "First they cut me off, and then I can't even get an operator!"

"The trouble's probably at the New York end, darling," said Carol. "They've only got a skeleton crew working. Most of the switchboard girls have left, and you can't blame them."

Finally an operator came on. She was maddeningly calm. She told David the circuits to California and to Palomar were busy. He begged her to get him through. She was properly sympathetic but very professional.

"I'll call you when we make the connection," she told David.

He paced up and down the floor, jittery, confused. He had to get through to Palomar, to get more details.

Francis had told him to come back, to take the first plane back. But there was that all-important meeting in the morning at military headquarters, wherever that was. He had some very important data in his brief case, and his presence would immediately be missed.

He was, in short, under orders to be there. From General Hawthorne. Maybe the Old Man was big enough to defy the top brass.

But *he* was only David Hughes.

And he could be slapped down, and hard, for not showing up at that conclave. It could mean a drumhead trial, a prison, a firing squad, maybe. In times like these they weren't too particular. The area between the civil and the military had faded into a nebulous no man's land.

No matter how much the Old Man protested that David had returned to the Coast under his, Dawson's, orders, an Army court would be sure to take the simple and disastrous view that General Matt Hawthorne, four stars, had ordered him to be there.

There was also another, and far more important, consequence.

Suppose the data in his brief case was valuable, *really* valuable?

Suppose the figures, diagrams, and conclusions, all neatly itemized on paper in his brief case, proved the key on which the men at the meeting made their decision?

Suppose, on the basis of what he was bringing to that all-important meeting in the morning, they decided to throw any further caution out of the window and strike at Russia immediately?

It was possible. It was horribly, damnably, and obviously possible that he, David Hughes, might be carrying the match for the fuse there in that shiny leather bag on Carol's table. By his not going to that meeting, by his failing to present that data and interpret it for the group, they might make a mistake and start the inferno.

Or, failing David's presence with vital information, they might make a different mistake and hold their attack, when the sound decision would be to strike. They might hold it a little too long, and the Soviet might beat them to it.

At this moment, David realized miserably, at this hellish moment, he was an unwilling giant on a world stage, carrying a hot torch he didn't want and couldn't handle.

It was too much, he thought. It was too much to ask of any one man. Even if the Old Man himself had asked him to come back.

But had he?

David didn't know, he wasn't sure. He didn't know whether the order for his return had actually come from the Old Man, or whether something had happened to Dr. Dawson, and Francis had called David on his own authority.

He turned suddenly to Carol. "Can I send a telegram out of New York?"

She shook her head. "The telegraph offices closed two weeks ago, David."

Then the only way to reach the Coast was by phone. The instrument lay on its cradle now, a black and shiny demon, grinning at him. The operator hadn't called him back. He yanked the phone up in a sweaty hand and tried again.

"I'm sorry, sir," the operator said. "All circuits to California are busy. I'll call you when we have one clear."

There was a faint note of irony in the operator's voice. She gave the impression that he'd be lucky if they phoned him back by morning. David frantically tried to explain that it was vital, an emergency.

She was sympathetic, she was sorry, but there was nothing she could do. What with the evacuation, with every relative trying to call every other relative, with most of the circuits already given over to the Army, there was nothing she could do.

She could only keep trying.

David slammed down the receiver.

"Sit down, darling," Carol said soothingly. "Sit down. Try not to worry for a while, David. Whatever it is, I'm sure everything will be all right."

She didn't know about the meeting, she didn't know on what kind of hook he was impaled. And he couldn't tell her. But she sat there, looking up at him and holding a fresh drink toward him.

He took the drink, had another. And another. Then he went to the phone and tried to get Palomar again.

The operator was very sorry. The circuits were still busy, and there was no way of telling when they would be free. There was no point in David's calling every ten minutes; she would call him when the lines were open again.

And finally David thought, The hell with it, the hell with everything. There's nothing I can do except wait.

And if worst comes to worst, if I hear nothing from Palomar, I'll go to that meeting anyway, no matter what Francis said. I've *got* to go!

But as he talked to Carol, as they sat close together, as the liquor began to take hold, he recalled Francis's voice before it had been cut off on the long lines, how it had shook and trembled, as though he were terrified, and the fear that something had happened to the Old Man nagged David like the throbbing of an exposed nerve.

He tried to forget it for a while. He asked Carol about the city, about New York, what it had been like living there in the last few months. Her face sobered, and she was suddenly afraid. He could see it in the quick brightness of her eyes, in the drawn, taut look of her face, in the sudden trembling of her fingers as she deliberately crushed her cigarette in the ash tray.

Finally she took a deep breath and then she started to talk, as though she'd been dying to talk to someone about it for a long time, to get it off her chest. The words came tumbling out in quick, rambling sentences, and as she went on they came faster and faster, as though she were determined not to leave any space between them, not to give the incipient hysteria a loophole in which to creep in and take possession.

"Of course it's like a bad dream, David. You wouldn't believe it —living here in the city now, I mean. It's simply fantastic. Even so, you can get used to it after a while, in a way. When Mother was alive—well, I remember what she used to say, 'You can get used to hanging, if you hang long enough.' I don't know. Anyway, it's not so bad during the day, really it isn't. It's the nights. Without the lights, the streets simply pitch-black—well, it's pretty nerve-racking. There've been all kinds of holdups and muggings. It's not that the authorities are trying to black the city out—that wouldn't do any good against those guided missiles or whatever they call them. It's just because they haven't enough men to run the power plants. That's why the subways and the els aren't running either, even if they had the men to run them. And food—David, you just can't imagine. You have to walk blocks before you can find a place that has anything to sell, and when you buy it, you pay fantastic prices. It's all black market, of course. People want to make money fast and get out before it's too late—and you pay ten times what food is really worth. Five dollars for a pound of butter, David. You can't get it for less anywhere, if you're lucky enough to find it. But if it's an apartment you want, that's different. They're just giving them away. A penthouse on Park Avenue—you can have it for the asking. It's ridiculous, David. There are just thousands of empty apartments going begging. People just left with what they could carry in a suitcase—left their furniture and everything behind. There aren't more than a few thousand people left in town, so you can imagine.

"Of course nothing makes sense any more. But I forget, there's the heating problem. Lucky for me this building is fairly new, and we have individual heating units for each apartment. The people left in the old buildings with a central heating system didn't get any heat, and so they simply moved to one of the new buildings—just like that. As for getting around the town—well, you know something about that, David, you already know how hard it is. The only way is a taxi—if you can find one. The drivers have thrown away their meters, and they charge you what they think you can afford, and of course they think you're all millionaires.

"And oh, the network studios—not to mention the Telecast Building—they're all madhouses now. You have to show your pass and wear a badge and go through the third degree at least five times, and show them your handbag to prove you haven't got an infernal machine in it, before you can get in to broadcast. It's insane, of course, but everyone's on edge; it's what they call Security. I know you think I'm mad to stay here, David, but we were asked to volunteer, at least until they set up new short-wave transmission studios in the Middle West. It won't be for much longer, darling, just another week, they say, and——"

She had averted her face from him ever since she started to talk. Now she stopped as he gently took her chin and turned her face up toward his.

Her eyes were blurred with tears, and they were scared, and suddenly she was in his arms.

"David! Oh, David, David!"

She was a terrified child, clinging to him, shaking violently in his arms, crying his name hysterically over and over. He held her tight, comforting her, soothing her, murmuring to her, pressing his lips against her cheek so that they became sticky with her tears.

It's all been building up in her, thought David; it's been building up for days and weeks.

Finally Carol drew away and wiped her eyes. "I'm sorry, darling. I'm sorry."

"Sorry for what?"

"For blowing up like that." She sat down and said faintly, a little ashamed, "I made up my mind I wouldn't cry, I wouldn't break down, I wouldn't get hysterical, like so many of the others. *Now*— look what happened!"

"You had it coming," said David. "Anybody would in a setup like this." He lit a cigarette and gave it to her. "But that's all over with now. You're going back to the Coast with me tomorrow."

She shook her head. "But, David, I can't."

"You're going back with me, and that's that!" he insisted. "I've got a plane reservation back tomorrow afternoon and a super-high priority in my pocket. I'll get another seat for you on that priority if I have to tear down the airport."

She tried to reason with him. "David, David, you don't understand. We promised to stay on the job; it's supposed to be important. The Department of Information says our broadcasts are getting through—to Europe. The people over there are hearing them, David, in spite of the Russians, in spite of everything——"

"To hell with all that," he said roughly. "It's too late for that boring-from-within propaganda stuff. They're all whistling in the wind. The blowoff'll come any hour now, and it won't be a question of propaganda, but of a lot of other weapons a million times more lethal. You've done enough, Carol; you've been here long enough, longer than anyone has a right to ask. After all, you haven't been drafted, you're just a volunteer——"

"That part of it doesn't matter, David." She was looking at him steadily, and it irritated him. He took the expression in her eyes as accusation and blazed at her.

"All right, all right, maybe I'm not a great patriot. Maybe I've no right to talk, sitting up on my nice, safe, remote mountaintop back at Palomar. But maybe I've got some information you don't know about, Carol. And I'm just not patriotic enough to let them murder my own fiancée." He walked about in a rage. "The damned fools! The crazy idiots running this government, and the Soviet government, and the others. If somebody could persuade these morons in striped pants to look upstairs for a minute and take a good long look at the stars, they'd find out that this infected speck of dust they call the earth isn't big enough to fight about, isn't worth the trouble——"

"David," she said gently. "You don't have to make a speech."

He looked at her, and suddenly he felt awkward and foolish, like an adolescent kid on a high school platform. I'm a little drunk, he thought, that's it, I'm a little drunk, and shooting off my mouth like a street-corner reformer.

Get off the soapbox, Hughes, get back to earth.

"Carol," he said, "all I know is that you're inviting suicide every minute you stay here. You've got to come back with me tomorrow."

She shook her head, and he knew it was final. "David, David, believe me, I'm not trying to be noble or anything like that. But I've *got* to do what I'm doing! I've *got* to go through with it!" She pulled him down to the couch with her and pressed her cheek against his. "Darling, darling, please, let's not quarrel. Not now."

She clung to him, and to David the room became a kind of blur, like a background out of focus, a hazy cubicle hemming them in. He was drunk now, drunk with the whisky, drunk with the feel and the scent of her, drunk with the warmth of her body against his, the perfume of her hair, the caress of her lips on his ear.

"David, will we really be married soon?"

"As soon as you get out to Palomar." He almost added "if."

She kissed the lobe of his ear again, his cheek, his throat, his mouth. He was afire with the feel of her, and he thought, I can't, Carol, I can't take any more of this. Carol, Carol, I can't take any more!

"What are we waiting for?" he whispered. "What are we waiting for?"

"No, David, no, darling, no."

She drew away from him, held him at arm's length, looked at him. It was perverse of her, he thought wildly, one of those baffling things women do without rhyme or reason. There was compassion in her eyes, but he resented it, he didn't want compassion now.

He could have fought it, tried to overwhelm her.

He could have shouted: "Now, now, or maybe it'll be never. Maybe there'll never be any tomorrow, or the day after tomorrow. Carol, for the love of God!"

But he didn't.

Instead he rose abruptly and glanced at his watch.

"Two-thirty," he said, almost too casually. "I'd better go."

Carol nodded.

He picked up his brief case, and the feel of the leather and the bulging papers within brought him back to his dilemma. He went to the phone again, dialed the operator.

"I'm sorry, sir," said the operator. "But the Army took over all long-line circuits ten minutes ago. They may be released by morning. I'll call you."

He hung up, and he thought, That's that. It's out of my hands, there's nothing I can do. Nothing, except—wait for tomorrow.

He turned to Carol. "What was the name of that hotel again?"

"The Rutherford," she answered mechanically. "It's east of Fifth, on Fifty-sixth."

"The Rutherford," he repeated.

He waited for her to rise, to say something, to see him to the door. But she did not stir from the couch. Instead she lay there motionless, watching him, appraising him, measuring him. Something had come into her eyes. They were hard to read at the moment; they said nothing, really, except that they expected *him* to do something, to make the next move.

The wail of a siren screamed up suddenly from the dark canyon outside. It tore the silence of the room with its shrieking din. Then it threaded away somewhere in the night, fading as fast as it had come.

They were apart now, out of each other's arms, and the Outside had come between them again. The realization was in her face, and he knew it was in his. The little island they had inhabited briefly and together had slipped into the dark sea, and they were both afraid and swimming for their lives again. The Fear, by some subtle osmosis, had penetrated through the walls; it was in the room again, a cold and oppressive shroud enveloping them both.

"Hope I can get a cab," he said.

His voice sounded strangely false. Still she said nothing, made no move to get up. He turned his back on her, acutely conscious that she was watching him intently as he walked toward the foyer. He picked up his coat and hat deliberately from the chair where she had left them, and turned to her.

"David," she whispered suddenly. "David—don't go!"

He stood there transfixed, staring at her. Mechanically, unaware of what he was doing, he put his hat and coat down again. The blood rushed hotly to his face, his heart pounded, and he began to tremble violently.

"Carol . . ."

"Don't go out there, darling." Her voice was husky. "Don't go out there—and leave me alone."

The morning light was streaming in the window when Carol said: "David, I've got to get down to Radio City. We've got an early broadcast, and one of the announcers still has his car in town. He's picking me up on the corner, and if I don't meet him I'll never be able to get down to the studio."

He made a last try. "You won't change your mind about flying back with me this afternoon?"

"No, David," she said quietly. "I can't."

Then Carol thought of something, made a sad face. "I didn't realize it was so late. And, darling, I *did* want to make your breakfast. There isn't much food in the refrigerator, the times being what they are, but——"

"Forget it," he said cheerfully. "I'll throw something together."

He turned on the small portable television set in the bedroom. A Negro girl at a piano came on with some wake-up-and-sing stuff. She was dressed as a maid and was obviously at her mistress's piano, her broom and mop leaning against the instrument.

The mistress came into the picture, and the Negro maid grimaced in alarm, as though caught poaching on her employer's time. But the woman of the house was very pleasant about it. She motioned the girl to stay at the piano; it was apparent that she would rather have music than have her house cleaned.

A moment later, the woman of the house, caught by the music, joined the girl in a duet. They laughed and swayed and made eyes to the rhythm of the song. There was a clock on the piano to give a visual picture of the time, and there was a face painted on its dial. The face grinned and grimaced, too, and had a wonderful time. Now and then it waved its hands jerkily, like an agitated and happy puppet.

It was pleasant stuff, early-morning stuff for the housewives, and David and Carol couldn't help smiling at it.

But then the scene was wiped out abruptly into a blank screen.

A surge of documentary news-of-the-day music came up, and a spinning globe of the world appeared. A streamer brightened and swept around it, and the legend announced:

NATIONAL NEWS

David's smile froze. He and Carol stood there, motionless, hypnotized, listening.

The announcer underplayed his news and made it effective. His words were measured and somber, and his voice was a steady monotone.

> *"Early reports from the Soviet Union indicate that the last-minute conference between Mr. Allison of the State Department and Foreign Minister Bakhanov has failed. There is a rumor that Allison has already left Russia by plane, and the tension is mounting hourly.*
>
> *"Meanwhile, the Army has announced that Washington has been completely evacuated, the last government bureau moving out two days ago.*
>
> *"The President, it is reported, is waiting a personal report from Allison at his secret headquarters somewhere underground. It is reported that he is resisting strong pressure from some of his advisers to take the initiative before it is too late. The health of the Chief Executive has given some concern. Since Congress stripped itself of power to declare war and gave the President authority as Commander in Chief to make whatever instantaneous decision necessary, the strain and responsibility have been overwhelming.*
>
> *"Flashes of unexplained light were detected early this morning over Labrador. Observers at Hopedale and Northwest River are unable to account for the phenomena, except to say that they resembled the tails of illuminated rockets. . . .*
>
> *"There are rumors that New York, Chicago, Detroit, Philadelphia, Los Angeles, and, in fact, every city of over five hundred thousand will be totally evacuated by Army order*

*this week end. Emergency facilities have been set up in the
hinterland for those without relatives or friends residing
in——"*

"David, shut it off!" Carol's voice rose hysterically. "Shut it off!"

He turned the switch and the picture dissolved to a tiny rectangle
of bright light, which finally drowned in the dull, gray screen.

"Why don't they stop?" Carol cried. "Why don't they stop?"

"They don't know how to stop," David answered quietly. "Not
any more."

After Carol had left, David tried the long-distance operator
again.

The lines were still tied up, and he swore softly as he hung up.

He prepared a hasty breakfast, but he had no appetite. His
ignorance of what had happened back at Palomar kept gnawing
at him; the trembling in Francis's voice over the phone haunted
him.

He checked his watch.

It was nine o'clock. And General Hawthorne had named the time
of the meeting at eleven, somewhere outside the city itself. He had
to make a decision, and make it quick. He might be too late by now,
as it was.

He went to the phone and asked the local operator for military
headqarters, New York area, R-Section.

A couple of voices finally routed him to a Colonel Hatch.

"Hughes?" The colonel was curt. "Where have you been? We've
been waiting for you."

"Sorry, Colonel, I——"

The colonel interrupted, asked for the address. "You damned
near missed that meeting, Dr. Hughes. As it is, we'll have to work
fast to get you out where you have to go. We'll send a car up for
you right away!"

The colonel hung up, and David fidgeted about Carol's apartment, waiting. He washed the dishes, put them away, turned on the

television set, turned it off again, sat down, got up again, paced the room.

What had happened at Palomar?

He looked at his watch again, did some rapid calculating. The meeting was at eleven. It might take hours, probably would. He would be lucky if he got out of it by late afternoon. The decision they expected to make wasn't a quick, cut-and-dried affair. There would be a lot of argument back and forth.

In any case, he couldn't get to a phone and find out what was going on back at the observatory. Once in that meeting, they'd lock the doors and seal them with MPs.

Maybe they'd be through at five, he thought. Maybe. He might be able to call the Coast then, the lines might be clear. Might, might, might. He'd try Carol once more over the phone; he'd know something then, know it for sure. If they decided to let go, to start it rolling, to throw the first punch, he'd have to come back and get Carol.

It might be very tough getting out of town. He had a reservation, a high priority. But only for one seat, not two. He'd have to find a way, some way to——

The phone rang.

David sprang to the instrument.

"This is the long-distance operator calling Dr. Hughes, Dr. David Hughes."

"I'm Dr. Hughes," he almost shouted.

"The lines have just been cleared, sir, and Palomar, California, is calling." There was a pause, and David waited rigidly. Then the operator said: "Here's your party."

A voice came thinly, distantly, over the wire.

"Dr. Hughes. Dr. Hughes, is that you?"

"Francis!" David yelled into the mouthpiece. "Francis, what's happened out there?"

The steward's voice came over clearly now. "Dr. Hughes, I've been trying to get you all night. I wasn't sure you got my message before we were cut off."

"What happened, Francis? What's it all about?"

"We had hoped you'd be on your way by now, sir. Dr. Dawson wanted you here. Oh, one moment." There was a pause. "Here's Dr. Dawson now, Dr. Hughes."

Thank God, thought David. Thank God the Old Man was all right.

Dr. Dawson came on. His voice was strange, feverish; it shook a little.

"David, I want you back here as fast as you can make it. Take the first plane out. Don't delay a moment, do you understand?"

"But, sir, what's it all about?"

"I can't tell you over the phone."

"But the meeting, Dr. Dawson. They expect me there——"

The Old Man's voice suddenly became harsh. "Forget the meeting, David. There is no necessity for you to attend. I'll guarantee you immunity for any consequences resulting from your absence. You have my word for it. The important thing is to get back here to Palomar—*at once!*"

The Old Man hung up.

David Hughes put the receiver back on the hook numbly.

There was no rebelling against an order like this—not the way the Old Man had put it.

The hell of it was, he *still* didn't know what was happening at Palomar.

Dazed, his mind whirling in a pinwheel of confusion, David put on his hat and coat and tucked his brief case under his arm.

Then he walked out of the door and heard the lock snap shut behind him.

4. Thursday morning, on the seventeenth of November, in the year 1960, was crisp and sunny.

The air was invigorating; it had a winy snap to it and was cleaned and sweetened by a northwest wind.

The sun was bright; it razzle-dazzled the rivers and glinted on the windows of New York and warmed the brick and stone walls of the canyons.

As David walked rapidly up Cathedral Parkway and then turned right down Broadway, he reflected on the incongruity of the weather.

It was not the kind of morning to expect sudden death, not the traditional backdrop for cataclysm. In the operatic and literary tradition, such events were augured by black skies, flashes of lightning, roars of thunder.

But the weather was not being literary or operatic this morning. It refused to be moody and provide a stage. Whatever schemes man was contriving, it was having none of it. It simply insisted, contrarily, on being itself.

Thus Nature, in what might have been its own version of an unfunny jest, had provided the kind of morning lyrics were written about, topcoat weather with a tang, the kind of morning to walk through the park, or to take that long ride through the country and forget the office.

To David Hughes, visually at least, Broadway presented rather a cheerful appearance. True, there were only a few vehicles on the street, but there seemed to be more pedestrians abroad. The night before had been desolate, the street a black graveyard, but perhaps the sun had drawn the inhabitants from their concrete warrens, lured them out with warm promise, infused them with its own optimism.

But the faces of the people belied the mood of the morning.

They were still stamped with the Fear; its imprint was indelible. They were gaunt and strained, and they did not smile. They knew that the Fear was still there, that it walked in the sun as well as in the darkness.

And David Hughes, as he hurried down Broadway, knew it too.

He kept watching the side streets, on the alert for a cab. Two or

three taxis went by, but they were loaded with passengers. David
kept on the west side of the street, going downtown. The traffic, or
what there was of it, seemed to be moving in that direction.

At 180th Street, David heard the sound of a siren shrieking up
Broadway.

It was an Army car, and moving fast. Instinctively he shrank
back into a doorway. Then when the car sped by he stepped out on
the walk and watched it.

He saw it swerve, with brakes screaming, and turn left into
Cathedral Parkway, two blocks away.

It was the vehicle the Army had sent for him.

The men in it would find him gone; they would find Carol's
apartment empty. The big strategy meeting, wherever it was being
held, would go on without him now. And whatever decision the
generals, the Secretary of Defense, and the consulting scientists
made, it would be made without Dr. Dawson's data in the brief case
David carried under his arm, and without David's interpretation of
it, as the Old Man's representative.

They would miss him, and General Hawthorne would find him
and ask some pointed questions. He, David Hughes, was in effect
and at this moment a hunted man, a fugitive from military law, and
subject to its consequences.

He quickened his step, and now and then, furtively, he turned his
head to look back up Broadway.

The olive-drab car from intelligence would emerge in a few
moments, when they found him gone. Its occupants would be watching the streets, looking for him. By their very lack of numbers, all
pedestrians were conspicuous, and suddenly David felt almost
naked on the wide Broadway sidewalk. It was possible that he might
be picked up before he had hardly started.

Between 106th and 105th streets he found a candy-and-tobacco
store open, one of the few still doing business. It occurred to him
that it would be a good place to hide, to get off the street until the
Army car went back.

David opened the door and went in.

There were several men in the place, all apparently regulars. At least they all seemed to know the man behind the cigar counter, a short, bald man with thick glasses. David had entered in the middle of a discussion. One of the men lounging on a stool at the now inactive soda fountain was saying to the proprietor:

"So you sent your family to the Catskills, Sam?"

The proprietor nodded. "Ellenville. I figured they'd be pretty safe there till I sell out and close up." He glanced around at his depleted stock. The store was almost empty of goods. "And that won't be long, Bernie. Tomorrow or the day after, maybe."

He turned to David, and David bought a pack of cigarettes. The price was a dollar, the transaction matter-of-fact. The man behind the counter continued:

"The way I figure, Bernie, if the Reds hit us with a bomb, the blast won't get up into the mountains."

"Yeah," said Bernie. "*If* they hit us with a blast. But they won't."

"What do you mean?"

"The Russians are too smart for that. They got something else up their sleeve. Radiation."

The proprietor was fascinated. "Radiation?"

Bernie nodded knowingly. "Radiation. That's it. That's the pay-off. I was reading a piece in the *Daily News* before all the papers folded up in town," he said. "It was something one of these big-shot scientists said, Sam. He said there's no place that's safe any more. Not even the mountains. Nowhere. And all on account of radiation."

"How do you mean?" Sam was suddenly worried.

"Here." The man named Bernie took a torn sheet of newspaper from his pocket. "I got the clipping right here." He spread it on the fountain top. "Listen to what it says at the end."

Bernie paused for a moment, then read the final paragraph slowly. " 'In any case, there is no defense against these lethal particles, no place of escape. There is no cave too deep to hide away, no mountaintop too high or remote. As long as men must breathe air and Nature provides winds, the human being, no matter how fast he runs or to what destination, is helplessly and pathetically vulnerable.' "

The man at the counter folded the clipping, his fingers trembling, and thrust it into his pocket. The bald head of the proprietor, Sam, was shiny with perspiration, and there was agony in the eyes behind the thick lenses. It was easy to see what he was thinking. People breathe air in the Catskills; the winds blow there too. . . .

"Christ," someone said, breaking the silence. "Christ, what a world!"

Amen, thought David, watching through the window.

The conversation turned to rumors. Everybody had heard a rumor. A fat man with a mottled face said:

"I heard that they stopped the salt-water fishing fleets from going out and won't let anyone sell any more deep-sea fish."

"Yeah?" Bernie wanted to know. "Why?"

"They think maybe the Reds dropped a lot of pills in the Atlantic and the Pacific, near the coasts. Made the fish radioactive. Lights 'em up inside like Christmas candles. Eat 'em—and good-by!"

"That's a new one on me," said a man thumbing through a magazine on the wall rack. "Remind me to eat hamburgers from now on."

"God," said the proprietor, finally joining the discussion again. "I had fish last night—mackerel."

The fat man laughed harshly. "I hope your wife doesn't divorce you, Sam."

"What do you mean, Paul? Why should she?"

"Once you get these radioactive particles in you, they tell me, you're no good in bed. A lot of guys working around this here plutonium stuff found that out. So did their girl friends." He grinned at the others and turned back to Sam. "But I wouldn't worry about it, Sam. You're no kid. You've had your fun."

No one grinned back. The would-be humorist said good-by and eased his huge bulk through the door.

The proprietor was still worried. "How do we know what's going on right now? Maybe we're all standing here and breathing in this stuff now, without knowing it. How about it, Bernie? How do we know we ain't radioactive right here and now?"

"One thing's sure," said the man with the magazine. "None of us have any Geiger counters. We couldn't tell if we wanted to."

"Maybe you guys can't" said Bernie. "But I can."

They looked at him curiously, and he drew a small camera from his pocket. It was the ordinary and popular type which developed film within the camera itself, after a few moments of waiting.

He held up the camera to the others. "I got my own Geiger counter right here," he said triumphantly. "If you did a lot of reading up on this radiation stuff like I have, you'd know film can give you the tip-off."

They watched him hypnotically. The man called Bernie, now a savant, savored his moment.

"Like to see whether there's any radiation around right now?"

They pushed in close to him without replying, their faces tense. David moved in with the others, as interested as anyone else, already knowing what the man was up to, knowing that the camera was capable of indicating, at that moment, life or possible death.

Bernie did not touch the shutter. Instead, with the air of a demonstrator before a spellbound audience, he pressed the developer button and pulled out a paper tab. He ticked off the seconds on his wrist watch as the developing reagent worked on the unexposed film within.

Finally, with a flourish, he opened the back of the camera and took out the print.

The print was clear.

"Well, gents," said Bernie impressively, "we're still okay. There's no radiation around. Y'see, if there was, it'd go right through the camera like X rays and fog up the film. If this picture came out all fogged up, brother, *we'd* be in trouble."

There was a moment of silence.

Then someone said: "You've got something there, mister. But won't you find out a little late? What I mean is, if the picture's fogged, you'd already be radioactive, wouldn't you?"

"Yeah," agreed Bernie. "No getting around that. The question is: how *much* would you be lit up inside? They tell me you can take a certain amount without dying. But the minute you see any fogging at all—that's the time to scram."

"Scram where?" asked Sam.

Bernie shrugged. There was no answer to that one. Still, the men in the candy store seemed impressed. It was something to *know* whether you were dying or not, even if it might be too late. Automatically their eyes strayed to a case in back of the cigar counter, where there was a stock of film. The proprietor took out a fistful of the rectangular yellow boxes and stuffed them into his pockets. The others quickly bought the rest of his stock.

David turned toward the window again, watching for the Army car. Bernie's demonstration had been a simple but familiar one. Back at Palomar he had seen the effect of radiation on sensitive film many times. There were other ways to detect it, of course: by the comet's tail of ionized particles in what was called a Wilson cloud chamber; by the action of an electroscope in discharging; and of course by the clicking of a Geiger counter.

But now, in David's mind, there was a serious doubt. *Was the attack, when and if it came, going to be atomic at all?*

Back at Palomar General Hawthorne had been sure that it was something else, something bigger, something perhaps on a cosmic scale. He had come to Palomar to talk to the Old Man personally, so strong was his belief, so determined was he to recruit Dr. Dawson, the greatest of them all in the affairs of the heavens. He had been convinced that the Russians had a secret weapon and that they were applying it when it suited them, as a series of steps to resolve the cold war and break the American morale without entering a full-scale atomic battle.

If the Russians *had* something new, thought David, their use of it in this respect made sense, from their point of view. The United States was a rich land, and if the Reds could bring it down and exploit it without too much damage, that would be to their benefit. The trouble with a victorious radioactive attack was that it left

nothing to the victor. It was fatal, not only to humans, but to live-
stock and animals. It polluted the waters and the crops, the buildings, and bridges, the very land itself, contaminated it all with a
coat of death. And in the end it left nothing but a vast, desolate, and
diseased waste, of no good to the Russians or anyone else.

Suddenly, through the window of the candy store, David saw
what he had been watching for.

The olive-drab Army car came in view. Its siren was silent now,
providing no warning. It cruised down Broadway slowly, and
David saw the soldiers in it scanning both sides of the street.

He shrank back from the window guiltily, and the vehicle went
by.

The skin prickled along his back. He was hunted now, and
Hawthorne would be the hunter. He was a fugitive, and there would
be harsher names the general would call him, deserter, saboteur,
traitor. The brief case he held burned hot in his hands.

The thought occurred to him that if General Hawthorne were
informed of his disappearance early enough, he, David, might
be stopped at the airport before he had a chance to take off.

He began to regret the decision he had made, almost wished he
had disregarded the Old Man's order to return to California without
attending the meeting.

At any rate, it was too late to do anything about it now. He had
to get out to Idlewild, and get there fast.

David opened the door and was just about to step out on the
sidewalk when a cab drew up to the curb. The driver got out and
walked into the store, leaving his motor running. David saw that
there were two other men in the cab, and for a moment he found
it impossible to believe his luck.

The driver was buying cigarettes from the proprietor when David
asked:

"Got room for one more?"

"I might," said the man. "Where you going, buddy?"

"Idlewild Airport." David tried hard to keep the eagerness out
of his voice.

"That's a long way out of town, Buddy," said the driver, his blue eyes studying David greedily. "Clean out to the end of Queens, and these days there ain't any fares coming back. It'll cost you some dough."

"How much?"

"A hundred bucks," said the man casually.

David nodded. He had no disposition to haggle. He had the cash, and it was worth everything for him to get to the airport in a hurry.

The driver stuck out his hand. "In advance, buddy."

David paid him, and as the man stuck the money in his pocket he said:

"I've got a couple of other guys to drop off first. Then we'll get going."

David squeezed into the back seat beside the other two men, and they started to move down Broadway. The others showed no inclination to talk, and David was grateful. He had a lot to think about.

First of all, he wondered how the Old Man was going to protect him when he got back to Palomar. The Old Man was one of the world's great scientists, a Nobel prize winner, a power in himself. But even Dr. Dawson couldn't countermand an Army order and get away with it. Not these days.

It would take some kind of special magic, thought David grimly, to keep him out of trouble now.

And then there was Carol. . . .

The cab stopped at Columbus Circle, and one of the men got out. Then the driver swung east on Central Park South, toward Fifth Avenue.

As they were rounding Fifty-ninth Street into Fifth, at the Plaza, it happened.

It began with a noise, a low, deep, rolling ominous rumble.

The rumble blended into a subterranean roar, a throaty booming sound.

"Christ!" yelled the driver. "What the hell is that?" He stopped the cab in the middle of the street.

The booming continued, grew louder, echoed and re-echoed like an artillery salvo. David, in that terrible moment of panic, had a single objective moment, a flash of light on the lens of his eye. He saw a few pedestrians on the avenue, standing still, frozen, listening, their faces blanched with terror.

And then it came.

The street seemed suddenly to undulate in a slow wave.

The taxi began to shiver, then shake, then do a crazy, awful, lurching dance. It tossed from side to side, like a mechanical toy, as David and the others clung to their seats for dear life.

"It's the Reds," shouted the driver. "The goddamn Reds! They've hit New York!"

The roaring became louder and was mixed with sharp snapping sounds, as though great blocks of stone were being torn and ripped apart deep underground.

The buildings started to sway, and dance, and shiver.

David watched, fascinated, in sweaty terror, unable to move, unable to breathe. He saw whole panes of glass fall from the windows of the Plaza Hotel, the Savoy-Plaza, Tiffany's, Plummer's. They fell in sheets, in a great glassy, deadly rain, crashed to the street. He heard people screaming, saw them running for building entrances. One man fell, his head a mass of blood, almost decapitated by flying glass.

It thudded and smashed on the roof of the taxi, crashed against the cab windows. The shatterproof glass of the vehicle bent back and cracked but did not break.

The man sitting next to David suddenly screamed: "Let me out! Let me out of here!"

David grabbed him, tried to keep him inside. The man's eyes were bulging with fear, they were mad; his lips were flecked with saliva, his teeth bared in an awful grin.

"God damn you, let me out!"

He slammed David in the face, ripped open the car door, ran out toward the lobby of the Plaza. He had just passed the statue in the center of the Plaza when a large sliver of glass whistled down and slanted into him. He fell on his face, the blood gurgling from his body.

Carol!

David yelled her name above the awful roar. It vibrated on his lips as he was shaken and tossed in the rear of the cab. She'd be inside the RCA Building now, broadcasting in the studios at Radio City, nine blocks away.

And God knew what was happening within the buildings!

The marquee of the Savoy-Plaza broke off and hung at a crazy, limp angle over the sidewalk.

The water mains on the avenue broke, sending geysers of water shooting skyward. From somewhere far downtown there was a tremendous explosion, and a great cone of smoke puffed straight up and mushroomed in a swirling ball.

Glass was still falling out of the yawning windowpanes, slamming to the road and disintegrating in a shower of slivers, till the road was covered with it.

There was a single sharp tremor, and then suddenly the vibrating stopped. The roar faded to a rumble, which rolled off in an uptown direction.

It was still. It was over.

The driver and David stared at each other stupidly, white-faced, numb with the shock.

Outside a single pane of glass fell from somewhere far up, splintered in the road with a shattering report.

"They've started it," said the driver hoarsely. "It's the war— they've started it. Those Soviet bastards have started it."

He babbled on in the same vein, incoherently, still in shock, half-hysterical.

A man ahead, lying in a pool of his own blood, screamed. People started to pour from the entrances of the buildings, crazy with shock, shouting at the top of their lungs uncontrollably, retching at the sight of those who had been caught by flying glass, slipping and slithering over the glass-covered sidewalks.

They were all running across the street toward the open, toward Central Park.

The driver started his motor. He stepped on the gas; the car skidded on the slippery pavement. He spun it around in the middle of the Plaza.

"Driver!" yelled David. "Driver, get me down to Radio City!"

"You're crazy," babbled the man. "You're crazy, mister. I'm heading for the park, for the open. They may give it to us again any minute. It ain't over yet. We'll get it again. I'm going for the park with everyone else!"

"But I've got to get to Radio City."

"Then walk, God damn it, walk!" the driver yelled savagely. "Get outa my cab and walk!"

David opened the door. The driver, in his hurry to get to the park, hardly slowed down the vehicle. David jumped, fell, cut his hand on a piece of glass. He lay there for a moment, stunned, inert.

Then he looked at his hand. The blood was streaming from it, but luckily it was a superficial cut. He bound it with his handkerchief, unsteadily got to his feet.

Then he dazedly realized that he was without his briefcase. He had left it in the taxi, and the cab was gone.

To hell with it, thought David. It doesn't matter now. It's too late for that and everything else.

I've got to find Carol.

He began to run down Fifth Avenue.

It was hard going, slippery going. The glass-covered pavement was treacherous; he almost fell headlong twice. He dodged a number of white-faced pedestrians running in the opposite direction toward the park, heard others on the sidewalk and on the road, crying out, hurt.

But he did not stop.

He ran blindly through the spray of a spurting water main at Fifty-seventh Street, came out drenched to the skin, moved past the once proud giants of the most glamorous street in the world, Bonwit Teller's, Tailored Woman, Cartier's, DePinna, all long closed, their plate windows shattered out.

At Best and Company he saw what appeared to be a group of victims, all naked, flung crazily over the sidewalk. As he came nearer he saw that they were display mannikins which had been stripped and left in the window when the store had closed.

Saint Patrick's was windowless, but its doors were wide open, and people were running inside for shelter, anywhere to get off the street.

David fought for air; his lungs ached as he ran doggedly on, turning the corner into Fiftieth and Rockefeller Plaza.

A siren sounded, then another.

An Army truck came roaring up Fifth, its solid rubber wheels crunching the thick carpet of broken glass. It was filled with goggled men in monstrous costume: galoshes, gloves, coveralls, and masks. They were hunched over small black boxes and listening to earphones.

This was the Radiological Squad, and these absurd gnomes were the Geiger men.

The clang of ambulances added to the din; the special flying squads of first-aid men began to roll up in trucks. These were the catastrophe units of the Army, specifically designed for disaster action.

The wounded city began to swarm with mobile units carrying uniformed men; it was obvious that the Army had taken over.

David came into the center of Rockefeller Plaza.

It was a weird sight.

The pavements were hidden by piles of jagged, broken glass. The towering buildings surrounding the square—the RCA Building, Time and Life, Eastern Airlines, Associated Press—all glowered down blindly, their glass eyes gouged out.

The sunken rectangular plaza, which once had served as a skating rink in winter and a café garden in summer, was like a box of broken glass.

The great statue of Prometheus, standing watch over the sunken plaza, tilted crazily. David caught a glimpse of the legend:

Prometheus, teacher in every art, brought the fire that has proved to mortals a means to mighty ends.

David ran into the RCA Building, where the broadcasting studios were located.

It was jammed with people milling around, herdlike, afraid to go out, expecting another blow. They were white-faced, shouting, talking hysterically. They had been lucky. They had been safe within the building, and there was no apparent damage to the interior of the great corridor.

The babel rose and fell:

> *"Earthquake—felt like an earthquake."*
>
> *"Earthquake, hell! There's never been an earthquake in New York, not even a tremor. There can't be. This town's built on solid rock!"*
>
> *"It was the Reds! This is just the beginning!"*
>
> *"Everybody said New York would get it first. Well, we have!"*
>
> *"Must have been a bomb planted deep in the subway. Or maybe in the river."*
>
> *"Tried to phone home. The phones are all dead."*
>
> *"They may hit us again—any minute now."*
>
> *"God, what if this whole place is radioactive right now? Maybe it is. Maybe we don't know it. If it is, we're done!"*
>
> *"I could have got out. I could have got out a week ago. But like a damned fool, I stayed."*
>
> *"Charlie, we're done for. We're standing here and dying. It's the radiation. It gets into the marrow of your bones, eats up the blood, gives you tumors like cancer. God, we're standing here and taking it and dying!"*

The place was alive with white helmeted military police trying to keep the crowd in order.

David tried to get to the studio elevators. Only one was in operation, and that was guarded by an MP. He flung David back.

"Better check with the sergeant at the information booth, buddy."

David told the sergeant that he was looking for a Carol Kenny, an actress who, as far as he knew, had been broadcasting in some studio on the upper floors.

The sergeant wasn't inclined to be of much help; he let David know that he didn't have any time at the moment hunting up girl friends for a lot of guys.

"Remember?" said the sergeant. "We just had a little trouble around here."

David suddenly recalled his priority. It had been countersigned by General Hawthorne. He showed it to the sergeant, who immediately became co-operative. He opened a tally book, ran a thick finger down the last page.

"Carol Kenny. Yeah. She had a short rehearsal and then went out."

"She went out?"

"That's right. Just before this thing went off. With an announcer named Ray Graves, it says here. Probably went out for coffee or something. They were due back for broadcast ten minutes ago, but I guess that's out. They won't be broadcasting around here for a little while."

So Carol had gone out. Carol had gone out into the street. And that deadly rain of glass . . .

David felt a little ill. He thought, Maybe nothing happened, maybe she found shelter, maybe she's all right. Maybe . . .

He decided to wait.

An hour passed, and Carol did not show up.

He looked at his watch. It was almost noon. There was no way of finding out what had happened to her, not the way things were now. And he had to get back to Palomar. Something big was going on out there. The Old Man was waiting for him.

He could only hope that Carol was all right, that she hadn't been caught in the street, that she was alive.

David waited another fifteen minutes, then contacted the sergeant at the information desk, told him that he had to get out to Idlewild Airport and that it was an urgent matter of military importance.

The sergeant was very helpful now; the name of Matt Hawthorne was magic. He escorted David through the Forty-ninth Street entrance, hailed an Army car, gave the corporal driving it an order.

"Take this man to the Fifty-ninth Street Bridge, Corporal." He turned to David. "There's a staging point there for Army vehicles moving to the island, sir. If you'll show your priority to the officer in charge at the bridge, I'm sure you'll be able to get a hitch."

An hour later David walked into the terminal at Idlewild. He had just reached the reservations counter when he heard:

"David!"

He whirled and saw Carol running toward him. Stunned, unable to believe that it was she, he stood there, gaping foolishly. And then she was in his arms.

"Carol, what happened? How did you get here?"

"Darling, darling, I thought I'd go out of my mind. I didn't know what happened to you." She was crying on his shoulder. "All I knew was that you were coming out here to the airport. But they didn't have any record of your leaving—and I waited and waited, and finally I thought, back in town, maybe you'd been hurt, maybe you were dead. Oh, David!"

It was a little while before she was coherent enough to tell him the rest.

"I'd just gone out for breakfast, David. With our announcer, Ray Graves. We usually do that between rehearsal and broadcast on a morning show. Anyway, we went over to Sixth Avenue, and we'd just gone into the restaurant when it happened. Everything. After that I knew there wouldn't be any broadcast or anything else. And I kept thinking of you. You'd be out here at the airport, or on the way out. I had to meet you then, to go out with you to California, and Ray—Ray was wonderful. First we went to his place to see if his wife was all right, and she was. Then he drove me out here, went way up to the Triborough Bridge and up the parkway, that way, because the Army wouldn't let any civilian cars cross the Fifty-ninth. Oh, David, I was so afraid something had happened to you. I've been here, waiting and waiting for—well, it seems *years!*"

There was still the problem of getting a seat on a plane for Carol.

David had his reservation and priority, but the reservations clerk swore that he couldn't assign another seat on the next plane going to the Coast.

At the last moment, however, there was a cancellation. One of the passengers hadn't been able to make it, had been delayed in town for a reason unknown. But it could be guessed at, and the guess was pretty grim.

At Chicago they had been delayed for three hours. Now it was just getting dark as the stratocruiser glided across the Arizona border and began to eat up the last lap to San Diego.

The radio was on in the lounge cabin, and an announcer was broadcasting from a Chicago origin. Suddenly he was cut off, and an announcer from New York came in, told his listeners that the transmitters were working again from that city. The passengers in the cabin sat up and listened as he gave them the first news fragments from the metropolis:

". . . the over-all damage to New York, it can now be reported, was surprisingly small. The modern structures in the city stood firm, although a few antiquated wooden buildings collapsed. Casualties, according to early estimates, amounted to some five thousand persons, killed and injured, for the most part, from flying glass.

"The main damage has been to morale. The vibrations, although doing little damage in a material sense, caused panic among those still left in the city. The Army has declared the city under martial law and has ordered the population evacuated.

"The rumor spread through the shaken city that the Russians had struck with an atom bomb buried deep underground, that they would strike again. Army authorities deny this, pointing out that an atomic underground explosion would cause far more serious effects. They report, too, that their Radiological Squads have found no sign of deadly radiation. I repeat— there is no indication of any lethal particles in the air.

"*Seismologists are at a loss to explain the strange vibrations. They point out that New York has always been considered tremor-proof and earthquake-proof, that it stands on solid bedrock, and that it would take a tremendous internal force to cause a fault in the rock.*

"*Meanwhile, the entire nation is being swept by the rumor that the Soviet Union has a secret weapon quite different from but more potent than the atom bomb. The rumor states that the Reds have used the weapon before, and used it to create a tremor in New York this morning as one of the final stages in the war of nerves. The Department of Defense has not confirmed or denied this.*

"*A sensational story is now going the rounds that America's top-ranking military men, at a special meeting this morning, have confirmed the existence of this secret weapon. This story, entirely without confirmation from any official source, states that the decision has been made to attack the Soviet Union in self-defense, that tremendous pressure is being brought on the President as Commander in Chief to give the signal. The story goes on to say that he is, at the moment, resisting all pressures and awaiting a fuller and more complete seismological report, on the off-chance that the tremor may have been a natural phenomenon.*

"*There is even a wilder story, put forth by a former Washington correspondent now at the temporary capital, that the President was about to yield to the advice of his military advisers, when he received a mysterious long-distance phone call from California. According to Frank Landon, the newspaperman responsible, the President was on the phone a half-hour. When he emerged from his office he was deathly pale and changed his point of view abruptly, refusing to order the attack.*

"*I repeat, these are only rumors; there is no official confirmation from any responsible quarter.*"

The stewardess came in and turned off the radio.

"Please go back to your seats and fasten your safety belts," she said. "We'll be coming into San Diego in a few minutes."

5. At Lindbergh Field, David immediately went to a phone booth and called Palomar.

It was Francis who answered. "Dr. Hughes! Where are you, sir?"

"In San Diego. I've got Miss Kenny with me, Francis."

"Oh. Dr. Dawson was worried about you, sir. We all were. After hearing what had happened in New York—well, you understand, Dr. Hughes. Was it very bad?"

"Bad enough. Tell you more about it later, Francis——"

"They say the Russians——"

"Yes, I know," interrupted David impatiently. He wanted to know, he wanted to find out fast. Everything. The phone calls. The urgent order from the Old Man to return. "Francis, what's going on at the observatory?"

"I don't know, Dr. Hughes." Francis sounded dead tired. "All I know is that I've been on the phone, calling astronomers from all over the world, ever since yesterday evening, asking them to come to Palomar at once."

David remembered the operator's remote voice the night before, as he had tried to get Francis, calling Rio, Amsterdam. . . .

"They've been coming in ever since last night and early this morning," continued the steward. "There must be twenty of them in all. Dr. Dawson's been locked in his study with them for hours. They're in there now."

"Francis, who are they? What are their names?"

"Well, Dr. Hughes, there's a Professor Ellender of Harvard, Professor Manning of Mount Wilson, Van Vreeden of Leyden, in

Holland, Dr. Perez of Rio de Janeiro, Bornson of Stockholm, Professor Varanov of the Pulkovo Observatory in Leningrad, Dr. Graves of Cambridge Observatory in England, Dr. Smythe of the Royal Astronomical Society, and oh—several others."

David hung on the phone, spellbound.

Ellender, Manning, Graves, Van Vreeden, Varanov.

These were names, the Greats and the near Greats, the select of the Who's Who of astronomy. Ellender in stellar interiors, Manning in stellar evolution, Van Vreeden in astrophysics, Perez in novae and nebulae, Varanov in comets and meteors, Bornson and Smythe, quantum mechanics.

These were the giants, almost as big as the Old Man. And now, for some fantastic reason, they had flown to Palomar from all over the world.

But why? Why?

The question drummed and throbbed in David's head as Francis continued to talk:

"It started only about an hour after you left for New York, Dr. Hughes. Dr. Dawson came out of his study and he looked—well, I've never seen him look that way. He looked pale—almost *wild.* For a moment I thought he'd had an attack. He gave me the list of names and told me to switch the astronomers to the private phone in his study after I made the connections. Then he asked for you." The steward's voice shook a little through its weariness. "He was so excited that he'd even forgotten you'd gone to New York. After that I tried to phone you and the wires went dead, and finally this morning we managed to get in touch with you."

"And you've no idea what the doctor said to these other men, Francis?"

"No, sir."

"Francis, listen," said David, watching Carol through the glass door of the phone booth. "If you can get to Dr. Dawson, tell him we're going to have a bite to eat here at the air terminal and then start out for Palomar. I've got my car parked in a garage in Dago. And by the way, have you any room for Miss Kenny?"

"Yes, sir. It's quite crowded in the colony now, Dr. Hughes, but I think I can arrange it."

"Thanks, Francis. See you in a couple of hours."

David hung up and walked out of the booth. Carol saw the stunned expression on his face.

"David, what is it?"

He told Carol briefly what was happening at the observatory. But she was unimpressed.

"With the earth ready to blow up, David, does it really matter what happens up there in the sky?" She smiled at him wanly. "And, darling, can we get something to eat now? I'm famished."

He relaxed a little over sandwiches and coffee, and they talked of other things, mostly themselves. And Carol asked finally:

"David, when will we be married?"

"Tomorrow, if you like. We can come back down to Dago here in the morning and stay at a hotel."

Her eyes suddenly filled with tears. "Here comes the bride, darling." She smiled. Then she leaned over the table and kissed him. "And speaking of brides, I'm going to be practically naked. All I've got is the dress I'm wearing, not even a toothbrush. David, I know you're in a hurry, an awful hurry, but when we get your car in San Diego, will you give me a little while, just a few minutes, so that I can buy a few clothes, anything, as long as it fits? Be a darling, say yes."

He grinned and said yes, and kicked himself mentally for not meaning it.

He needed the time; he begrudged it to her.

He wanted to get to Palomar—fast.

They were well out of San Diego now, speeding through the starlit night along the broad road to Palomar.

David kept his foot down hard on the accelerator. They turned off Route 101 at Solana Beach, raced past Rancho Sante Fe, Lake Hodges, through Escondido, the southern gateway to Palomar. And then they began the long, tortuous climb up through the

San Jacinto range, pointing for the solid hogback of granite that was Palomar itself.

"So *this* is what the newspapers call 'The Highway to the Stars,' " said Carol.

"Yes."

She sniffed. "It looks like any other road."

"Naturally. Why shouldn't it?"

"I don't know," she said. "I expected it to look more—well, *glamorous.*"

He smiled. "It will after we get off the plain here and start to climb."

The country grew progressively rugged, a vast and silent wilderness of broken hills and canyons, the star-bright sky painting the patches of snow in old silver and playing weird tricks with the shadows deep in the gorges.

David felt Carol shiver close to him.

"Cold?" he asked.

"No." She laughed apologetically. "I guess I'm just a little scared."

"Why?"

"Well, in the first place, you're driving awfully fast. And in the second place, it's so wild and lonely up here in the mountains. And the way this road curves around and around the mountain with those deep canyons dropping off on both sides——"

"Don't worry," he reassured her. "I've driven this road so many times, I think I could do it with my eyes shut and one hand tied behind my back."

They kept climbing for a few minutes before either of them spoke again. Then Carol said thoughtfully:

"Funny what a difference a little distance makes, David. Back in New York—and yes, even in San Diego—there was always that terrible pressure, that awful *waiting*. But this mountain seems so remote, so far away from everybody and everything. It's another world—a whole new peaceful world."

He nodded. He, too, felt the release. What had happened back in New York seemed now an ugly and nightmarish dream. Whatever happened to the cities, he had thought, even if they were blasted clean off the earth, these mountains would still be around.

But then he remembered the group in the candy store back on Broadway. The talk of neutron radiation, the proprietor, Sam, worrying about his family in the Catskills.

And he thought, The mountains would still be around, but not for man or any other living thing.

Carol leaned her head on his shoulder and dozed a little. He drove on, now and then looking up through the Plexiglas roof of his car, up into the cold night sky. The heavens were blazing, as though some mighty hunter had raised his gun in glee and spattered the black backdrop with a million silver buckshot. His practiced, professional eye picked out the buckshot one by one— cold, dull red Betelgeuse, yellow Capella, familiar Polaris, white-hot and blue-hot Vega and Rigel, and the brightest of them all, Sirius.

He had seen them often enough, studied them through the months and years, and yet he could never get over the wonder of them. There they were, up there now, swimming around among the deep-sky objects—the galaxies, open and globular clusters, diffuse and planetary nebulae, and the bright riot of the Milky Way. They had been moving in their courses billions of years ago, and they would go on, thought David. They would go on in their preordained courses, through astronomical and infinite time, long after the earth had ceased to be.

The Old Man and he had enjoyed many a long talk over early-morning coffee, after the night's work was done and the droning motors closed the dome against the paling sky. On cloudy nights, when the dome stayed up, they played chess in Dr. Dawson's study, and after that, over their brandy, they had often talked all night. And more often than not, the Old Man talked of the sky in non-astronomical terms. David recalled something now that the Old Man had said in one of these sessions.

"Consider the sky, David," Dr. Dawson had said. "The nonprofessional, perhaps, has never realized that what he sees overhead on a clear night is the most amazing drama ever offered. The curtain rises for him, on any clear night, to reveal a superb play written by a divine hand, and the layman barely gives it a glance. But to you and me it has always been a wonderful antidote for sanity when we compare it to the agitated and unpredictable little madhouse on which we live and quarrel and come to blows and die.

"Yes, David," the Old Man had continued. "You and I are astronomers and, therefore, fortunate. We can always retreat from the turbulence around us to our sanctum sanctorum, the sky. It gives us an exact ruler to measure by, a precise order of ideas. And in the presence of the orderly march of illuminated worlds up there in the void, this cold war, this new threat which currently plagues our fourth-rate planet, seems to be only a local affair of some badly run asylum."

Carol stirred and lifted her head from his shoulder. "How far is it to Palomar?"

"Only a little way. We'll be there in a few minutes now."

Carol pressed her nose against the car window and stared out into the night for a minute. Then she asked: "David, why did they pick *this* isolated mountain for an observatory, anyway?"

"For two reason," he answered. "In the first place, the 'seeing' is good."

"The seeing?"

He laughed at her blank look. "Astronomical argot. It refers to the degree of unsteadiness of the image in the observing instrument, as it's affected by the atmospheric refraction of light rays. And the atmosphere itself here is clear the year round—makes for ideal observation. It's comparatively windless. Oh, there are storms during the winter, of course, but they're pretty short—blow over fast."

"You said there was another reason why they built it here."

"Yes. Palomar's almost earthquake-proof."

"Why?"

He grinned down at her. "Are you really interested?"

"Of course I am. If I'm going to marry an astronomer and live up in the observatory colony, I've got to know *something* about my husband's business! Now then, Doctor, you were saying about earthquakes . . .?"

"Well, it's a little technical, but you asked for it. You see, darling, a few million years ago the flat top of Palomar was on a level with the plain round it."

"Well, I must say it's changed since then," she murmured. "It's certainly grown up to be a big boy."

"And still growing. Geological forces from within have pushed it up until now it's six thousand feet above sea level. This mountain happens to be a solid rock of granite, bounded by two fractures, and it can't be shaken very much by any faulting or quake tremor from within. Any shock spreads through it in a fast-moving wave which has a very small force—too small to damage seriously the instruments and 'scopes in the dome."

"Thank you, Doctor," she said gravely.

He grinned and bowed his head elaborately. And at that moment they plunged out from among the trees and into the open, on the summit of the hill. Carol gave one quick gasp.

"Palomar," said David.

The great central dome leaped out of the ground and thrust itself upward with almost breath-taking suddenness. With the great burnished hemisphere reflecting the sky in a silvery sheen, it looked like a half section of some fantastic, inverted dirigible. Behind the central dome, like some infant it had spawned, stood the tiny dome that housed the eighteen-inch Schmidt camera, and distantly, on an outer ridge, glinted the dome of the forty-eight-inch. The power-house topped another rise, flanked by a brood of shining water tanks. A cluster of small buildings and houses hugged the slope of the mountain, close to the dome. It was an austere sight, and yet a kind of silvery fantasia, a geometric fairyland.

"Well, Carol, how do you like it?" There was a note of pride in David's voice.

She groped for words. "I—why, it's almost fabulous, David—it takes your breath away! It looks just like one of those pictures you see in nursery books about the Wizard of Oz or Puss in Boots. You know, where the king's castle is balanced on top of a mountain, surrounded by little cottages perched crazily around on the sides, and a winding road going up."

David grinned. "Come to think of it, it *does* look like that."

As he spoke he saw that the dome of the big building was up, and for a moment it didn't register. This was a clear night, the sky nearly perfect. Then suddenly he remembered. The Old Man wasn't running any takes of the sky tonight. He was closeted in his study with the big shots of the world's observatories and discussing . . . *What?*

With mounting excitement he drove through the gate of the high wire fence and parked the car in the yard. They stepped out into the sharp, sub-zero cold, and once out of the car, the heavens seemed to come down and blaze and crackle about them, so that the stars seemed almost tinselly artificial in their brightness, and Carol almost fancied that she could actually hear them pop around her shoulders.

They walked halfway around the great, squat, round building before they came to a small door, not much bigger than a house door and almost lost in the massive circular wall. Through this, after identifying themselves to a sergeant at the door, they entered a foyer tastefully and simply furnished in early American and softly lighted by hidden lamps. The reception room beyond the foyer was in the celestial motif, topped by a miniature dome supported on oval arches.

A stout man with iron-gray hair, ruddy-cheeked and neatly dressed in a suit of shiny alpaca, rose from a desk and came forward to meet them. It was obvious that he was dead tired. His face was lined with fatigue, and there were shadows under his eyes.

"Hello, Francis," said David. "Dr. Dawson still in the study with the others?"

"Yes, Dr. Hughes. I didn't dare disturb him—even to tell him you were here. They've been in there for hours."

"Maybe I'd better not barge right in then. I'll wait till they've finished." David suddenly remembered that Carol was at his side. "Oh, darling, this is Francis, our steward, receptionist, and general major-domo of Palomar. He arranges for all the earthy wants of this stargazing colony, and if you ever need anything, call on him. Francis—this is Carol Kenny."

The stout man smiled. "In a way I've already met her face to face, sir. Welcome to Palomar, Miss Kenny."

Carol looked puzzled for a moment until David grinned and said: "Francis is a great radio and television fan. One of your admiring public. He's seen your lovely face on the video screen many a time. In fact, he never fails to keep me posted when you're scheduled to go on."

"Oh." Carol looked gratefully at Francis. "Thank you for reminding him. And of course he's written a lot about you in his letters. He spent half of one whole letter raving about the veal paprika you serve."

Francis blushed. He was obviously pleased as he took their coats and hung them in a closet. When he turned back David looked at him solicitously and said:

"You look all in, Francis."

"It *has* been hectic, sir. Getting all those phone calls through for Dr. Dawson—ordering extra food and setting up extra cots in the auditorium—and then of course arranging for Tom and Guido to drive the station wagons down to San Diego to meet the planes and pick up the astronomers as they came in." Francis shrugged. "Well, sir, you can imagine, none of us have had much sleep in the last twenty-four hours."

"How's Dr. Dawson taking it?" David was concerned. "You know he can't stand too much, Francis—not with his heart."

"Yes, sir. I know. Mrs. Dawson phoned the observatory here from the house three times in the last hour. She's tried to get through to the doctor, and I know she wants to get him home for some rest, but he won't talk to *anyone*. He's just locked himself in the study with the others, and he hasn't had a bite to eat since early this morning."

David thought of the galaxy of names closeted with the Old Man. Then he asked:

"Did you say, Francis, that Varanov of the Pulkovo Observatory was here?"

"Yes, Dr. Hughes."

"Funny they let him leave Russia at a time like this."

"He wasn't in Russia, sir. We located him in Mexico City. He was working on something with Professor Martinez down there. Dr. Dawson had some trouble with the officer in charge of the military guard here. At first he wouldn't admit Varanov into the observatory, but finally Dr. Dawson won out." Then the steward abruptly changed the subject. "Was it really terrible in New York, sir? The radio and television have been broadcasting all kinds of stories."

"It was bad, Francis," admitted David. "But not as bad as a lot of people think. The buildings weren't damaged, outside of the windows, and those people who got hurt were caught in the streets."

Francis shook his head. "I don't know, Dr. Hughes, up here we're so far from everything. They say the Soviets are responsible, that they've got some kind of new and terrible weapon. But I don't know. I just don't understand how it ever got to this. Another war, after the last one . . ."

Suddenly the steward remembered his duties and turned to Carol. "Oh. You must be tired after your trip, Miss Kenny." And then to David: "I've saved her one of the small guest cottages, sir."

"Thank you, Francis," said David. "I appreciate it."

"And so do I," added Carol. "But somehow I'm not the least bit tired right now——"

She broke off abruptly as a tall, regal-looking woman with snow-white hair came through the foyer door.

"Well, David!" Her bright eyes showed relief as Francis hurried to her and helped her off with her coat. "We were half afraid you weren't coming back!" Then she looked at Carol. "And this is Carol."

"Carol," said David, "this is Mrs. Dawson."

"You're right, David," Emily Dawson looked at Carol appraisingly. "She is lovely. And I'm glad you came, Carol; this young man was eating his heart out." She took Carol's hands in her own and smiled warmly. "Welcome to Palomar."

"Thank you, Mrs. Dawson."

Emily Dawson had met the Old Man when he was a student at Harvard. David could never look at her without thinking that she must have been a beauty in those days, in the days of her youth. Her features were chiseled so straight that they were almost severe, but her warm smile and the gracious welcome in her lively blue eyes belied any reserve. Her hair was startling, almost showy in its whiteness, and her skin was smooth, delicate in texture, and gave the illusion of being almost transparent.

It struck David, as he watched Emily Dawson and Carol standing together, that the Old Man's wife was still a beauty, in a great and gracious way, in a different, antique frame.

Those who knew the Old Man said she provided the only earthbound competition to the stars in his affection. She fussed over him, worried about his food, bought his clothes, saw that he carried his heart tablets in every suit. And, as Mrs. Dawson once said to David:

"I'm not a wife to the doctor, David. I'm just his caretaker."

But she was his wife. The Old Man was utterly helpless without her. And now Emily Dawson was holding Carol at arm's length and smiling into her eyes.

"Well, my dear! You're going to be an astronomer's wife. How do you think you'll like it?"

"I think I'll like it very much."

"Wait, child, wait!" The Old Man's wife shook her head dismally. "You'll be the most miserable woman in the world in a little while. No sensible girl in her right mind should marry an astronomer."

"But why not?"

"Astronomers work nights, my dear. You'll never have any social life. If you want to go to the theater, you have to consult the weatherman and make sure you buy your tickets on a cloudy night. If you want your husband to take you to a concert, you pray for rain. Sometimes, when the weather is clear and you've been home alone night after night, you could scream for a few friendly clouds to come along and cover the sky, so that your husband can come home from the observatory and keep you company."

She shook her head again, dolefully. "Take the advice of an old woman, Carol. Learn to knit or take up solitaire—anything to occupy those long evening hours. Otherwise you'll be horribly bored and start thinking of how nice it would be to be married to someone in the plumbing-supply business."

David grinned at the Old Man's wife. "Before Carol has a chance to answer, Mrs. Dawson, and before you have any more chance to break up my happy home before it begins, *I'd* like to put *my* two cents in."

"Yes?"

"I've known you for a few years, and I can't remember ever seeing *you* knitting, or playing solitaire either. And I'd be willing to bet you aren't bored."

The phone buzzed. Francis answered it and then stiffened tensely at his desk.

"Yes, Doctor," Francis was saying. "Yes, sir, Dr. Hughes is here. He just came in with Miss Kenny. Yes, I'll tell him. What was that, sir? Bring the small radio into the study? Yes, Doctor, at once."

Emily Dawson went to Francis quickly. "Tell the doctor I want to speak to him."

She took the phone. "Charles, you've got to stop. You've got to come home and get some rest. . . . I know, I know. It's important, it's always important. But this time, Charles, you're overdoing it. I don't know what you're up to—you've never told me—but nothing is that important." She listened for a moment and then hung up.

Her eyes were dull now, her lighthearted mood gone; she looked tired, worried.

"I can't do anything with him. I can't do a thing with him, David. It's the first time. And whatever this thing is, he'll kill himself."

So the Old Man wanted the radio in his study, thought David. Ordinarily Dr. Dawson hated the radio and television both. They intruded with affairs that didn't interest him, that disturbed him, that violated the tranquillity of his own kingdom.

But now he was asking for it. Funny, thought David. The Old Man was closeted in his study with a group of top men, the greatest astronomers of them all, whose only horizon was infinity.

But a radio was an earthly affair, confined to earthly matters. It had nothing to do with nebulae or island universes millions and billions of light years away.

They must be talking about something very close to home, guessed David.

But if so, *what?*

He thought of the wild rumors sweeping the country, the phenomenon at New York, the Russian secret weapon General Hawthorne had talked about. Hawthorne had said that it was something on a cosmic scale.

Maybe, thought David, maybe the general was right. Maybe Hawthorne had something, after all.

Maybe that's what they were discussing in the Old Man's study right now—looking down at their feet instead of over their heads.

"Dr. Dawson wants to see you in a few minutes, Dr. Hughes," Francis was saying. "He told me to tell you to stand by."

David nodded. Then, as the steward was helping Emily Dawson on with her coat, David took Carol's arm.

"Carol, you don't have to wait——"

"I'd like to, David," she said. "I'm not tired at all, and I'd like to see the observatory. I'm terribly curious."

"If you wish, Dr. Hughes," said the steward. "I could——"

"Thanks just the same, Francis," interrupted David. "But you've got plenty to do as it is. Anyway, I'd like to show her around myself while I wait for that meeting to finish."

Mrs. Dawson offered Carol the hospitality of her home for the night, but David thanked her on Carol's behalf and told her that Francis had already made arrangements. Then the Old Man's wife turned to Francis and said:

"Francis, I'll be waiting up. The moment the doctor finishes, call me. I'll come for him myself." Her face sagged a little now, it was haggard, but she smiled as she turned to Carol.

"Please come and see me tomorrow, my dear."

After Emily Dawson had left, and as Francis was disconnecting the small radio from his desk, David said with an attempt at lightness:

"Come on, Carol. I'll take you on the dollar tour."

He led her through a door and onto the ground floor. This was a circular corridor, severely simple and paved in rubber parquet. From it, on each side, ran the astronomers' offices. Then he conducted Carol past the small auditorium and lecture hall, the library, the cafeteria, and the kitchen, gleaming in white tile and monel metal. They walked by a series of darkrooms, and finally he led her into his own office.

"Like it?" he asked.

She studied the leather furniture, the bookshelves recessed in the paneled walls, the deep gray rug, and the illustrations: David's graduating class picture at Columbia, an etching of the original Harvard Observatory, a drawing of Galileo peering through his telescope lens, an air view of Palomar itself, and finally a picture of herself on the leather-topped desk.

"It's very nice, David," she said. "But it's so plain—it needs a little color——"

"Oh no, you don't." He grinned. "No frilly feminine touches for me—not here, anyway. This is my retreat, and if it's monastic— well, I like it that way. I don't care what you do to the cottage we're going to live in—that's your department—but in my office, no colored pottery, no chintz curtains on the windows——"

"*What* windows!" She laughed. "There isn't a window in this whole darned mausoleum!"

He took her back in the rotunda and up the stairs to the mezzanine. He pointed out the lounge, rest rooms, drinking fountains, exhibits of meteoric rock under glass, a model of the observatory itself, literature in racks, illustrations of the planets, and finally a large reception room displaying the history of the 200-inch reflector, in photographs, drawings, and text.

"Now *this* looks a little more comfortable," Carol remarked.

"Yes. The mezzanine here is our concession to the public. People come up here in droves every Sunday, not only from San Diego, but even from Los Angeles."

David had forgotten his somber mood of a few minutes ago. This personal little tour was something he had planned for a long time, and now that Carol was here, he was enjoying her reactions.

"But, David, why should they come here? Isn't the Mount Wilson observatory much nearer to Los Angeles?"

"Sure." He smiled. "And ten years ago, back in 1950, before Palomar was really open to the public on a tourist basis, Wilson used to get all the business. But now *we've* got the biggest eye in the world, while Mount Wilson has to struggle along with a puny 100-inch. And you know people—they like to see the biggest and the best."

"What on earth do you do with them when they get here?"

"Oh, show 'em around—lecture 'em on the theory of operation—open and close the dome for them—let 'em look at the telescope."

"That must keep Dr. Dawson pretty busy on Sundays."

"The Old Man? *He* doesn't wet-nurse the tourists." David made a wry face. "*I* do!"

She laughed up at him. "Well, the public is lucky to have a handsome barker like you. But, David, what do you do, line them up one by one when they want to look through the telescope?"

"Look through *what* telescope?"

"Why, the big one that's here." She was taken aback by his sudden and mock-stern expression. "David, what's the matter? What did I say?"

"Oh, nothing. Nothing but blasphemy, heresy, and sacrilege—at least for an astronomer's wife. I'm glad no one overheard you."

"But all I said was——"

"I know. You see, my darling, you don't *look* through a reflector or mirror telescope. Not a big one like this, anyway. You just take photographs."

"But in all the pictures I've ever seen," she protested, "the astronomer always has his eye screwed up against a little eyepiece at the bottom of the telescope when he's looking at stars and heavenly bodies and things."

He looked even more pained at that. "Sure. But they were looking through a refractor, or lens telescope. They're more romantic—much more photogenic for movies or magazines. As I said, we don't *look* through a reflector like the Big Eye here at Palomar—we get *into* it."

"You what?"

"We ride up to the top of the telescope and climb down inside of it. Or at least the Old Man does. He takes all the observations and makes all the complicated calculations. I just stay below near the switchboard and give him the position settings."

She looked incredulous. "You mean you really get *inside* the telescope?"

"Come on." He grinned. "I'll show you."

He led her out past rows of switchboards protected by roller sheets of metal, and they climbed another flight of parquet stairs into a kind of transparent cubicle completely enclosed by glass, walls and ceiling alike. A tiny glass sign said: "No Visitors Allowed Beyond This Point."

"Well," said David quietly, "there it is—the Big Eye."

"Oh, David!" Her whisper was almost inaudible.

It was a thrilling, awe-inspiring sight. The huge telescope, like a great monstrous robot, loomed up almost vertically, sheer into the shadowy arch of the dome, where its soaring spiderwork disappeared entirely. It was big—big beyond description—almost frightening in its vastness. Its north and south piers, squat and solid and massive, came out of the floor and held up the great apparatus like two hunched shoulders. The two cylinders in its yoke were bigger than railroad cars as they reached out for support into the horseshoe of the frame. The telescope tube itself rested silently, delicately, on its trunnions.

It was still, motionless, now. Yet Carol, as she stared at it, almost had the feeling that it was alive, that it had a beating heart and nerves and muscles, that it was sleeping now but soon would bestir itself, yawn, and then reach up and up toward the stars, its five hundred tons creaking and groaning in the joints as it stretched itself.

"It gets you, doesn't it?" said David softly.

"Oh yes, yes," she whispered. "David, what—what does a Thing like that *do?*"

"More than any man ever dreamed would be possible." He spoke almost reverently. "The Big Eye right out there has reached up into billions of light years of cold space, Carol. It's pulled down stars and nebulae and supernovae we never knew existed before, and dropped them right into our laps. It's discovered new and remote worlds—millions and millions of them—some of them vast enough to make our own look like a microscopic speck of dust floating around in a stadium." He was staring up into the dome, talking half to himself now. "It's brought enough light down through what we call the tube and onto that big mirror to make real studies of the galactic systems, the binary stars and their separation, and the secret of the expanding universe itself——"

"I'm not sure of what you're saying," she interrupted. "But just hearing it makes my head swim."

He nodded. "Unless you're an astronomer, Carol, I suppose this *is* so much Greek. But putting it in layman's language, that big 'scope out there is already giving us the story of how stars are born, how big they are, how hot they get, and how long they have to live. And that isn't all. From that kind of data we're already getting a hint of how long *we* have to live right here on earth."

She stared at him. "How?"

"Well, it's this way, Carol. The sun itself is a star—and pretty small potatoes, a poor relative, as far as stars go. In terms of stellar distance, the earth is practically glued to it. When we find out how old the sun actually is, we'll be able to predict how much longer it's going to shine, giving us light and heat." He smiled. "See? We're kicking around in this particular universe on borrowed time. We've hitched our earthy wagon to a star, but someday that star's going to lie down and slowly die on us!"

She shuddered. "What a horrible thought!"

"Don't worry." He laughed. "We're still good for a few billion years yet." Suddenly he sobered. "Or—we were. Now—I don't know. It looks as though man, with his little atom bomb, is going to beat the sun to the punch and get rid of himself first." He took her arm. "Come on, Carol. I'll take you up to the top."

"You mean—way up there?" She looked apprehensively up into the shadowy dome.

"Sure. Up to the observer's cage, inside the top of the 'scope." He led her back down the stairs and into the corridor. "We never take the public into the observation room itself. You see, Carol, crowds generate heat from their bodies, and just a couple of degrees' rise in the observation-room temperature would be enough to throw several of the delicate instruments right out of whack. And of course we rarely give anybody a ride to the top. You ought to feel very flattered."

"Thank you," she said weakly. "But right now I'm beginning to feel scared."

He went to a locker, pulled out two heavy fleece-lined suits, fur hats with ear muffs attached, heavy mittens, and scarves. "We'd better put these on," he said. "If we're going for a ride to heaven, we'd better be dressed for it. Gets pretty cold up there in the dome. From the way it felt when we got out of the car in the yard, it's well below zero."

They wriggled into the heavy clothing, and then David led her to a small automatic elevator. In a few moments they stopped at the main floor, and as the elevator door opened, a cold blast of air hit them. David stepped out, went to a control board, and pushed a button. A motor droned somewhere, and the hemispheric roof opened into two halves. Only an almost imperceptible hum and a faint lightening of the shadows indicated that the roof was opening at all. Carol, craning her neck and looking straight upward, finally made out a faint segment of blue-black sky and two or three faint stars almost hanging onto the end of the 'scope as it thrust up vaguely into the slice of night between the parted dome.

David came away from the control room, smiling. "Of course this is just a demonstration. We're not going to take any observations or anything like that. I just wanted you to know what it was like when the dome was down."

He led her back into the elevator, and they stopped on a narrow balcony. From here they climbed a short, circular iron stairway to what David called the "jump-off" bridge. They were already at a dizzy height, and he could feel Carol holding his hand with almost frantic pressure. A blast of icy-cold air blew down upon them through the open dome.

"All right, darling?" he asked.

"I think so," she said in a small voice. "But as far as I'm concerned this is the end of the world."

He held her close. "In a way it is. From here on we take a scenic railway to the stars."

He pressed a push button on the bridge. Carol gasped as a flying conveyor car raced down a curved track from an invisible perch far up under the dome and stopped at the bridge. David grinned at her discomfiture and motioned her to step onto the narrow car.

She looked at him and shook her head, a little pale. "Don't be afraid," he said gently. "Just hang onto me." He held her by the arm, and gingerly she stepped across the abyss beneath and onto the car.

David closed the small swinging gate on the conveyor car and locked it. "Hang onto the rail with both hands," he said.

Then he pushed a button, and somewhere below motors began to sing a muted song. The cage glided away, then soared outward

and upward in a dizzy, fantastic ascent toward the top of the telescope. Now they were two fur-covered pygmies whirling up into the
vault of the dome, riding a steel carpet toward the stars. Finally the
car slowed and came to a stop next to a catwalk. The observation
floor yawned far below, and they were almost fifteen stories from
the ground level itself.

For a moment Carol clung to David, trembling as he held her. He
was immediately penitent. "Maybe I shouldn't have brought you up
here."

"No, no," she said faintly. "I—just for a moment I felt—well, a
little sick. I'll be all right."

"Sure?" He was really concerned now.

She nodded. He held onto her and pointed down into the top of
the telescope. She saw a cisternlike cubbyhole, a cylindrical steel
well, with a curved bottom and an instrument desk coming up
through the floor. There was a strange-looking little chair at the
desk which rolled around on rails within the well, and an instrument panel opposite the desk, set with dials.

"This is the observer's cage," said David. "The Old Man sits in
that chair and through the voice-power phone signals to me down
at the control board for star settings. When I start the Big Eye moving, he rides along down there inside of it, watching those luminous
dials until they indicate the exact observation position. Then he
pushes his photographic plateholder into position, pulls out the
slide—and that's the 'take.' "

He said nothing more for the moment. They stood there, clinging to the catwalk. Carol felt David's arm slip around her waist,
and she leaned against him. A strange, almost wild feeling of ex-
altation filled her, and she looked up through the dome into the
indigo sky. The stars seemed to be floating by across it, moving
through it like tiny lighted ships at sea.

They had escaped from their own planet now, and they were
standing in space. They had stepped off the earth and ridden up
into the mysterious bosom of the heavens and thrust their heads
among the stars, into the vault of the universe itself. Up there the

illuminated stars moved along their ordained paths through infinity, through everlasting tranquillity. The earth was not a few feet below, but a million light years below, a remote and troubled and diseased speck of dirt swimming around in the void, crawling with microscopic and cannibalistic organisms.

"It's wonderful," Carol whispered, "wonderful. I've never felt so exhilarated, so *free*." She stole a look at David's face, saw his reverent, faraway look.

It's like being close to God up here, she thought, so close that you could almost see His face.

The phone suddenly buzzed down in the cisternlike cage. Like a noisy burglar, it broke the silence and the spell. Up here at the top of the telescope, they had for a moment soared into the heavens, but now they knew that it, too, was earthbound.

David turned to Carol. "Somebody below wants us," he said. "Do you think you can hang onto the catwalk here for a moment?"

She nodded. He walked to the top of the telescope and clambered down a series of pipe rails into the cage. The phone buzzed again, and he hunched over it like a furry dwarf, fumbling with the receiver in his heavy mittens.

He spoke briefly, put the receiver back on the hook, and then looked up at Carol from the cistern below.

"That was Francis. We'd better go right back down. The Old Man wants to see me now."

6. As they descended to the ground-floor corridor they heard the news coming over Francis's radio, muffled in the Old Man's study.

They were back on earth again.

Outside of Dr. Dawson's study they saw small knots of men gathered, talking in low voices. David was struck by the fact that their faces were taut and grim, that they seemed strangely quiet, without animation.

He picked them out one by one—Ellender of the Harvard Observatory, the shaggy man with the ill-fitting suit; Manning of Mount Wilson, a giant of a man, bald as a billiard ball; Van Vreeden of Holland; Perez of Brazil, rotund and swarthy; Varanov, the Russian from Leningrad, a white-bearded man with ice-blue eyes; Dr. Smythe of the Royal Astronomical Society, a wizened hunchback.

There were others, too, whom Francis hadn't mentioned. Duval, who watched the heavens from the Swiss Alps, Wallace of Aberdeen, Alvarez of Chile. Many of them were refugees from Soviet-dominated Europe and Asia.

What was the matter with them? thought David, bewildered. Where was all the excitement of the new discovery, *if* there had been something new. Why were they speaking in hushed tones? Why were their faces so grave, so pale and rigid, like puppet masks?

David walked up to Dr. Ellender and extended his hand. Ellender had been his mentor at Harvard and had been largely instrumental in getting the Old Man to invite David to Palomar. But Ellender seemed hardly to recognize him; his gray eyes seemed to look through and beyond David.

"Hello, David," he said absently. That was all. Ellender turned and followed the other men down the corridor. His hand, in the brief moment it had touched David's, was damp and limp and cold. And his forehead, too, was wet with perspiration.

As they drifted off, Francis came out of the reception room and met David and Carol near Dr. Dawson's door. Then he added almost apologetically:

"Dr. Dawson just rang for me, Dr. Hughes. He asked me to bring in both of you."

David looked puzzled for a moment and then knocked on the door. A gentle voice spoke from within, almost inaudibly.

"Come in."

A man was seated at a desk piled with a jumble of books, slide rules, photographs, pencils, and yellow scratch pads covered with computations. Carol looked at him curiously as he rose to greet them. So this is Dr. Dawson, she thought. This is the Old Man of the Mountain, the Wizard of Palomar, one of the great men of all time, whose back yard was the universe itself.

Carol lived in a world of celebrities, of Big Names, and she was used to them. She was one herself, in a modest way. Yet in the presence of this man she suddenly felt an almost embarrassing humility. There was nothing blatant about his appearance, nothing particularly bizarre or striking. Yet in a roomful of men you would pick him out among all the others for some baffling reason. You would know instinctively that here was a great man, a man who attracted others by a personal magnetism of sheer intelligence glowing from within and radiating outward.

"Dr. Dawson," said David. "This is my fiancée, Carol Kenny."

The Old Man offered her a thin, blue-veined hand. "Welcome to Palomar, Miss Kenny."

He spoke mechanically, almost without interest, as though he were hardly aware she was there. He seemed preoccupied, a million miles away. He was courteous enough, but there was no warmth in his voice, no welcoming smile.

The Old Man's just going through the motions, that's all, thought David.

It was unbelievable, he thought, unbelievable. He'd never seen the Old Man act like this before. Ordinarily Dr. Dawson was an unfailing gentleman in his relations with others. He put them at their ease, and they took to him immediately. No matter whom he met, in whatever station of life, he gave others the impression of humility, made them feel that it was *his* privilege to meet them, listened intently to what they had to say, as though every word they spoke were a word of wisdom. David knew that this appreciation of others was genuine. The Old Man was no poseur. Yet now he was almost rude.

It was plain that something had shaken him deeply, that he was laboring under some kind of tremendous tension. There was no other answer. After all, he wasn't meeting a perfect stranger in Carol. He had always been keenly interested in her, had asked David a hundred questions about her, had looked forward to meeting her. Now . . .

"You must be tired after your trip, Miss Kenny. Francis here will take you to your quarters if you wish."

His voice was gentle, but it was an obvious dismissal. David, shocked, glanced at Carol to see how she was taking it. He wondered: What is she thinking of the Old Man now—especially after the way I built him up?

But Carol was sensitive and a good actress. She could see that the Old Man wanted to be alone with David. She only smiled gratefully and said: "I *am* a little tired, Dr. Dawson. Thank you for being so thoughtful." David saw her to the door with Francis and squeezed her hand. "See you in the morning, darling," he said. Then he closed the door and turned to face the Old Man.

"Sit down, my boy," said Dr. Dawson gently.

David sank into one of the deep leather chairs. His curiosity was like a mouse in his belly, gnawing away at his innards. What was the Old Man waiting to tell him?

Slowly, almost deliberately, Dr. Dawson reached into his desk, took out one of the small cigars he favored. He lit it, and as he did David saw that his hand trembled.

"My boy, I don't have to tell you that something tremendous has happened. You know that I would not have countermanded General Hawthorne's order and exposed you to grave charges without a very good reason."

David nodded. The Old Man puffed on his cigar for a moment and looked steadily at his protégé. Then he said suddenly:

"David—do you believe in God?"

David's mouth dropped half open at the question. It stunned him by its very suddenness, by its irrelevance to anything he had even remotely expected. But the Old Man was dead serious, his eyes demanded an answer, and David managed to falter:

"Of course, sir, of course—I believe in God."

The Old Man paused. He seemed to look deep into David, weighing the sincerity of his answer. Then he said quietly:

"I know what you must be thinking, my boy, and I don't blame you. But I have not gone suddenly mad, and I am not yet senile. We have known each other for some time, David, and for some reason we have never touched upon this subject, this subject of faith, or religion, if you like. Now, in view of what has happened, I had to ask you, I had to know."

In view of what has happened, the Old Man had just said. Well, thought David, what *has* happened? And what did God have to do with it?

Dr. Dawson seemed to anticipate what David was thinking. He went on:

"Here at Palomar, David, you and I, as astronomers, have seen the great procession of stars and planets move in their immutable courses. We have named and classified them, measured them in precise terms—positions, orbits, velocities, temperatures, luminosities, compositions, and absolute magnitudes. If, in doing this kind of work, we have thought of our relationship to God at all, we have marveled at the orderly manner in which He has arranged the expanding universe."

Dr. Dawson put his cigar on a tray and leaned back in his chair, his eyes half closed. Then he continued:

"There are men of science who, since they cannot measure God, weigh him, or produce Him in chemical synthesis, are not concerned with his existence. Yet even *they* must have reflected that once, at the beginning of time, there was an original nebula that filled the void of the universe with equal density everywhere. They must have asked themselves, 'Where did it come from? How did it get there? Who put it there?' If a Creator did not create it, *who* did? If the agnostics and atheists among us do not admit the role of a Creator here, they must at least admit that it is an undefinable mystery.

"At any rate, David, whatever the innermost conviction of each man, it is only the fool who does not at least admit the mystery of creation—who thinks that everything just 'happened' somehow."

Dr. Dawson paused, looked steadily at David. "Forgive me, my boy, for all this preamble. But it is very pertinent to what I have to say." He measured his words. "In the past few months, David, I have seen a miracle. I have witnessed the *hand of God* suddenly appear in the universe."

"*The hand of God?*" echoed David stupidly.

The Old Man nodded. He reached forward on his desk, picked up a batch of enlarged photographs.

"Look at these."

David stared at the top photograph. So *this* was the project Dr. Dawson had been working on so feverishly through the Big Eye. This was why, at the Old Man's urgent request, Ellender, Perez, Varanov, and the others had come running to Palomar from all over the world. They *were* concerned with the sky, after all, and not with earth-bound matters.

He studied the photograph eagerly. It was that of a familiar constellation, and his practiced eye picked out at first glance what seemed to be a normal astronomical pattern. His mind clicked over like a comptometer, identifying the various members in the group.

Then suddenly something jarred his vision.

It was a tiny patch of light where no light should have been.

Dr. Dawson hadn't even labeled it.

David tried to place the intruder, tried to identify it. But it was foreign to him; he had never seen it before. He shuffled through the other photographs. There it was, again and again, the annoying and insistent extra patch of light, hanging on like a bright little leech. It changed its position as the dates of the observations changed, but it was there every time, sharp and clear.

It was all the more mysterious because Dr. Dawson had neglected to give it a name.

David stared at the photograph again, and his mind leaped to the possibility of asteroids or a new comet, but as quickly abandoned the idea as he shuffled through the other photographs.

David looked up at the Old Man, bewildered.

"I don't understand it, sir. It's something I don't recognize—something that doesn't belong——" He caught his breath as he saw the expression on the Old Man's face. "You mean it's something brand new—something we've never seen before?"

The Old Man nodded. "You and I are among the first to see it, David, with the help of the 200-inch telescope. But in the not-too-distant future it will be visible not only to other astronomers with smaller telescopes, but finally to the naked eye of the whole world. It was only by sheer accident, by the most remote chance, that I stumbled on it first, late in September, while doing some routine observations."

"But what is it, sir," asked David, "that extra point of light?"

"A new planet," answered the Old Man quietly.

"*A new planet?*"

"Yes, David. A strange new intruder into our solar system. Not an ordinary planet in the conventional sense, for it doesn't revolve around our sun at all. But a planet in size and mass and every other detail."

Dr. Dawson paused a moment as David kept his eyes glued to the tiny patch of silver. Then he continued:

"As you know, the last planet discovered was Pluto, back in 1930, at the Lowell Observatory. At the time of its discovery, before it was officially named Pluto, it was designated as Planet 'X.'

"Therefore, I shall name this newcomer—Planet 'Y.' "

Planet "Y"!

David was staggered. He stared at the Old Man stupidly. For a moment he could not believe what he had heard. No wonder the greatest astronomers alive had dropped whatever they were working on and answered the Old Man's summons!

This was one of those dream discoveries, the greatest triumph of the Big Eye, an astronomical miracle. He thought dazedly of what would happen in the observatories of the world when the news came out officially. That is, if the world was still around.

They'd go crazy, he thought, crazy!

So *this* was the answer! *This* was what the Old Man was talking about—the *hand of God*. This was it, this extra patch of light. There it was, planted on those photographs, sharp and clear.

For as long as men could remember there had been only nine planets revolving around the sun.

And now—now there were ten.

Now, as the Old Man had put it, there was a strange new intruder in the sky, a kind of heavenly stepchild, a celestial Johnny-come-lately.

Planet "Y."

"It's a massive body, as planets go," the Old Man was saying. "Much bigger than the earth. And it's traveling through space with fantastic velocity, far greater than that of the earth. It made the orbit difficult to calculate. In fact, two years ago it would have been impossible, before Morrissey built us his analogue computer."

Dr. Dawson's voice leveled off into a monotone, as though he were delivering a lecture before a science forum. "Although we can now see it and trace its orbit, we don't know where this wildcat planet came from, and we never will. The origin of Planet 'Y,' David, does not fit into any of the present cosmogonies. If we accept the Weizsäcker hypothesis as correct for the formation of our own solar system, we must reluctantly conclude that there are exceptions to it as a rule. For Planet 'Y' must have been born in the fiery explosion of a supernova."

David nodded. "I would agree, sir. It seems to me only the expanding wave front of a bursting sun could have given it the initial velocity necessary to bring it toward our system at its present speed."

As he spoke he reflected on what a triumph this would be for the Old Man. To discover a new planet was tremendous enough, but to add to it a major contribution to the theory of planetogenesis was enough to shatter the calm in every observatory in the world.

"At any rate, David," the Old Man went on, "Planet 'Y' was born. It was hurled off into space, traveling like a fantastic juggernaut, drifting through space for thousands or millions of years.

Then at last it came into the gravitational field of a star, was caught and held. It is plunging toward that star now."

"And that star," said David, "is the sun."

"Yes."

"It's a great discovery, sir." David's voice shook a little. "No wonder you called those men to Palomar. It'll create a sensation."

Yet as David spoke he wondered, even so, even in the face of this tremendous new phenomenon, why had the Old Man ordered him back in such a hurry?

"As you say, David," continued Dr. Dawson, "this new intruder into our solar system will create a sensation. But it is more than just a new planet. The consequences of its appearance are staggering beyond the limits of human imagination and there is no doubt it will profoundly change the pattern of human life. If this new planet is anything it is the hand of God."

There he goes again, thought David. The hand of God.

The Old Man seemed obsessed with the idea. Dr. Dawson was a scientist, through and through, and yet what he was saying now was curiously unscientific. Of course, David said to himself, it was a miracle, but you could figure it on a cause-and-effect basis. A fragment from a distant star coming within the sun's gravitational field and swinging in an orbit around it.

It was the longest long shot possible, but theoretically it could happen.

In fact, it *had* happened.

But that wasn't all, apparently. There was more that the Old Man was getting ready to say. David could see it in his face, read it in his over-bright eyes.

There was something else coming. Something big.

But *what*?

What could top a discovery like this? The Old Man had said something about the planet's changing the way men lived. It struck like a jagged fragment in David's mind. Where did *that* belong in all this?

"David," said the Old Man, "everything I have discussed up to now has been a kind of preamble, by way of preparation for what I have to tell you now. A minute ago I asked you if you believed in God, and I said I had a reason for the question. If your belief is sincere, if your faith is deep-rooted, then it will give you strength to meet the revelation I am about to make to you, and even help you gain some comfort from it." Dr. Dawson hesitated a moment. "Now, David, I must ask you to prepare for a shock—a very great shock."

David sat rigid in his chair, fascinated, watching the Old Man. His collar suddenly seemed to be unnaturally tight, and he felt the goose flesh rise on his body. For a moment neither of them spoke.

Finally the Old Man picked up a chart from his desk.

"This chart illustrates the future orbit of the new planet, David. I've been plotting it for days, but I got my first result about an hour after you left for New York on Wednesday."

David looked down at the chart.

Then suddenly it swam before his eyes as the full implication of what he saw smashed into his brain. The sweat broke out in a cold ooze on his forehead, his mouth went dry, a cruel hand seemed to be curling itself around his throat, stifling his breath.

It was right there before his eyes. The awful and incredible denouement to the Old Man's discovery.

Planet "Y" was headed for an elliptical orbit around the sun. But its orbit intersected that of the earth, and the chart showed both bodies reaching the intersection point simultaneously.

Long before the geometric point of intersection, Planet "Y" would come close enough to exert a tremendous gravitational pull upon the earth, send it flying out of its orbit and toward Planet "Y" itself. And that would mean—*planetary collision.*

The end of the world!

It was right there, right there in neat circles on that crisp piece of graph paper. Dr. Dawson had indicated the point where the clash would come. He had marked it with a tiny "x." X marks the spot, thought David foolishly; x marks the spot where the accident would occur.

Like a man in a dream, he put his finger on the point.

unexplained earthquakes that were driving New York inhabitants
from the city. The other two were Dr. Charles Dawson, the "Wizard
Palomar," and his gracious wife Emily.

Dr. Dawson, scanning areas of the heavens never seen before,
just made a discovery that he dared not release until he con-
d with other leading astronomers. It was a discovery that was
ct every person on earth in a way which even Dr. Dawson
uld never have dreamed.

ughes knew nothing of this as he hurried to Carol's
ime, he vowed, he would accept no more argu-
to take her with him to California.

David picked up the phone to hear Dr.
b urgency. "David," rasped his boss, "I
ar immediately. *Immediately.*"

when I release to the world the

Dr. Dawson's voice grew

ask more, but
by that
He

The BULLETIN
PRESENTS
The April 1950 Selection

THE
BIG EYE
BY MAX EHRLICH

The BIG EYE

By Max Ehrlich

ONE OF THE MOST UNUSUAL NOVELS The Dollar Book
Club has ever found for its members is *The Big Eye* by Max Ehrlich.
This breathtaking book plunges into a daring theme of how vibrantly
living men and women find, under the threat of a strange peril, the
true secret of how to make the world a good place in which to live. It
is built on two engaging love stories . . . one young and hopeful,

one mature and serene, each affecting the other.

On a certain November night, four people
hovered on the brink of destiny. One, young
Dr. David Hughes, was executive assistant
Palomar Observatory. He was winging hi
from California to New York in a str
anxious to take his fiancée Carol Ken
Palomar with him. Carol, hard at w
vision commentator, was determin

PUBLISHER'S EDITION $3.00

MEMBERS' EDITION $1.00

*"I went over my figures again an
again," Dr. Dawson said. "I alw
came to the same staggering*

at
s way
atoliner,
ny back to
ork as a tele-
ed to ignore the

j
vays
result.''

of h...

D...
had ...
sulted ...
to affe...
himself wo...

But David H...
apartment. This t...
ments; he was going ...

But the next morning, ...
Dawson's voice, harsh wit...
want you to return to Palom...

"But Dr. Dawson . . ."

"No buts, David. I need you here ...
greatest news in all history."

"What on earth have you discovered?...

"It's terrifying and wonderful, David."...
awed. "I've seen the hand of God!"

"The hand . . . ?" David swallowed and started to ...
Dr. Dawson had hung up. Whatever Dr. Dawson meant ...
strange phrase, David knew he would have to return immediately ...
found a cab and ordered the driver to take him to Radio City, where ...
Carol worked. No matter what Dr. Dawson had found, David was
going to take her along.

Suddenly the street beneath them heaved. The cab screeched to
a halt. Another earthquake! The cab driver jumped and fled, ignor-
ing David's yells. David too jumped from the cab and raced through
showers of falling glass toward Radio City, wondering if it still
stood . . . and if Carol were unharmed . . .

This is only the beginning of one of the most gripping stories you
will ever read. What was causing the strange earthquakes in New
York City? What tremendous discovery did Dr. Charles Dawson
make through the Big Eye of Palomar? To tell you more would rob
you of a double-barreled surprise climax that will have you sighing
with complete satisfaction. This unusual novel will keep you on the
edge of your chair right up to the end.

THE DOUBLEDAY ONE DOLLAR BOOK CLUB • 105 BOND ST. • TORONTO 2

The Old Man nodded. "The point of final gravitational attraction, David. The cosmic collision point."

It was impossible, of course. In the infinite sweep of space, the earth was merely a speck of dust. So was this new planet, this Planet "Y." Every law of chance was against it. A billion billion billion to one.

But there it was, right there in the diagram. There were the orbits of Planet "Y" and the earth.

And there was the point of collision. And nothing, nobody could stop it.

The end of the world.

The end of the world! The end of the world! It beat through David Hughes's head like an awful refrain.

It was fantastic. It was something you toyed with in your imagination, or read about in those weird fiction stories. Soothsayers from the beginning of time had been predicting it, religious fanatics had seen it in their visions, and every year some crackpot predicted the exact day and hour of the catastrophe.

But people just laughed or shrugged and went about their business. The newspapers sent a photographer to take pictures of the cranks and their followers, usually kneeling and praying on some mountaintop as the appointed hour drew near.

But the hour came and went, and the earth kept right on rotating on its axis, and the photographers got their pictures. And the crackpot and his followers finally gave up and sheepishly went home.

And the next year there was always a new prophet and a new flock, a new day and a new hour. And a new picture in the press for the people to smile at the next day.

But this new prophet was not a crank. He was the man sitting at the desk, the man watching him with compassion in his eyes. He was Dr. Charles Dawson, a man of science, who placed no reliance in visions or dreams.

"At first I couldn't believe what I saw," the Old Man was saying. "I went over my calculations again and again. And invariably I always came to the same result—the same staggering result.

"It was then that I called the men from the other observatories —the only men in the world who knew the necessary mathematics for this problem—the best research astronomers in the world. I wanted them to check my calculations. I didn't dare trust myself.

"Furthermore, David, I could not announce this terrible phenomenon to the world alone. The responsibility would be too great, and there would be skepticism. After all, the world would have only my word, only one man's word, that the catastrophe would occur. But if the announcement came simultaneously from a group of the greatest astronomers in the world, then there would be no room for doubt, it would then be accepted as the truth it is."

Yes, thought David, this white-haired man sitting here in this quiet room was the true prophet, whose gospel and predictions were made on cold, hard facts. And these facts had been attested to by other true prophets like himself.

"Then that tremor we had in New York—those other phenomena General Hawthorne spoke about . . ." began David.

"Are all the result of natural stress and strain from the intrusion of this new astronomical body in the solar system," said the Old Man. "The fact is, they should have been even more violent and widespread, and in our discussion here we were puzzled as to why they were not. The only explanation we can offer is that, curiously enough, the other celestial bodies in our system seem to have moved into a new position of balance, compensating the strain. And so we can count on a little more time than we had expected."

It was clear to David now—*too* clear.

"Then there's no Russian secret weapon, after all."

"No, David. And as far as I know, there never was. What happened in the city of New York was a cracking of the bedrock, a minor earthquake fault in the rock. The other phenomena can no doubt be similarly explained."

David could have sworn that he saw the flicker of a smile on Dr. Dawson's face as the Old Man continued:

"Professor Varanov of Leningrad is here at Palomar, David, as you probably know. And I have it from him that the same kinds of baffling phenomena have taken place recently, not only in the Soviet Union, but in Soviet-dominated Europe and Asia. There has been an earthquake in Warsaw and tidal waves at both Naples and Vladivostok, to name a few. The Russians are sure *we* have a new and terrible weapon of some kind."

David suddenly recalled the news broadcast aboard the strato-cruiser as they were coming into San Diego a few hours ago.

"Then it was you who called the President, Doctor?"

The Old Man nodded. "I told him about the planet, told him it was on its way, and begged him to hold off any positive move for a few hours, until we were absolutely sure there would be a collision. Now—we are." Dr. Dawson paused for a moment. "We had to stop the fools from destroying each other before the planet ended their natural time."

Before the planet ended their natural time.

When? When would it strike?

That was the question, the question he avoided, the question that stuck in his throat, that he did not dare ask.

But now it was insistent, it wouldn't stay down, it demanded an answer.

"Do you know when the collision will come, Dr. Dawson?"

The Old Man nodded, but he did not answer immediately. It was still in the study, very still, except for the regular ticking of the clock in the corner. Then finally he spoke.

"A decade ago, as you well know, David, even a rough conclusion would have been impossible. But we have come a long way since then, with the new instruments we have developed and the new mathematical techniques we have evolved, and indeed with the 200-inch reflector itself. But now, although it is too early yet to calculate the exact hour, we have been able to calculate the day."

"When will it be?" asked David. He was impatient; he wanted the Old Man to get to it, and get to it quick. "What day will it be?"

"The end will come in two years and one month," answered the Old Man quietly. "On Christmas Day, 1962."

Christmas Day, 1962!

"A date not without its irony," Dr. Dawson was saying. "And yet an appropriate day, when one considers that almost two thousand years ago a miracle had been ushered in by a new heavenly body shining in the sky. It had heralded the birth of a new idea and then disappeared off into the void." The Old Man's voice was hushed now, almost inaudible. "It would almost seem, David, that it had made a complete circuit of the heavens and returned, this time in a different and final role."

Yes, David thought wildly, one thing was certain. Planet "Y" didn't just happen, it *couldn't* have just happened; the odds were stacked against it, millions and millions to one.

Whatever it was, it was a sign, a sermon in the sky, a divine wrath, a terrible judgment upon the creatures who called themselves men.

There could be no other answer. The Old Man was right. It *was* the hand of God!

David stared at Dr. Dawson. "What do you think will happen to people when they find out, sir?"

The Old Man leaned back and closed his eyes. "No man can tell, David. All we know is that there'll be profound changes, not only in our social and economic patterns, but in our mental processes. In a way, I got a preview of that this morning. When we started to go over my calculations, two of the astronomers present were confirmed atheists, and others were agnostics. They had believed in a kind of divinity of order, because the system of the heavens had functioned according to a kind of heavenly Hoyle ever since time began.

"But when they learned about this outlaw, this huge gob of matter, plummeting into our lives from nowhere, it smashed their faith or lack of it. The runaway planet up there was the great dissenter, the disrupter of order, the harbinger of chaos. It was the first and final exception to the rule they had worshiped, and they could not escape its timeliness and significance. And when they walked out of here a few minutes ago, David, they were men of religion."

"Two years and one month," murmured David. "It isn't very long."

"No. It's precious little time, David, for man to put his house in order after cluttering it with the refuse and the mistakes and the prejudices of centuries. But I suspect that Planet 'Y' will turn out to be a large and efficient broom."

They sat there silently for a minute, each lost in his own thoughts, listening to the methodical ticking of the clock. Finally David roused himself and asked:

"When will you break the news, sir?"

"Tomorrow morning. Better phone the news syndicates and the radio-television people immediately, David. Oh—and have Hartschorn make slides of those photoplates so that they can be used in the auditorium projector. I'll want you to run the slides off for the press while I lecture."

"Yes, sir," said David mechanically. "I'll call them for tomorrow at ten."

The Old Man nodded. "I'll inform the staff of what's happened at a preliminary meeting and then meet with the other astronomers before we go in."

David hesitated. "You're sure you want to break this—this whole thing, Dr. Dawson?"

"Yes. We decided at the meeting that there was no point in withholding the news. In the first place, we wanted the world to know before it had a chance to blow itself up. In the second place, people would know sooner or later anyway, if they survived themselves. The planet's traveling at tremendous speed, David. And of course it will become visible long before the end comes."

The Old Man rose, put his hand on David's shoulder. His voice was marvelously gentle.

"David, I'm an old man. This coming catastrophe may rob me of some of the years of my life—but not many. It's people like you —you and Miss Kenny—who'll be cheated. I—I don't know what to say to you now. I don't know what any father would say to his son at a time like this." The Old Man hesitated a moment. "I can only say this, try to console you with this—there's still faith. You must have faith."

"Faith?" echoed David. He thought of Carol and the future they had looked forward to. His calm suddenly disappeared, and a wave of bitterness took its place, and he began to tremble a little. Faith. The word stuck in his throat. He looked at the Old Man.

"Faith? Now? Faith in what, sir?"

"In a miracle," said the Old Man quietly. "Another miracle. A miracle of redemption, David."

Not much chance of *that*, David told himself cynically. That planet was on its way, on its regular course up there around the sun, and the earth would be drawn into it, and slam against it on schedule, sometime on Christmas Day, 1962. That was the scientific fact, that was what the Old Man's calculations and charts had said, and they were never wrong, they were as final as doom.

But now the Old Man seemed helpless, seemed to be groping for another sign in the sky. Now he had no calculations, no charts, no telescope photos, no slide rules to conjure up any future miracle. He was without benefit of these comforting things now; he could only fall back on an intangible they called faith and pass it on to him, David Hughes.

And another miracle in another two years was a little too much to hope for.

At the door to the study the Old Man suddenly took David's shoulders and turned him around so that their eyes met.

"Don't let it get you down, my boy. Face it. Try to live normally. Get married. Have a child."

Funny, thought David as the door closed; he had been shaken for a moment, but now he felt better. The Old Man's eyes had been compassionate, they had been serene with a strength of their own, and somehow they had poured that strength into David.

Try to live normally. Get married. Have a child.

That was what Dr. Dawson had said. But the Old Man was tired, he wasn't thinking.

If Carol had a child, if she became pregnant almost immediately, it would live hardly more than a year.

7. It was well past midnight when David made the last phone call from his office.

"Corey talking." The tired voice over the receiver belonged to the managing editor of the World Press in Los Angeles.

"Mr. Corey, this is David Hughes, Dr. Dawson's assistant here at Palomar Observatory."

"Yes?"

"Dr. Dawson has an important announcement to make. Will you have a representative here at ten o'clock tomorrow morning?"

There was a moment of hesitation at the other end. Then: "What's it all about, Mr. Hughes?"

"I'm sorry. I can't tell you over the phone."

Corey's voice became a little querulous. "You don't seem to realize, Mr. Hughes, that L.A. right now is a ghost town and I've only got a skeleton staff on hand. Under ordinary circumstances anything that Dr. Dawson had to say would be big news, and naturally we'd be more than glad to cover it. But with all hell due to break loose at any moment, you understand I couldn't let a man go all the way up to Palomar unless it was a really big story."

It was all David could do to stop himself from yelling what he knew into the phone. That fool down there in L.A. prattling about how big a story he wanted, thinking in terms of columns and half columns and paragraphs!

Instead David said quietly, "It's a bigger story than you think, Mr. Corey. So big that some of the world's greatest astronomers have flown in to Palomar here to consult with Dr. Dawson. They'll be at the press conference tomorrow."

Corey seemed to be somewhat impressed at this. Then he said:

"Look, Mr. Hughes, if you could just give me an idea of what it's all about over the phone, I could have a rewrite man take it down and give you my solemn promise that we wouldn't break it until you gave us a release with the others."

"No," said David. "I'm sorry. Your man will have to be here. Dr. Dawson will make his announcement personally."

"I see." Corey seemed a little bored now, weary. "And who'd you say would be there besides Dr. Dawson?"

"Well, to name a few, Ellender of Harvard, Bornson of Sweden, Smythe of the Royal Astronomical Society, Van Vreeden of Holland, Varanov of the Pulkovo Observatory in Leningrad——"

"Varanov? The Russian?" Corey's voice leaped suddenly like an electric spark. *"He's* at Palomar?"

"Yes."

David could almost hear Corey's mind clicking over, savoring the news value of this. "How'd he get out of the U.S.S.R. at a time like this? They won't let a sparrow across the Soviet border now."

"We located him in Mexico City."

"I see." Corey was eager now. "Do you think he'll talk?"

"Talk?"

"Yes. About the threat of war, I mean. About the Soviet point of view. As a Russian scientist, he——"

"I can't say," interrupted David sharply. "But he'll be here at ten o'clock in the morning."

"All right," said Corey crisply. "We'll have a man up there then. Thank you very much, Mr. Hughes."

David hung up. He felt a little ill. Corey had been no different from the others. They had all been a little difficult, the press and radio people alike. Not so long ago, as Corey had implied, the mere announcement that the Old Man would have something to say was enough to send a horde of reporters scurrying up to Palomar.

Now, what happened in the heavens was small potatoes, compared to what *might* happen on earth.

It was almost amusing, thought David, in a macabre sort of way. He had actually been forced to "sell" the greatest story of all time.

He felt tired, very tired now. He snapped out his hooded desk light and shuffled out into the darkness of the observatory. It was quiet in the great circular hall, a kind of brooding and unearthly quiet, almost sinister in its overtones. He started for the light switch and then changed his mind. Somehow he didn't feel like facing the glare of lights now.

He walked noiselessly along the corridor, his feet making no sound on the rubber-inlaid floor. He passed the cafeteria, the library, the auditorium and lecture hall. Then he paused for a moment as he saw a crack of light coming from under a door.

The Old Man was still up.

David hesitated, debated whether to knock on the Old Man's door and tell him the press meeting was all set for the next morning. Then he decided against it and went through the door and down the stairs to the ground floor. The night light was on in the reception room, dull blue under its shade, but Francis was gone.

David took his hat and coat from the foyer closet and stepped out into the night.

The cold wind hit him broadside, making him gasp. He turned up his coat collar and walked out of the yard and onto the road, heading for his room at the Monastery a short distance down the road. It was a moonless night, but the heavens, nevertheless, suffused the entire area with light. He had never seen the constellations blaze so brightly. They tipped the domes of the observatories with silver and similarly etched the various buildings of the mountain colony —the water-supply works, the electric plant, the cottages down the road.

David's eye swept the heavens as he walked, glancing momentarily at each illuminated island universe—and then moving on. Yes, they were really putting on a show tonight—Hercules, the Kneeler; Pegasus, the Winged Horse; Sagittarius, the Archer; Cassiopeia, the Lady in the Chair; Canes Venatici, the Hunting Dogs.

And finally his roving eye caught and held the patch of sky where, plummeting onward, cold and lifeless and remorseless,

Planet "Y" was moving on its inexorable and fatal arc, bent on cosmic destruction.

Two years and one month . . .

How long was that? Figure it out. Two times fifty-two. One hundred and four weeks. Plus four, more or less.

One hundred and eight weeks—seven hundred and fifty-six days.

You could go on like that. You could break it down into hours, minutes, and even seconds. But it all added up to the same thing.

Two years and one month. And then—*Merry Christmas.*

How much life could you pack into two years and one month, even by living desperately, with the ticking of the clock loud in your ears? In two years and one month, he, David Hughes, would be thirty-two. A man in his prime. Young enough to enjoy life vigorously, old enough to know how precious it could be.

And even now, as he walked along Observatory Road, he was walking on borrowed time. It was beginning to slip away from him already. These minutes and seconds here on top of Palomar Mountain were now part of a precious stack of chips.

And they were beginning to slip away, he was already beginning to lose. And there was no way of winning them back.

He looked up again, fascinated, at the constellation in which the Old Man had first sighted the killer planet. One night in the not-too-distant future that empty patch would be punctured by a tiny silver pin point. The pin point would get bigger until it became a disk, and then a bigger disk, and then bigger and bigger as it came nearer and nearer, night after night.

And it would have your name on it, and the precise time and date.

And that was the agonizing thing about it—to know exactly when you were going to die. Like the convict in the death house awaiting execution, you would live with your eyes on the clock, cherishing every miserly minute.

But unlike the condemned man who awaited the chair or the hangman's noose, you could not hope. You could not hope for a pardon, or clemency, or a stay of execution, or even an escape.

For you there was no hope, no clemency, no escape.

David Hughes was suddenly afraid—afraid to be out there in the open, in the sharp night, alone. He had been all right back in the Old Man's office, but now—now it was beginning to get him. He began to hurry, to walk faster and faster, like a boy hurrying past a graveyard, his feet crunching on the graveled road.

A kind of panic swept through him as he hurried along, his head up, staring at the sky. Somewhere back in the recesses of his memory he recalled a Mother Goose story, something he had learned as a child in first or second grade:

> *One day Henny-Penny was walking in the woods. An acorn fell from a tree and hit her on the head. "My, my," said Henny-Penny, "the sky is falling, and the world is coming to an end. I must go and tell the King."*
>
> *Then Henny-Penny met Ducky-Lucky. "Where are you going in such a hurry?" said Ducky-Lucky. "The sky is falling," said Henny-Penny, "I must go and tell the King." "Wait for me," said Ducky-Lucky. "I will go with you and tell the King."*
>
> *Then Henny-Penny and Ducky-Lucky met Turkey-Lurkey. "Where are you going in such a hurry?" asked Turkey-Lurkey. "The sky is falling and the world is coming to an end," said Henny-Penny and Ducky-Lucky. "We are going to tell the King. . . ."*

The panic possessed him. It shook him, drove him on, so that now he was half walking, half running past the rows of darkened cottages on each side of the road. He envied the people who slept in them, the telescope mechanics, the steward and the cook, the janitors, the chauffeur, the handy men, the power-plant and Diesel personnel, the others on the Old Man's staff. They and their families slept peacefully now, with nothing on their minds, not even tomorrow.

But tomorrow would be another day. Then they would know what he knew now. And after that they would never again sleep soundly. . . .

He came to the small guest cottage where Carol was staying, and abruptly he stopped.

The cottage was dark, like all the others. Carol was in there, and by now she would be asleep.

Carol . . .

He remembered that night back in her apartment, back in New York. He had been afraid then, although it was nothing like the awful Fear that clutched him now. He had held Carol in his arms, close, very close, and the Fear had gone away, it had ceased to possess him. He had lived for the moment then, and the hell with tomorrow.

He needed Carol again, now. He needed her more than he had then. He needed her more than anything on God's earth. His need of her was like a crying hunger.

He turned and went up the walk and onto the porch. He knocked on the door, softly at first, and then louder and louder, in an almost frantic tattoo.

The lights went on inside the cottage. A curtain parted in a window. Then there was a sound of a key turning, and the door opened.

"David!"

She was standing there in the doorway, shivering in a thin robe, staring at him.

He shut the door behind him and without a word swept her into his arms.

It was two minutes before ten o'clock in the morning.

The reporters, the radio and television men had already been shown into the small auditorium by Francis, and the buzz of their conversation filled the room. But the Old Man and the other astronomers hadn't come in yet. They were holding a last-minute meeting in the study.

David stood in the glass-walled projection room of the auditorium, fumbling with his slides, nervously tinkering with the projector. Throwing sky images up there on the screen above the platform was nothing new to him. He had gone through the routine a hundred times, not only for Dr. Dawson and his colleagues, but for the tourists who visited Palomar.

But now he was jittery, and his hands were all thumbs. He wondered how the Old Man would break the news to this press and radio crowd.

He wondered how they would take Planet "Y."

How big did printers' type come, how black and bold? How loud could headlines scream? And would there be any of those silly melodramatic affairs you saw in the movies, those rapid-fire conversations between the city editor and the foreman of the pressroom?

> *"Stop the presses, Joe. We'll need a first-page replate!"*
> *"Make it the next edition, Mac. We're already rolling."*
> *"I said stop the presses!"*
> *"Okay. Okay. I suppose you got something big, Brisbane!"*
> *"Big? Listen, Joe, this is terrific—the greatest story of all time. The world is coming to an end!"*

At a time like this, thought David, you could think of the damnedest things. You felt a little lightheaded; your mind played tricks on you, with fanciful images. . . .

He looked at the clock. Five minutes after ten. He wished the Old Man would come in and get it over with. He was getting more of the jitters all the time. And he had a busy day ahead.

Late in the afternoon Carol and he were driving down to Dago to get married.

It was wonderful the way she had taken it, the way she had taken the news early that morning. He had made love to her first, savagely, as though it were his last chance on earth, and she had responded wordlessly, without questions, without asking an explanation.

She had sensed how much he had needed her, and that was enough.

Later, when he was spent and the Fear had gone and he was calm again, he had told her. He had given her the whole story, simple and straight, and he had expected hysterics afterward. But there were no hysterics. She was funny, he told himself, she hadn't even cried. She was funny, and wonderful. She had rested there in his arms, saying nothing for a long time. And then finally:

"We'll still have two years together, David. We can make it a lifetime together."

"Then you're not afraid, Carol?"

"No, David. I'm not afraid. Not like this. Not with you."

She was funny, and she was wonderful. She hadn't even cried.

He listened to the conversation of the newsmen as they waited for the Old Man. They were frightened, you could see that. It was plain in their taut faces, in the way they spoke.

They were, in a sense, beaten men, thought David as he watched them through the glass-enclosed projection room. They had no hope in themselves, saw no hope of anyone else averting the tragedy. They had already accepted the war as a *fait accompli*, and now they looked backward at what had gone before.

David listened to their chatter eddying up to the projection room:

"Look, Ed, we had a temporary monopoly of the bomb back in the forties. Remember? And what did we do with it? We muffed it. We sat on it and watched the Reds gobble up Europe and Asia, watched them like a hypnotized bird watching a snake, gave them a chance to dream up a firecracker of their own."

"The Baruch proposal, the Marshall Plan, the Atlantic Pact, the Eastern bloc, and the rest. And the Reds playing it cagey all the way . . ."

"Christ, Frank, when you think of it, the whole thing's like a bad movie. And now here it is, right around the corner— A-Day!"

"In a way, I suppose it's partly our fault. Maybe we could have made it one world. We had a world weapon, and we made a nationalistic gimmick out of it. You know, we've got a gun and you ain't. Be good guys now. Do it our way—or else!"

"I could have sworn it was going to be all right, Fred. Roosevelt and Truman, back a few years ago—they were trying. And all those conferences later . . ."

"Talk, talk, talk, talk. Everybody talking about the international control of atomic energy and nobody doing anything about it . . ."

"Funny how it all happened, Ed, when you look back at it now. For a while, there, it looked swell. The Russians finally dropping the veto power in the Security Council and even agreeing to international inspection . . ."

"Are you kidding, Frank? It was what they call 'agreeing in principle.' But they weren't putting that one over, not on me! I was with Globe Press at the time, and I drew the assignment with the Control and Inspection Commission in the Soviet. Sure, they showed us Moscow and Kiev and Leningrad. But when we started to head east, into Siberia and Manchuria, we began to be 'delayed.' And it was the 'Mystery Cities' we wanted to see—Dudinka, Norylsk, Petrovsk, Yakutsk, Seimchan, Magadan, and the others. Well, we never did. And, brother, that's where the Reds were really radioactive. Anyway, we hung around awhile and finally came home. What was the use?"

Joe Morgan, David's roommate at the Monastery, joined David briefly in the projection room. The Old Man had just broken the news to the rest of the staff, and the spectrograph man was pale under his sandy hair.

"Listen to them," said David. "They're like mourners talking at a wake."

"They don't know what we know," responded Morgan dully. "They don't know that there won't be any wake because there won't be any mourners. Listen to 'em, David. What they're saying now sounds like prattle—childish prattle."

They were two men playing God for a moment, it occurred to David, he and Joe Morgan. Knowing what they knew, they could see these men as crawling microorganisms in a laboratory test tube, crazily running around and around the inside of the glass in awful and pitiful futility.

"*What the hell is the President holding out for, I ask you, Fred? Look at what happened in New York. It's obvious that the Reds have got a new gimmick! What's he trying to do, get us to commit national suicide?*"

"*I hear they got him backed against the wall. He's getting it from the generals, from senators, from the Cabinet, everybody but his wife. They're all in favor of lighting the fuse quick.*"

"*Yeah. But what's he holding out so long for?*"

"*Wants to be morally sure we're right, I guess.*"

"*Hell, that's what I call old-fashioned. Someone ought to give him the facts of life. You can't even spell 'morally' in Russian.*"

"*It's ten-fifteen already. I've got to get back to the office. What's holding Dawson up, anyway?*"

"*I don't know. I kicked like a steer, Al, when the boss assigned me to this. I said, 'Look, Manny, the excitement's down here, right here in the office, and to hell with spending half a day way up at Palomar.' Well, said Manny, it might be a new comet or meteor Dr. Dawson's discovered, you know, one of those things he pulls out of the sky now and then. And I said: 'So what, Manny, and who cares? What's an item like that worth now? Page 10? Page 20?*"

"*I wish the Old Boy would walk in and get it over with, Frank. I've gotta get out of here and be back in L.A. by one.*"

"*Maybe this clambake will turn out okay, Ed. After all, Varanov's here. A big-shot Soviet in the U.S. now. It's a good angle.*"

"*Yeah. I'm going to try to get to him, like the rest of you guys, right after this lecture, or whatever it is. But if I know these Reds, we'll all be lucky if we get a 'nyet' out of him.*"

"*Wait a minute. Here comes Dawson.*"

The door at the rear of the auditorium suddenly opened. The chattering of the newsmen suddenly stopped as Dr. Dawson came in, followed by the others. One by one they filed in—Smythe, the gnomelike hunchback of the Royal Astronomical Society, his face like a wrinkled gray mask; Perez, the muscles of his round face working with emotion; Manning, the giant of Mount Wilson, his thin mouth a hard line, his bald head shining with perspiration; Varanov, the massive white-bearded Russian, his eyes hard and cold like two blue agates; Perez, Van Vreeden, Wallace, Ellender, Duval, and the rest.

The newsmen stared at them with sudden respect and a kind of awe. These were, after all, scientific men of international reputation, and the simple fact that they were here, gathered in one room, was an event out of the ordinary. But these days, when it came to news, everything was out of the ordinary.

The news- and radiomen were there to get a story. They would listen politely, even expectantly, to what Dr. Dawson had to say, and spot it on an inside page or after the middle commercial on the news broadcast. But they had their minds on other things.

Grimly and quietly the astronomers took their seats together on the left-hand aisle. All except the Old Man. He walked up to the platform and turned to face his audience.

For a long moment he stood there, his eyes straying over each of the newsmen. He's a born showman, thought David Hughes. He's a showman in the way he's standing there now and looking at them. He commanded their deference and held them.

The auditorium was quiet as the Old Man began to speak.

"Gentlemen, as representatives of the press and radio, you are preoccupied at the moment with current events of a highly unusual nature. But now, for a few moments, I ask you to take your eyes from the affairs of our own planet, the earth, and look at the sky.

"I summoned you here this morning because something completely extraordinary has taken place up there in the domain of the heavens—something not only extraordinary, but completely unprecedented. I stumbled upon this phenomenon a short time ago, and upon learning of its overwhelming implications I immediately summoned these gentlemen, my colleagues, from their posts all over the world. They have checked my observations and my calculations, and they will attest to all I am going to tell you now."

The Old Man paused for a moment. Then he said with gentle irony: "Gentlemen, I ask for your undivided attention for five minutes, and I promise you a story for page 1."

The Old Man looked over the heads of his audience and nodded to Francis, who was standing at the light switch in the rear of the auditorium.

The auditorium was plunged into darkness.

"All right, David," said the Old Man. "Give me the first slide."

The Old Man was through.

David shut off the projector. Its whirring sound slowed and died in the dead silence of the darkened auditorium.

Then the lights went on.

The men in the auditorium sat there in the bright glare, stunned, paralyzed, as though under a powerful narcotic. They sat stiffly, like waxen images in a museum gallery, like rigid figures in a still picture. They stared fixedly at Dr. Dawson, their jaws slack and sagging, their faces ashen with shock and horror.

"My God!" someone moaned softly in the back row. "My God, my God!"

That was all. The one voice—and that was all. Then silence again, dead silence. And finally another voice, rising and cracking, shrill in hysteria:

"It's not true! *It can't be true!*"

It was Langley, a radioman. He had half risen from his seat, his eyes bulging, his face dead white.

"I'm sorry, Mr. Langley," said the Old Man quietly. "It *is* true, and there is no chance of error. My colleagues are ready to substantiate what I have said."

The others began to stir and sigh and rustle in their seats, like men coming out of a dream. The first smashing impact was beginning to wear off. Then, with almost a single accord, their voices rose, loud, protesting, incredulous, hysterical. They rose from their seats almost all at once, talking in a wild babel.

"Please, gentlemen." The Old Man raised his hand. "Please. If there are any questions, please ask them one at a time."

The babel stopped as suddenly as it had started. Some of the men fell back in their seats, others remained standing. Finally a newspaperman named Graham spoke, his voice breaking into a cracked falsetto.

"Dr. Dawson."

"Yes?"

"Is there any chance of this catastrophe being averted? Is there any chance at all—of this Planet 'Y' taking some other course?"

The Old Man shook his head. "Nothing I know of can stop it." He paused, then said softly, "Nothing but a miracle."

"But the end of the world! It *can't* happen! It's crazy—fantastic!" The man from World Press, the man Corey had sent up, was sobbing out the words. "I've got two kids. They're young. Why, they won't even have a chance to grow up. Two years and one month!" Then he blurted foolishly, "Dr. Dawson, for God's sake, there *must* be something we can do!"

The Old Man looked at him for a moment. Then he spoke, gently and compassionately.

"It's out of our hands. I know it's clear to you, as well as to myself, that this is a divine punishment. Any man, whether scientist or dreamer, minister or atheist, can draw no other conclusion. In a sense, even in the face of the coming catastrophe, we are fortunate——"

"Fortunate?" someone cried hoarsely. "How?"

"We have been preparing to exterminate ourselves by our own hands in the very near future. Tomorrow, or the day after that, or the next week, perhaps, or next month. Now, at least, the immediate tragedy will be averted. We have been given the opportunity to live a little longer. Perhaps we will make good use of the time remaining to us, make our peace with God."

A thick, foreign voice came from the left. "Dr. Dawson is right, gentlemen."

The news- and radiomen turned their heads and stared at the speaker.

It was Varanov, the Russian.

"When I walked into Dr. Dawson's study yesterday, I did not believe in God. I do now. So, too, will all my people in the Soviet Union. There can be no other answer to what has happened.

"Neither can there be any further conflict. Now it is over, this threat of war is over. Communism—capitalism—these systems are nonsense now. Our Red soldiers will lay down their arms, as yours will. For there is no use destroying each other, when all will finally be destroyed. Men who are facing the same execution for the same reason do not hate each other. And two years is not a very long time to live."

Varanov sat down. The men in the auditorium stared at him, fascinated. For a moment there was dead silence. Then Perez, the Brazilian astronomer, rose.

"Senhor Varanov is right. One must concede that there is divine purpose in this terrible miracle. I am no philosopher, senhores, and I am no politician. But even I understand one thing. We have been given these years of grace, this little time that remains, for a purpose. It did not just happen that way. Consider this and call it a curious kind of logic, if you wish. But if God wished to destroy us by the cosmic explosion of a star, if this was the method He chose, He did not have to reach far out into the universe and explode the distant star from whence this Planet 'Y' came. The sun is a star, senhores, very near and quite convenient for this purpose. Had He been instant and quick in his wrath, had He chosen the sun instead of this other and far-distant star for His cosmic explosion, this little planet of ours, the earth, would have vanished instantly in a blast of heat and a puff of smoke."

There was a moment of silence. Then a reporter named Brewer cried out hysterically: "The hell with all this double talk. Nobody wants any sermons or platitudes now!"

He jumped to his feet and, his face livid, pointed his finger at Dr. Dawson.

"We're going to die!" he cried shrilly. "You and me and every damned one of us! Why didn't you keep it quiet? Why did you and all these other scientists tell us about it?"

"We had a moral duty to do so," answered the Old Man. "We discussed it, my colleagues and I, in my study. We felt that if men had been given these two years of grace, they should be so informed before they took matters into their own hands and destroyed each other. Furthermore, had mankind, by some miracle, compromised their differences and let each other live a little while longer, they would have seen this planet come into the sky and come closer and closer with each succeeding day. They would have asked questions then, and these questions would have had to be answered."

"You should have kept quiet about it," insisted the newspaperman sullenly. "What kind of a life do you think we're going to live, knowing the date of our own execution, watching that damned thing in the sky come closer day after day?"

"I think we'll all live a better life," answered the Old Man quietly.

"I'm not interested in your theories of reforming, Dr. Dawson," flared Brewer hysterically. "All I know is that on Christmas of 1962 I'm going to die. So is my wife, and so is my little girl and my little boy. As far as I'm concerned, that's the only important thing."

"Is it?" The Old Man spoke patiently. "I wonder. No doubt death is a great tragedy to all of us. But in a larger sense, an astronomical sense, what does it amount to? Man is, after all, merely a microscopic organism living on a grain of sand revolving around a fourth-rate star." He paused. "As a matter of fact, we really have no right being alive in the first place."

"No right? What do you mean by that?" Only Brewer and the Old Man were doing the talking now. The others hung on the discussion, quiet and absorbed.

"Did you ever hear of an English astronomer named Eddington, Mr. Brewer?"

"No."

"Well, Eddington pointed out that actually we are interlopers in creation, intruders. We really have no right to be here. We are here because one chemical element out of the whole ninety-two—carbon —happened to be able to combine with others in thousands of different ways. We are, in short, here on this earth as a freak of nature, unique in all the universe.

"Think of this, Mr. Brewer, consider this extraordinary state of affairs. We are alive only because we cling to a tiny bit of dust just the right distance from the right sun. Around us the vast bulk of cosmic material is either blazing at temperatures of millions of degrees, or else scattered remotely in the cold absolute void. A small deviation in either direction, a slight jarring of our lucky position —and we would be wiped out in an instant." The Old Man stopped and then said very quietly, "That deviation has now come."

There was a full minute of silence. The Old Man waited on the platform for someone to speak further. No one did.

"Are there any further questions, gentlemen?" the Old Man asked.

No one broke the silence.

"Very well. I know you gentlemen will want to contact your offices immediately. You'll find a telephone in the reception room and others in the various offices off the corridor. You're welcome to them." The Old Man nodded. "Good morning, gentlemen—and thank you."

David Hughes, standing by the projector, watched the newsmen curiously as they rose and slowly moved toward the door.

They had the greatest story on earth, but they did not rush for the phones in a frantic race to get the story in. On the contrary, they seemed almost reluctant to leave.

They shuffled out of the auditorium as though they were walking in their sleep. The look of the condemned was already upon their pallid faces. Already their heads were shaved and their trousers slit for the electrodes and they were hearing the last rites.

8. An hour later the whole world knew about Planet "Y."

The shock radiated outward from Palomar and shuddered through the earth like a great earthquake.

The phones at the observatory rang incessantly, and already the Highway to the Stars was choked with cars racing upward into the San Jacinto range, toward the new magnetic center of the earth. The military guard at the observatory was alerted for trouble.

The people of Palomar were nearest, and they came to the observatory first. Almost with a single accord the staff astronomers, the physicists, the mathematicians and calculators, the telescope mechanics and maintenance men, the janitors and Diesel workers had dropped whatever they were doing. They had gone to their homes, gathered their wives and children, and, like the Israelites drawn to the temple in time of crisis, had headed for the main observatory, as though somehow they would find salvation there.

Now they gathered in little voiceless knots, their faces white and dazed. Some of them, without knowing why, had dressed in their Sunday best, they and their wives and children, as though it were a holiday. They searched each other's faces dumbly, looking for hope, but they saw no hope. All they saw in each other's faces were mirror reflections of their own. They wandered about aimlessly, like pale automatons, eddying and flowing through the corridors and foyers and reception rooms.

They gathered before the closed door to Dr. Dawson's study, waiting for a word.

But there was no word.

And finally, inevitably, they climbed the parquet stairs toward the transparent partition blocking off the telescope from the rest of the observatory.

The Big Eye seemed to hypnotize them. They pressed their noses against the glass wall and stared at it mutely, as though somehow it could rectify what it had done, as though, by merely stirring itself, it could make amends for its crime.

"*What have you done to us?*" the staring eyes on the other side of the glass said. "*What have you done to us?*"

But the monstrous apparatus, soaring up into the semi-darkness of the dome, was silent. It stood there, unmoved, vast and massive and triumphant. It seemed to leer back at the white faces malevolently, as though it were well aware of what it had done, as though it knew the havoc it had wrought.

Yes, the great telescope was conscious of its power and proudly flaunted it. It had a right to revel in its own strength. After all, it had created all the havoc merely by producing only a tiny glint of light deep in its Pyrex cornea.

To those who watched it through the transparent wall, it was a Thing, it was alive. Its massive piers, its yoke, its girders and cylinders were muscles which it flexed in glee on ball-and-socket joints. Its burnished eye was invisible, but they were aware that it was mocking them. They almost expected a bellow of triumph to roar up and out from the yawning mouth of the giant and echo through the dome.

It was the telescope who was alive, not those who watched it. They were inanimate, dead. They could only stand and stare, like images of fleshy wax.

Had the heavily armed soldiers not been there, as stunned as anyone else, but still watchful for the first sign of violence, the hatred might have bubbled out of the onlookers and exploded into hysteria. They might have come to life, a wild and avenging mob. They might have found axes and sledges somewhere, surged forward, smashed through the glass partition, and rushed toward their leering tormentor, chopping and hammering at it, blinding its eye and hacking at its muscles until it came crashing to the floor.

Elsewhere the great observatories of the world were attacked by mobs. Unlike Palomar, they had been unprotected, caught off guard. The attacks came simultaneously, shortly after the announcement, and they came without warning. In the rioting, millions of dollars' worth of delicate precision instruments were smashed and destroyed before guards could be summoned.

But at Palomar they could not move, they could not act. They could only stand and stare at the telescope through the partition. No one spoke; the silence was like that of a death watch.

Finally a pair of lips in one of the white faces against the glass moved, muttered:

"You big bastard. You big bastard. *What have you done to us?*"

By early afternoon the observatory yard was choked with cars. And still they kept coming up the steep road to Palomar.

They had no valid reason for coming, no real purpose, blindly seeking the oracle, perhaps hoping for a crumb of comfort from the same mighty source that promised them disaster.

The observatory was crowded with newsmen, photographers, Army officials, public officials, and just plain people, dazed by the shock.

Everyone wanted to see Dr. Dawson.

But the Old Man would see no one. He was locked in his study with David, and they had Francis's small radio turned on.

None of the regular programs was being broadcast. There was nothing but music—somber music—funeral music. David twisted the dial to station after station, with the same result.

"You're sure the President is going to make a statement, Dr. Dawson?"

The Old Man nodded. "He assured me he would, when I spoke to him over the phone yesterday, David. Just as soon as we could give him absolute confirmation of this phenomenon, beyond any element of doubt."

The dirgelike music continued.

David remembered something like this a long time ago when he was a boy. It was the day Franklin D. Roosevelt died, fifteen years ago. There was the same interminable music, like this.

And yet it was nothing like this.

Then, back in 1945, the people mourned for one man.

Now, in 1960, they mourned for themselves, and the music was their *own* requiem.

The music occasionally stopped and then resumed jerkily. Sometimes there were long blank spaces of dead air. Sometimes a hesitant voice came in from somewhere and then was cut off in the middle of a sentence. The whole radio frequency dial, from left to right, was uncertain, jittery, frightened. The networks had been caught short. Their organization had broken down. The studios were still there; the microphones, the transmitters, they were intact. It was the people operating them who collapsed.

Like everyone else, they had been stunned by the blow, numbed by the shock; they had lost control.

David and the Old Man listened to one station playing the same transcription over and over. Someone in a studio somewhere seemed to have gone out of his mind. He put the needle on the record, ran it through, began it all over again. It didn't occur to him to turn the record over or put a new one on the turntable. It was enough that something was on the air, anything.

"They've gone crazy out there somewhere," David remarked to the Old Man.

He recalled something Carol had once told him.

Back in New York the networks had prepared and recorded dramatic obituaries of every living great man. When one of them died the studios could almost instantly broadcast his obituary. They'd been making up these transcriptions in advance ever since they got caught short when Roosevelt died.

But this was one obituary they didn't figure on, thought David grimly.

This was *everybody's* obituary.

The music stopped abruptly and a shaky voice broke through:

> *"Ladies and gentlemen, we bring you a special message— from the President of the United States. The next voice you hear will be that of the President."*

The announcer's voice broke off. There was a long silence, perhaps a minute of dead air. Then suddenly they heard the President.

His voice trembled with emotion; it was halting, still almost incredulous:

"This morning, only a few hours ago, a dramatic announcement was flashed to the entire world from the Palomar Observatory in California. By now there are few in this country, and indeed in every other nation of the earth, who do not know that our days are numbered. At this very moment, this cosmic body, this Planet 'Y,' is speeding toward us from somewhere out of the limitless heavens, bent on our complete and final destruction.

"In this solemn hour, this hour of tragedy, there is nothing I can say to give you comfort. To those of you who are still skeptical of this coming catastrophe, I bring bad news. I have been reassured that for us on earth, and for the earth itself, there is no possibility, no hope of escape.

"No one can doubt that we have been visited with some kind of divine judgment. We must accept it as such and try to face it tranquilly, and with resignation.

"I ask you now, the people of the United States, to remain calm in this great crisis. We cannot, we must not, fall prey to violent and destructive hysteria. We cannot, we must not, have anarchy or chaos. As Commander in Chief of the armed forces of this nation, I have already instructed the Army to keep order wherever necessary. I now call upon the governors of every state to alert the National Guard for any local emergency that might occur.

"For some months we have faced the threat of terrible war, the prospect of possible destruction. Now—this period of uncertainty is over. Now our destruction has been made certain and complete by a far higher Power than man—perhaps in

*righteous retribution for our own sins. And we are powerless
to avert our terrible destiny.*

*"I ask you now to turn to God Himself for solace and for-
giveness. I ask you now to go to your churches and temples and
pray."*

The President had finished. There was a moment of silence after
his last word had died away. Then a famous clergyman followed
with a short prayer. And after him the mournful music again.

And finally a news announcer, the first David and Dr. Dawson
had heard, pouring out early fragments of information in an almost
hysterical voice:

*"The whole world is stunned and dazed. In the cities
throughout the country people have left the factories, the
offices, the homes, and swarmed out into the streets, tying up
traffic. All transport has been halted, all schools closed as
hysterical parents called for their children. The streets are
jammed with surging crowds. Authorities fear mass panic.*

*"From China it is reported that soldiers of warring factions
have throw down their weapons and embraced each other.
. . . The Pope is preparing to address the world from Rome.*

*"A report from Kirensk . . . The Leningrad astronomer,
Professor Varanov, is already on his way to Russia by plane to
report personally to the Soviet Premier. . . .*

*"Members of both houses of Congress are now meeting in
secret and emergency session somewhere in America. . . .
Riots, violence, and looting have already begun in many sections. Observatories all over the world have been attacked,
valuable instruments destroyed.*

*"At Sing Sing, Dannemora, Leavenworth, and other prisons,
inmates have begun to riot, demanding their freedom. The
governor of New York State has postponed two executions
scheduled for tonight. . . . Thousands of people are beginning to jam airports and railroad stations, moving back to
their homes in the evacuated cities. . . . The Secretary of*

Defense has ordered every man in the armed forces, air, land, and sea, to stay at his post."

There was a knock on the door of the study.

The Old Man waved his hand, signaling to David to turn off the radio, and then admitted Francis.

"Dr. Dawson," the steward began apologetically, "there's some. one waiting to see you."

"I told you I didn't want to see anyone else right now," interrupted the Old Man.

"Yes, sir. But it's Professor Kellar."

"Kellar? *He's* here at Palomar?"

The steward nodded. He seemed to have aged ten years since the morning; his shoulders sagged under the alpaca coat.

"He drove up from Los Angeles, sir. And he insists on seeing you."

The Old Man hesitated for a moment. Then he said, "Show him in, Francis."

David awaited the appearance of Kellar with more than ordinary interest. Andrew Kellar was a giant in his own field, recognized as the greatest physicist alive. He was reputed to know more about nuclear fission than any other man. It was he who had assembled the first bomb they had ever dropped in New Mexico, he who had been the scientific brain behind the vast Manhattan project of World War II, and more than any other single man, he had been responsible for the bombs dropped on Hiroshima and Nagasaki fifteen years ago.

Since that time, however, Kellar had virtually dropped out of sight, along with many of his colleagues. He had been taken in hand by General Hawthorne, hemmed in and badgered, a virtual prisoner jealously guarded and secluded in a kind of rigid cocoon.

And for fifteen years his genius had become impotent in everything except research for war.

"Dr. Dawson!" The nuclear scientist, a tall spare man, came hurrying into the study. "Thank God, Doctor, for what you've done!"

David stared at Kellar.

His eyes were overbright. They shone behind his thick spectacles; they seemed a little wild, a little mad. Kellar's aged shoulders were straight back, his sunken cheeks unnaturally flushed. His step was springy and buoyant; he almost danced into the room.

He was alternately laughing and sobbing, his voice cracking in falsetto. He grabbed the Old Man's hand, pumped it up and down, wouldn't let go.

He's mad, thought David. He's surely mad.

"I'm free!" babbled Kellar. "Do you understand, Doctor? I'm free now, and so are all of us—Eckert, Davidson, Walker, and the rest of my colleagues on nuclear fission—we're free! *You* set us free! For the first time since Hiroshima, we can sleep nights!"

It was shocking, almost obscene, to watch him, a happy man, delirious with his happiness, mad with it, a lone celebrator in a world of mourners.

"Thank God for that planet you found! Thank God for it, sir, we welcome it. We're out of it now, we're absolved. No one's going to use the bomb now, Doctor, thanks to you. The world may be blown up, yes, but not by *our* hand. Not by our hand, *now!*" He took the Old Man by the shoulders, almost shook him. "Do you realize what it's been like, Doctor, the fifteen years since Hiroshima? We've been *haunted*, living with a stone around our necks. We've seen what we've created desecrated into an instrument of slaughter rather than of new power, of curative medicine. We've been made to feel that *we* were responsible for the destruction of humanity!" He released Dr. Dawson and slumped back into a chair, exhausted. "But now it's out of our hands, thank God. No one can point a finger at us now!"

Dr. Dawson watched Kellar. His face was set and hard, his eyes stern; they showed no sympathy. The physicist quieted down; he stirred uneasily under the Old Man's steady and accusing gaze.

And when the Old Man finally spoke, his voice was as cold and sharp as the edge of a knife.

"If you've suffered, Professor Kellar, you've no one to blame but yourself. You should never have let the atom get away from you."

Kellar spread his hands. "What could we do? You know what happened. There was a war. The Army stepped in. They *took* the atom away from us! We had nothing to say; we had to stand by helplessly." He appealed to the Old Man. "We didn't have a chance. You remember, Doctor, back in the late forties and early fifties, how we tried to warn the world. You remember why we formed the Emergency Committee of Atomic Scientists."

The Old Man nodded.

"We raised a million dollars for propaganda to make the public aware of the destructive nature of the bomb. We told them that it would inevitably lead to war, that there was no particular secret about nuclear fission. We told them, again and again, that the only solution was international control, until the words we were trying to get across simply became clichés." He rose and began to pace the room. "But you can't say we didn't try, Doctor. We went before Congress, talked to a hundred committees—to public meetings— drove our message home over the radio and through the *Bulletin of Atomic Scientists* we issued. And don't forget one thing."

"Yes?"

"We weren't publicity men. We were scientists—amateurs at this business of propaganda. We had to come out of the laboratory."

"Very true," said the Old Man quietly. He lighted one of his small cigars very deliberately. "The trouble was, Professor Kellar, you didn't come out far enough."

"I don't understand, Doctor."

"The point is, Professor, that we scientists have been blind for hundreds of years. We've dealt only in precise things—pounds, feet, degrees, designs, formulas. We've been scientists in everything but the most important of them all—the science of the human mind." The Old Man was emphatic. "But that's wrong, Kellar, *wrong!* It's not enough to be a good scientist any longer."

"Are you suggesting that a scientist become a psychiatrist too, Dr. Dawson?"

"More than that, Professor," snapped the Old Man. "He must

become a sociologist, a philosopher, a humanitarian, a reformer, and yes—even a preacher. Let's look ourselves straight in the eye, Professor. Let's own up to what we've done!"

"Well?" asked Kellar. "What *have* we done?"

"We've been criminally negligent. You and Eckert and Davidson and the others work out nuclear fission. And then instead of weighing the consequences, instead of going slowly and asking, 'What will they do with the atom, and are they ready for it?' you blithely give a fused stick of dynamite and a match to a schoolboy and go back to the comfortable and familiar sanctity of your laboratories."

Kellar did not speak for a moment. Then: "Are you suggesting, Doctor, that we deliberately stop the progress of science?"

"What I am suggesting is that we *control* it and judge whether whatever we create will do more harm than good when it is released."

"I don't think scientists are capable of judging——"

"Then it's about time they started to learn," interrupted the Old Man hotly. "Take myself, Professor. I am an astronomer. My worlds are universes. I use giant telescopes to study them. Should I then condescend to turn to a microscope and study the microbes on my own pitiful planet? The answer is yes. And again, yes! Perhaps I am lacking in nobility, in the pure scientist's approach that the truth is the thing, and damn the consequences. But I believe our first responsibility is to the people with whom we live, not to the things we find!"

David had never heard the Old Man swear before, had never seen him so worked up. His eyes blazed, and he spoke passionately.

"Of course this whole discussion is really academic, Kellar. We haven't much time left. But we've a lot to atone for. We scientists have been responsible for many of the world's ills for a long time. We've failed to understand that science moves fast, it is revolutionary, while the human mind is slow, *evolutionary*. As a result, we have a gap of thousands of years between scientific achievement and the human capacity to use it wisely."

"Then we have one of two alternatives," said Kellar. "In order to gain an equilibrium, we must either speed up the growing process of the mind or slow down science."

"Exactly," answered the Old Man. "One or the other. And of the two, the slowing down of our research functions is by far the more feasible. That comes into our province, Professor Kellar. Call it scientific sabotage, if you will. Call it anything you want. We should have put it into practice long ago. Now it's too late."

There was a commotion just outside the study. The door was flung open and two men burst in, sweeping Francis to one side.

One was the Secretary of Defense, and the other was General Matt Hawthorne.

Immediately after the first radio flash had hit their underground headquarters they had conferred briefly with the President. Then they had boarded a jet for San Diego, where an Army helicopter had picked them up and dropped them on Palomar.

General Hawthorne's face was livid.

"Damn it, Doctor, what the hell do you think you've done?" He pounded his fist on Dr. Dawson's desk. "Didn't you ever hear of something we call military security?"

"Yes, General," replied the Old Man quietly, "I have."

"Then why didn't you check with us before you released this information? The press and radio people went crazy on us—rushed the story through before our censors had a chance to stop 'em!"

David saw Kellar's face out of the corner of his eye. It was almost contorted with hate and contempt for Hawthorne. But the Old Man was unruffled as he answered:

"Rather like trying to stop an avalanche with a red pencil, isn't it, General? Besides," he continued calmly, "it was precisely in the interests of security that my colleagues and I released the announcement when we did."

Hawthorne began to retort hotly, but here the Secretary of Defense stepped in. A tall, thin, hawk-faced man, and a former insurance company executive, the Secretary was noted for his brilliant administrative ability and his coolness under pressure.

But now his face was flushed; he chewed his cigar nervously and spoke rapidly, jerkily, as though his mind were busy groping for a solution and had not yet caught up with his tongue.

"Dr. Dawson, we were on the verge of attacking the Soviet Union. As you know, there was a meeting near New York——"

"He knows it all right," interrupted Hawthorne angrily. "His boy here, Hughes, broke my orders and didn't show up. And by God, planet or no planet, I'm going to prefer charges——"

The Secretary looked annoyed, silenced Hawthorne with a wave of his hand.

"Let me finish, General." He turned back to the Old Man. "To repeat, Doctor, we were on the verge of attacking Russia, on the honest premise that it was in our best interests. We were in the process of convincing the President himself that this was the wise course to take, when your bulletin came through. You must realize, you must be aware of the disastrous effect it will have. Our men are at strategic outposts everywhere, ready for action. When they hear about this—this new planet—their morale will break down—their discipline crumble. There's sure to be a wave of hysteria, perhaps some sort of mass panic. Our men may simply throw down their weapons, leave their posts, and head for home, a demoralized mob." His voice rose a little. "And you, Doctor, speak of releasing this bulletin in the interests of security!"

"My colleagues and I, Mr. Secretary, were thinking of *world* security rather than just national security."

Hawthorne stepped in, his face a mottled red, and thrust it close to the Old Man's belligerently. "You say *that*, knowing that our whole military setup, let alone our war industries, may melt away overnight? Christ, man, don't you realize that'll leave us wide open for attack?"

"Attack?" said the Old Man softly. "Attack by whom?"

"By the enemy—by the Reds. Who else?"

For a moment Dr. Dawson did not reply. David watched the Old Man's face closely. He thought he saw a flicker of amusement pass over it for the second time that day. His blue-veined hands toyed with a letter opener, and he tapped it in a kind of rhythmic beat on the desk.

"Gentlemen, apparently you didn't hear the President speak on the air a few minutes ago. He himself has pointed out that the threat of war is over. As for myself, I am an astronomer, not a military man. Believe me, I appreciate your concern for the national safety. But you have mentioned the enemy and it is here I must ask you, General Hawthorne and Mr. Secretary, a pertinent question."

The Secretary's eyes narrowed. "Well?"

"What do you think the men in the *enemy* armies will do, gentlemen, when they hear of the coming catastrophe?"

The red slowly faded from Hawthorne's face. The Secretary, caught off guard, stared at Dr. Dawson.

"As you implied, Mr. Secretary, the men in our armed forces are human and will certainly react by throwing down their arms and going home. But the men in the Soviet armies are human, too, and they will do precisely the same thing. As I see it, this planet is not only scheduled to shatter the earth, but it will shatter some of the primitive notions we have nurtured since history began. Among other things, it will certainly vitiate the will to kill, to destroy each other."

The general and the Secretary listened, hypnotized, as the Old Man continued:

"In short, gentlemen, Planet 'Y' will automatically make a human dream of many centuries come true. It will outlaw war. Men who are threatened with a common disaster do not attack each other. After all, what is there to fight about now? A future? There *is* no future. Territory? Natural resources? Political systems? Ideology?" Dr. Dawson shrugged. "These things are meaningless now."

The Old Man was magnificent, David marveled. He had his two visitors riveted to the spot; they were unable to move, to say anything. David noted that Hawthorne's mouth had sagged open ludicrously and that the Cabinet officer's cigar had gone out.

Finally the Secretary of Defense stirred, fumbled for his hat, and said quietly:

"You'll forgive us, Doctor, if we have to rush off now. The President has instructed us to report back to him immediately." He hesitated and then added hopefully, almost wistfully: "If we could only tell him that there was some possibility, however remote, that this catastrophe may not occur . . ."

The Old Man shook his head patiently. "I'm sorry, Mr. Secretary. But I assure you, my colleagues and I have gone over our calculations, checked and rechecked them numberless times. And there is no escape."

The two men walked slowly out of the study, into the hall of the observatory itself, through the crowd of silent, white-faced onlookers who had come to Palomar.

And David, as he watched General Hawthorne's retreating back, was fascinated by the four stars on each shoulder. When the general had come in the stars had been highly polished; they had glittered brightly in the light.

Now, as he left, the stars seemed suddenly to have become a little dull, as though they had tarnished during the general's brief stay in the room.

It was late afternoon.

Carol and David were still miles away from San Diego when they heard the first faint tolling of the city's bells.

All along the road coming down, at Rincon, Valley Center, Escondido, Rancho Santa Fe, Solana Beach, and Del Mar, they had heard the bells.

Listen to the bells, thought David, listen to the bells. Bells went with wedding days. And this was his wedding day.

But these were funeral bells.

He had intended to postpone this wedding trip to Dago. They were going crazy back at the observatory. There were a thousand things to do, and he had volunteered to stay. But the Old Man would have none of it. He had insisted that David and Carol go through with their plans. And now, thought David, here he was with his bride beside him in the car, and they were racing down the Highway to the Stars to a justice of the peace and a wedding night in Dago. And tomorrow they would return to Palomar.

Listen to the bells. . . .

He was getting married this evening, and it was incongruous, almost ridiculous, on this day of all days. It was just too damned normal to be believable. Getting married was normal, if anything was. You said "I do" and she said "I do" and you went somewhere and had your honeymoon, and after that you settled down and planned for the future.

Or at least that was the way it had been in the old days.

But the old days were yesterday, and yesterday was another age, another era. Yesterday was the day before the Year One. One, two. Christmas Day, 1962.

Now you planned nothing, and there was no future.

Two years and a month. Twenty-five months. It was like walking through twenty-five separate rooms, each smaller and narrower, each with less ventilation and lower ceilings, each progressively colder and darker, each pressing downward and inward, until the last room.

And from this there would be no other escape, no other room.

"David," said Carol. "Listen to the bells."

They sounded nearer now, clearer. They were a great chorus of discordant calamity, wafted through the thin clear air by a hundred bronze mouths. They clashed and clanged and rang; they cried and wailed and sobbed. They welled up from the distant city and rippled across the plain and echoed faintly through the mountain canyons.

Ring out the old, ring in the new.

It was just getting dark when they drove into San Diego.

It was a different kind of darkness from what they had ever known or seen before. It was a darkness deafened and desecrated and made discordant with the awful constant clamor of the tolling bells. It had the feel and the texture and the weight of a great shroud.

It was a darkness of a special quality.

Every house in the city was ablaze with light, as though each held a mourners' wake.

The rooftops were black with people staring up at the sky, staring at something they could not see but knew was there. They seemed to be waiting in a kind of feverish anticipation, as though half expecting that the wildcat planet would somehow appear among the stars and plummet down upon the earth ahead of schedule.

Those who were not on the rooftops swarmed into the streets, thousands upon thousands of them, blocking traffic, moving aimlessly, mechanically, going nowhere.

And they, too, stared up at the sky.

They were close-packed and dense, men, women, and children, like animals huddled together for comfort and protection. They moved and swirled and eddied in an endless crowd, craning their necks upward. They were silent and sullen now, walking like automatons, shuffling along with slow and dragging steps.

But it was there within them, the threat of explosion, of awful hysteria, of terrible violence. It was ugly and alive in their white faces and frightened eyes. It bubbled and seethed and brewed and waited.

The din was deafening. The bells rang, seemed to grow louder by the hour. Horns honked as busses and cars moved by inches through the seething crowd. Newsboys hawked extras shrilly, with screaming headlines: END OF WORLD . . . PLANET HEADED FOR EARTH . . . DOOMSDAY, CHRISTMAS, 1962 . . . READ ALL ABOUT IT!

It was the only story in the newspapers; there was nothing else. There were pictures of Dr. Dawson, of Palomar Observatory, of the great telescope, a blown-up reproduction of the fatal spot of light.

The theater marquees blazed, the stores were brightly illuminated, the neon signs in the bars and taverns blinked reddened invitation.

But they were empty and abandoned. The people were on the rooftops or in the streets, out in the open, where they could look up and see the sky.

Only the churches were full. They were jammed to capacity, and the crowds choked their doorways and spilled out into the streets and waited in long lines. The wailing of prayer and the sound of lamentation came from their interiors, mixing with the din of the bells.

Already there were a few who had begun to make their peace with God.

David and Carol hardly heard what the justice of the peace had said. He mumbled the words in a kind of daze; his hands shook as he held the book.

He married them and signed the papers and took his fee. He was a man in a trance, going through the motions from force of habit. The chances were that he never really saw them, would never really remember them. Nor would they remember him.

Now David edged the car through the crowds, honking his horn. The people were no longer silent and sullen. Their nerves had been stretched taut, tighter than they could stand, and now they had snapped back the other way. They stopped looking at the sky and started looking at each other. They became animated, articulate, shrill.

There was the smell of hysteria in the air.

The streets turned into bedlam. As David and Carol drove toward their hotel they heard the crash of glass, the delighted yells of a great crowd. Someone threw a stone through a shopwindow, and the idea caught on. Soon they were breaking the windows of all the shops up and down the streets, swarming into the stores, ripping the merchandise from the shelves. Sirens sounded; the police fought the crowds. They surged forward and retreated, surged and retreated. Their faces red, their eyes wild and staring, they fought the police tooth and nail.

People who had never taken a drink, respectable people, middle-class people, solid citizens and regular churchgoers, now crowded the bars and taverns, or staggered in the streets, or lay in the gutters, dead drunk. Horns blared in an earsplitting din, women were openly attacked, the looting became general, shots were fired, cars tipped over, and busses turned on their sides.

The planet ended restraint, turning it into release. The pressure was gone, the emotional floodgates spewed wide open, and the people went wild in a kind of ugly ecstasy. They could soar now; they were free and untrammeled spirits; there was no future to face, only a future to forget.

Eat, drink, and be merry . . .

This was the first night of the Year One.

It was almost dawn now.

No one in the city had slept that night.

Carol and David, for the moment, lay quietly in each other's arms and listened to the sounds of the macabre holiday outside. They were still going on, the violent sounds, the honking of unrestrained horns, the distant sirens, the tolling of far bells, the sound of running feet on the pavement.

The hotel was a beehive; it was alive and awake. Its windows, from top to bottom, were ablaze with light, as though it were the hour after sunset instead of the hour before dawn. From them eddied anonymous voices, shrill, high-pitched in drunken laughter, hysterical, babbling, tinged with a kind of madness.

"To hell with it, Joe. Let it come outa the sky, this goddamn Planet 'Y.' I'll never see it—won't even know it's there. I'll be stiffer than a haddock for two years, Joe, see what I mean? Get myself so blind I won't be able to see it. Yeah. That's the ticket. A two-year bender—starting tonight. Have another drink, Joe!"

"Listen, Ann. You wanted that fur coat? Okay, you'll get it. That trip around the world? Sure. We'll go. Anything you want, baby. We're on the merry-go-round, honey. What've we got to lose? Sure, we'll take every dime we've got out of the bank—sell the business. Who cares about money now? Who's saving for the future now? What future? We got two years to have fun in, baby—two years. Let's start now, baby. You know what I mean. It's been a long time. Pull down the shades, baby. We're wasting time."

"The funny part of it was, Phil, this insurance agent was up to see me yesterday. Had me sold on a hundred thousand dollars' worth of life insurance. I was going to sign the papers today. Kind of funny, isn't it, when you think of it now? Who in hell would want any life insurance now? For what? Pour me another one, Phil. Make it weak though. I feel a little sick inside."

"Darling, listen, I'm calling from San Diego. I'll take the first plane I can get for home. How are the kids? Yes, yes, I'll be home just as soon as I can make it. I don't feel like being alone, either, at a time like this. Please, please, Helen, don't cry. Don't cry like that. Try not to think of it. Try to get some sleep now. Please, Helen, don't cry. Remember what we've always said? If we had to go, we wanted to go together. . . ."

"Listen, Frank, it isn't just dying that's hard to take. Everybody's got to die sooner or later. But it's knowing the exact date—that's what's hard, that's what's driving me out of my mind. Christmas Day, 1962, Christmas, 1962. That's all I can think of. Watching the calendar, counting the hours. Frank, for Christ's sake, how are we going to stand it, how are we going to stand it? And watching that Planet 'Y,' that thing up there in the sky, getting bigger and bigger, closer and closer, like an ax coming down on top of your head, and knowing you can't do a thing about it—except let it come. Frank, for God's sake, there isn't any more liquor left. Order up another bottle. I need a drink—I need it bad."

Finally the voices which had crawled through the blinds became a confused and distant murmur, without meaning and without identity.

And they were alone, the two of them, on their wedding night, clinging and blending, drunk with the desperate having of each other, living a moment of priceless time.

Afterward they lay exhausted, apart, and David thought, God, she was wonderful, wonderful, this wonderful girl who was his wife.

He could never get enough of her, there would never be enough of her, never. There never would be enough time.

From now on Carol and he would live in moments, in desperate moments, each more urgent than the other as the deadline came nearer, each hungrier, each more hopeless. They didn't have long, they didn't have much, only each other. And there would never be the easy anesthesia so mercifully provided by a benevolent Nature, the hope of a natural lifetime, the slowing down by time of youth itself, of passion cooling imperceptibly and painlessly, of "growing old gracefully."

Then finally David whispered:

"Carol."

"Yes, darling?"

"We've got to be careful, very careful. We can't have any children—not now."

She began to cry then, and he took her in his arms and tried to comfort her.

9. It was early evening, and the Year One was just two weeks old.

David Hughes sat in his own easy chair, in his own home on Palomar Mountain. There was a scotch and soda at his elbow, and the newspaper he always read was in his lap. He was a bridegroom of two weeks, and upstairs his bride was under the shower, and in a little while they would leave for the Dawsons' house, where they had been invited for dinner. After that the Old Man and himself would go to the observatory, leaving Carol and Emily Dawson and perhaps some of the other staff wives to talk about the little things that women talked about.

It was all very usual and very commonplace, or had been—once. Now the commonplace was a little dreamlike.

He glanced out of the window and stared at the landscape and thought, in a detached kind of way, that the snow was just as white and cold as it always was, it drifted in the same old way, it stuck to the trees in the same patterns. The sun was red on the horizon with its customary redness, and in its customary place, in that gap in the mountains, just to the left of the crimson-tinted dome housing the forty-eight-inch telescope. The kids near the place where the road curved were building a snow man, and it looked as all snow men usually looked, graceless and lumpy, with the same black coals for eyes, the same twig for a nose, the same wide gash for the mouth, the same resigned and patient look.

This was your own personal little picture, he reflected, your own miniature, drawn to accustomed scale, with the same strokes of the brush and the same colors.

Up close, nothing had changed.

But when you backed away from the picture and then looked at it, everything suddenly changed. You saw with a kind of numb horror that the perspective was all wrong, that the colors clashed and shrieked, that everything in it was monstrous and distorted and unbelievable, and that its theme of the commonplace was suddenly hideous.

The sun was too big and, although faceless, it seemed to leer and lean with oppressive weight over the horizon, like a round and overhanging and threatening stone. Its red had now darkened and deepened to the color of blood. The snow suddenly became pock-marked and old and dirty, and the trees, their branches and twigs loaded down with snow, no longer looked like delicate figurines of some frosted fairyland, but rather like white skeletons swaying and rattling hollowly in the wind. The dome of the forty-eight-inch, over the ridge, was no longer round and squat, but long and cylindrical, and its glistening tip was a shining fingernail on the end of a finger pointing straight up to a fiery spot which had suddenly materialized in the clear sky.

Even the kids playing and dancing around the snow man had changed. The red in their cheeks had dissolved away into ashen gray, and their chubby faces had suddenly become wasted and gaunt, and their laughing and yelling became a kind of dismal wailing. The snow man, too, had changed; his lumpy head suddenly seemed to tilt upward, watching the fiery spot in the sky, and there was a leering and malicious smirk on his face.

You'd been too close before to see it. But now that you were a little farther back, you saw that the picture had a black frame around it.

And as you watched, you could almost see the black frame contract and creep inward from all four sides, left and right and top and bottom, and begin to encroach upon the picture. You could almost see it blot out the picture little by little, first the sun, and then the landscape and the trees and the observatory on the ridge, and the snow man and the children playing around it, and the room in which you sat.

And the black frame kept spreading inward, until the picture became a miniature, and finally a tiny square cameo, and finally a pin point of fiery light—the light in the sky. It was like peering through a long black tunnel and seeing nothing at the other end but this blazing bit of light.

And then finally the black closed over the light and there was nothing left.

"David, did you see my nail file?"

Carol's voice came to him from upstairs. He stirred and shook his head, as though to clear it.

"It's in the drawer of the end table, I think," he called back.

It was a little amusing, this, Carol calling for her nail file with the world about to end. It was a little amusing, in a sardonic kind of way. You went through the motions, clung to the commonplace, kept your sanity that way. To go on with the traditional amenities, to hew to the regular routine, was the best defense against the planet, the only real defense. Work eight hours, play eight hours, eat three meals, a drink before dinner, wear blue ties with blue socks, white tie with tails, never trump your partner's ace, kiss your wife when you go out, and kiss her when you come in, remember her birthday and anniversary, and of course Mother's Day, if you had a mother, and see your dentist twice a year.

Otherwise the planet would get you ahead of its ordained time, as it had already gotten a lot of other people. They were running out in the streets, or going mad, or cutting their throats, or jumping off high buildings, or drinking themselves to death.

Already the earth was a kind of revolving madhouse, a spinning apple swarming with maddened ants racing in every direction. It was hard to see close up, but the newspaper on David's knee told him the story. He swallowed the last of his highball, picked up the paper, and let his eye rove over the glaring black headlines.

RUSSIAN DICTATOR
ARRIVES IN WASHINGTON

Goes into Immediate Conference with
President at White House

That was something for the book. Two weeks ago a visit from the King of the Martians would have caused a lesser sensation.

When the big Soviet plane with the red stars painted on its wings finally taxied to a stop at National Airport, the President and the entire Cabinet were there to meet the Generalissimo, and the United States Marine Band played the "Internationale."

The photographs of the meeting in the newspapers were not flattering. Both the President and the Soviet dictator looked like everyone else, like frightened little men. Their faces were haggard; they seemed dazed as they shook hands . . .

ARMIES DEMOBILIZED
ATOM PLANTS CLOSE DOWN

Experts Mull Problem
Of Bomb Disposal

The existence of the bombs was almost humorously embarrassing now.

You couldn't just dump them in some junk yard, or store them in some dusty warehouse somewhere, like obsolete merchandise.

You couldn't just bury them in the earth somewhere, or drop them deep on the ocean bed.

The astronomers had pointed out that the other bodies in the solar system had made a slight change in position to compensate for the onrushing planet. Luckily the earth would be spared any violent internal dislocations, but there would still be dangerous stresses and strains on the dry crust and the ocean beds—too dangerous for the deposit of bombs.

Maybe, thought David cynically, they ought to run a contest open to all comers—a million dollars for the best thousand-word statement on what to do with a non-producing atom bomb. Too bad it wasn't a missile like the old-time artillery shells they used a few decades ago. You could always polish up the casings and fill them with dirt and plant flowers in them. Or you could stand them on end and use them as floor ash trays. Whether they held geraniums or cigarette butts, you could get some use out of them, your money wasn't entirely wasted.

But there was nothing more useless than an atom bomb which wasn't working at its trade.

David's eye caught a headline:

MILITARY DISEASE
DEPARTMENTS DISBANDED

Reveal Plans for Bacteriological Warfare
To Supplement A-Bombs

Yes, thought David grimly, it would have been a nice little war all around. He read through a list of attack diseases at the bottom of the story:

Botulism, anthrax, pneumatic plague, measles and mumps, glanders, rabbit fever, undulant fever, yellow fever, dengue fever, tick-borne relapsing fever, spotted and "Q" fever, fowl plague, foot and mouth disease, melioidosis, hog cholera, rinderpest.

David shuddered and turned the page.

RAILS AND AIR LINES JAMMED AS
THOUSANDS RETURN HOME TO CITIES

TRAVELERS ON MOVE TO REJOIN FAMILIES

Food and Utilities Situation
Critical in Urban Centers

It was like a funeral in the family.

The planet brought everybody home, even relatives who hadn't seen each other in twenty years or who were bitter and quarreling enemies. There was nothing like a tragedy to bring people together in a kind of morbid brotherhood.

But this time it wasn't just somebody else's funeral.

WAVE OF SUICIDES AS THOUSANDS
BREAK UNDER STRAIN

MANY TAKE LIVES BY HANGING, POISON, SLEEPING PILLS

Heart Attacks Take Toll

Insane Asylums Filled to Overflowing

Ever since the first night it had been like that. The planet pressed down hard on the brain, and its shadow, although still invisible to the eye, already darkened the mind.

Many died before they were born. Thousands of women in the early stages of pregnancy arranged deliberate miscarriages.

GREAT RELIGIOUS REVIVAL AS
CHURCHES JAMMED TO OVERFLOWING

Planet "Y" the Millennium

In houses of worship all over the world, masses and services were continuous, day and night. People fought to get into churches as they once fought to get into a Hollywood première. The people of radio, the hucksters of Boxtop Boulevard in New York, Chicago, and Los Angeles, looked at their listener-rating reports and stared.

Religious programs, programs of church services and sermons, hit the highest Hooper rating of all time, far above the big-name orchestras and comedians and variety shows.

Right now, radio-wise, prayer was commercial, very commercial indeed.

Give the public what they want. And what the public wanted was comfort, and divine intervention, and deliverance.

What the public suddenly wanted, David concluded, was God.

GOVERNORS PARDON CONDEMNED MEN
LIFERS RIOT FOR FREEDOM

Let Us Live Last Two Years,
They Cry

INDUSTRIES PARALYZED
AS WORKERS STAY HOME

Stores, Offices, Schools Close

Wheels Grind to Stop as World
Staggers under Shock

RUN ON BANKS AS DEPOSITORS RUSH
TO WITHDRAW LIFE SAVINGS

Orgy of Spending, Black Markets,
Inflation Already a Threat

DAWSON DISCOVERY DISPUTED BY
SELF-STYLED HOLY MAN OF
HOGBACK MOUNTAIN, ARKANSAS

I Saw Planet First, Claims Ozark
Prophet, and I Didn't Need No
Telescope Neither

*Saw It in a Vision from the Lord
Swears Lord Promised World an
Extra Two Years for Extra Prayer
And Repentance*

David threw the newspaper on the couch and went upstairs. Carol, a vision of loveliness in a long black evening dress, was combing her hair before the mirror.

"Hurry, darling," she said, "or we'll be late for dinner."

It was almost a technique now.

You deliberately and desperately stuck to the commonplace, and it was a kind of pathetic game. You insulated yourself, never mentioned the planet if you could help it—tried not to think of it.

In order to stay sane, you had to make believe that it wasn't up there in the heavens and rushing onward.

But it *was* there.

That was the fact, the inescapable fact, and there was no privacy from it, no escape. Not even in sleep was there any escape any more, for the planet appeared in dreams, everybody's dreams, large and round and menacing and murderous.

As David unbuttoned his shirt he turned on the small television set on the night table.

The video screen focused on a crowd of people, and the camera panned over to a floodlighted entrance to the White House.

An announcer said something about a momentous meeting, and before he finished, the doors swung open and the President appeared with a bushy-haired man in a tight uniform and wearing the star of the Soviet Union.

They posed before the camera. Then, in an unrehearsed impulse, they threw their arms around each other's shoulders.

You had to hand it to the planet, David reflected.

Whatever it did, it was changing things—and changing them in a hell of a hurry.

10. In April of the Year One, a dramatic announcement came from Palomar.

Dr. Charles Dawson was preparing to photograph the face of Planet "Y."

He had hooked up a complicated photographic setup, using sensitive infra-red plates, and the apparatus had a special talent. It could ignore what it did not want to see. By scanning the face of Planet "Y" a hundred thousand times and delivering to the camera only the features which appeared on a majority of the pictures it saw, it could eliminate all distortions due to poor seeing or other temporary causes, thus taking full advantage of the light-gathering power of the Big Eye.

Already astronomers knew certain basic facts about the onrushing planet. It had a mass hundreds of times greater than that of the earth, and its period of rotation was eight months. They knew that it was a cold and inert body, surfaced by a frozen layer of methane and carbon dioxide, and that its reflective power was approximately that of sandstone.

It would become visible to the naked eye in September, a mere pin point in the sky, and thereafter would rapidly grow larger. And the catastrophe, the collision, would occur on the far side of the sun in relation to the earth's orbit.

But now the Old Man of Palomar was going to look straight into the face of Death itself. He was getting ready to give the world an advance showing on how the Killer would look when finally it hung in the heavens, clearly visible to the naked eye.

The news from Palomar was an immediate sensation. People all over the world showed a morbid and almost unbearable curiosity to look upon the face of their executioner. Newspapermen, astronomers, and other observers converged on Palomar.

This was the preview.

But whatever face Death wore, it would soon become as familiar to every man, woman, and child as the face of the man in the moon.

The night of the photographing was clear and cold.

David and Carol walked up the road toward the observatory. Carol had been in San Diego all day on a shopping trip, and she had insisted on coming along.

"Everyone's going crazy tonight, David," she had said. "You can cut the excitement with a knife. I've never seen so many newspapermen in one place before—not only from the American papers, but from the foreign ones too. They've been coming in all day. And I want to be in on the fun too."

He had noticed that she seemed pale, nervous, after her return from San Diego.

"It was the ride up," she had explained. "The roads, David, they were terribly icy. I thought we were going to skid right over a precipice a couple of times. And anyway, I kept thinking about tonight and worrying about the seeing. But they've already measured it, and I understand it's going to be good."

David had smiled a little at that. Already Carol was talking like an astronomer's wife. They never asked, like ordinary wives, how things were down at the office. They always asked anxiously how the seeing was. If it was one, that was excellent, the best. Two was good. Three was fair, and so on down the line.

The wind, as they moved up the hill, was like the edge of an ax, cutting deep into the bone, and they half walked, half slithered up the slippery road, huddling close to each other for both support and mutual warmth. The crunch-crunch of their feet as they passed the lighted cottages on each side of the road seemed abnormally loud, the only sound in the night.

Night and silence.

This was the normal state of the universe, thought David. Up there in the night of the sky, the stars and planets, like tiny illuminated vessels, moved slowly and silently across a dark and limpid sea. There were billions of them, pitiful suns lost in eternity, shining by their own light, driven by the breath of God. They were like specks of dust seen in a beam of light, or in the slanting rays of sunshine through a window, worlds and universes, lost in space, gliding, turning, spinning, whirling, drifting, vibrating.

Yet, thought David, so perfectly balanced were these bodies in the universe, so delicate and dependent were they in their rhythm upon each other, that a man, by the mere stretching forth of his hand, could theoretically change the moon on its course.

He thought of the planet, of Planet "Y," and he thought of the death it would bring. And he recalled Dr. Dawson discussing death one morning after the dome had closed and the work night was over.

"After all, David," the Old Man had said, "what is fourscore and ten years compared to the life of the stars and the planets? A lightning flash on a summer day? A drop of rain in a cloudburst?"

David had admitted the comparison, had agreed that it was no more than that when you stood away from a man's life and looked at it in proper perspective.

"But in a sense," he had said to the Old Man, "the whole concept of a man's life is in his own mind. To him a lifetime is forever, the beginning and end of all things."

"True," Dr. Dawson had replied. "But it is pure ego, David, for man to believe that all creation began and ended in his personal segment of infinity. In the heavens an eternity has already passed, and an eternity is yet to come. Up there some stars are being born, some are adolescent, some aged and dying, some dead. In the history of creation, a billion years, a hundred billion years, passes like a day."

But, David reflected, men didn't see it that way. They lived their pitiful era in astronomical time, as though the era would never come to an end. They lived, famously or humbly, making money or dreaming dreams, living in glory and living in sorrow, loving, fighting, sleeping, dying, goaded on by self-indulgence or ambition, believing with an incredible belief that *their* careers, *their* lives, *their* futures were the most serious, the most important, the most weighty in the universe.

Yet if there had been no Planet "Y," the earth, dependent upon the sun for life, would have died a short time later, a mere hundred million years later. The sun would finally lose its warmth and light and roll along through space, a dark and invisible and forgotten star, an icy graveyard.

And when Planet "Y" and the earth finally clashed, there would not be the sound of it in the void, nor even an echo, nor a ripple, to mar the still serenity of the universe.

David suddenly felt Carol tug on his arm, and they stopped walking for a moment.

"David," she said quietly, looking up into the cold and crackling sky, "where will we finally see the planet—up there?"

He bordered the constellation for her, pointed out a star. "That's where it is now, Carol. But when it finally becomes visible its position will have changed."

"Oh." Carol's face was rapt and dreamy. "It's funny, darling. Up to tonight I was afraid of it, of death. But now—now I'm not afraid any more. I keep thinking of life." She turned to him, and her eyes were suddenly wet with tears. "And do you know why?"

He shook his head.

"I was in San Diego today," she said. "But I lied to you, David. It wasn't because I wanted to do any shopping. I—I had to see Dr. Ramsey."

He stared at her. "Dr. Ramsey?"

"You see, David," she said simply, "I'm going to have a baby."

Up ahead on the summit, in the squat, curved white building, in Palomar Observatory, men were feverishly preparing to look at the face of their executioner; they had contrived instruments to do so, trembling in their anticipation.

But David had forgotten it now.

The affair of the heavens had for the moment become relatively unimportant. His mind was confused and whirling with an earthy problem.

His child would be a year old when the end came.

It was wrong, he thought savagely, wrong. When you brought a child into the world, you owed it a lifetime.

But he knew that his concern was partly selfish.

Carol was pregnant, and for the better part of a year she would be denied to him.

God damn it, he thought furiously, helplessly, he was human, as human as anybody. Why did this have to happen?

Why?

"Everything set, David?" asked Dr. Dawson.

"Yes, sir." David answered mechanically, almost absently, still preoccupied with his own intimate problem. "I've checked all the apparatus. Wallace had some trouble with the Bowen image-slicer. There was some variance in the temperature of the coudé room, and we were afraid it would distort the image delivered into the high-dispersion spectrograph. But everything's all right now."

"Good." The Old Man crushed his cigar in an ash tray and rose. "You've instructed the newspaper and radio people to stay in the auditorium until the experiment is over?"

"Yes, Doctor. Francis will be there to see that no one wanders out into the observatory."

"Well, David, I guess we're ready to go." The Old Man lifted his phone, dialed two numbers, and said: "All right, Fred, we're ready. You can bring the roof down now."

The Old Man's voice was almost dry in his calm. But David knew he was excited, excited inside. It was a big night, and the world was waiting. It was the biggest night they would ever have from here on in. The face of the planet was something you could not predict or calculate in advance, or even guess at.

Whatever the big telescope showed would be brand new, and it would be just as exciting to astronomers as to laymen.

They walked out into the observatory itself. It was silent now, bathed in the weird glow of soft red and green lights hidden in the cornice. The two men were alone, walking noiselessly on the rubber parquet as they headed toward the elevator.

David forgot his own troubles for the moment. The observatory still affected him, still awed him a little. Walking through it alone, he had always felt a little like an intruder. There was something about it, its hushed and reverent silence, its dim lighting, its echoing and arching vault, that reminded him of a cathedral. He had seen boisterous tourists enter it, and suddenly their voices had dropped to whispers, and they had taken off their hats and walked softly on tiptoes.

Being a little nearer to the stars here at Palomar was, in a sense, being a little nearer to God. The observatory was the last way station to the heavens.

Yet walking through the observatory now with Dr. Dawson, David felt somehow that they and the building itself were already in a kind of celestial motion. It was of course an illusion, you knew it was an illusion, you knew that this building was anchored firmly to the granite body of Palomar Mountain.

Still, here in this place, in the ghostly light and the complete silence, a kind of hypnotic spell stole over you, and already you were moving, soaring through space, as though the great round building had somehow burst from its earthy moorings and was carrying you along with it, a pygmylike passenger, through the starry vault overhead.

As they came out of the elevator on the mezzanine, a motor purred suddenly somewhere deep below. It began to throb and beat, throb and beat, like a great heart. The dome began to open, like an orange slowly unfolding into two perfect halves, and a cold blast of air came straight downward.

After the main floor, the transition to the mezzanine was almost startling. Men of the observatory staff were swarming about the place, running up and down stairways, carrying photographic plates, sheets of calculations, and bound on other errands. They seemed to be moving almost feverishly against a deadline, as though the onrushing planet overhead might decide to veer off and run away before they could catch it in their instruments.

The Old Man smiled. "It's a little like a railroad station around here tonight, isn't it, David?"

"Yes, sir."

"Tell you a little secret," whispered the Old Man. "I'm more excited than anyone else around here. Thank heaven there's only one setting I'll have to take. And I hope I don't fumble it."

The Old Man sounded as though he meant it. He went to his locker, pulled a fur hat fitted with ear muffs down firmly over his head, bundled himself up in a fur coat, and drew on a pair of heavy mittens.

"Well, David," he said, "let's go. And in a short time—if we're lucky—we'll have the answer."

David signaled for lights out and walked toward his desk control station. The lights died, except for one tiny hooded reddish lamp high in the dome. As the members of the staff scurried toward their separate posts, a kind of hush came over the place. But it was a hush that was alive, ecstatic with excitement, and yet filled with dread.

They watched the Old Man silently as he walked with measured stride along the balcony, and then, climbed the short iron stairway to the loading bridge. He looked up into the dome for a moment, as though savoring the drama of what lay in wait up there, far beyond the roof and the earth itself.

Then he pushed a button, and the flying platform swept down from the shadows of the dome, swung in on its curved track, and stopped. He closed the gate, the clang of the steel safety bar shattering the silence like a steely echo. The Old Man pressed another control button, and the platform, with its tiny figure clutching the rail, swept up the track and disappeared.

David stood quietly at his station and waited. His eye swept his control panels, the various switches, the indicators for right ascension and declination, the telescope's zenith angle, wind-screen position, sidereal and standard time clocks, the selsyn transmitters. They were as familiar to him as the dashboard of an automobile is to its driver.

But tonight their phosphorescent faces glowing sickly in the darkness seemed to take on a special and magic and almost human look, as though they, too, were aware that the drama was about to begin.

This was the night. This was the night they had waited for at Palomar for weeks.

Now they were ready, they were all ready to go. And in a few minutes their aching curiosity would be satisfied, theirs and the curiosity of millions of others in every corner of the earth.

The Old Man seemed to be taking a long time getting his call through, thought David. Maybe it was no longer than usual on the clock, but it seemed like an eternity. He pictured Dr. Dawson high in the cage, in the top of the telescope, checking the banks of three selsyn dials for right ascension and declination, as he had so many hundreds of times. The dials indicated rough, intermediate, and fine settings.

The phone buzzed suddenly. David picked up the receiver.

"All right, David," came the voice of the Old Man quietly. "Give me the setting."

David hung up and pressed the "execute" button.

And now the precise mechanical miracle that moved the 200-inch telescope to its appointed place went into action.

The human brain stopped functioning, and an electric brain took over. It was contained in a box twenty feet square, its brain cells were electronic tubes, and it could memorize, add, multiply, and divide billions in a fraction of a second. The name of it was EDVAC—Electronic Discrete Variable Computer—and in an hour it could work out a problem that it would take one human and expert mathematician fifty years to solve.

Now, through its motors, gears, electric circuits, and electronic tubes, it instantly calculated where the big telescope had to point in order to find Planet "Y." In effect, it solved the problem of holding the giant telescope with an accuracy of a single second of arc—a miracle of accuracy comparable to hitting a moving dime two miles away with a high-powered rifle.

It compensated for variable factors all at once—the change in object position caused by atmospheric refraction; the change in refraction owing to the temperature, humidity, barometric pressure, errors in the driving gears, the error owing to the deformation of the telescope itself under its own huge weight.

Then, through a system of cams, clocks, differential gears, and governors, the impulse was passed on to the great telescope drive system. And finally the huge tube swung into position, and the tracking motors took over and kept it aligned—a machine as heavy and as complicated as a locomotive, and yet a delicate instrument as precise as the finest microscope.

And up in a cage a man sat hunched over his instruments, photographing the face of Death itself.

Every seat in the auditorium was filled, and now it buzzed with excited conversation.

The first five rows of seats were taken by members of the Palomar staff, the rest by reporters and radiomen. In the rear a "remote" was set up, and two network men waited with earphones clamped to their heads, with microphones ready to broadcast the news to the world, while the television crews busied themselves with their cameras.

They were waiting for the Old Man now to come out of the photographic lab.

David stood at the projector and watched the faces of the men, listened to what they were saying. He remembered another occasion—the morning the Old Man had broken the news of the planet here in this same auditorium.

It seemed as though it were only the day before yesterday. But actually it was five months ago.

Time moved on wings now, it slipped by fast, it was desperately precious. It was no longer leisurely. Before the planet came, a man could watch the hands of a clock, and they would seem to stand still or barely crawl around the face.

But now you could see them move, you could watch them voraciously eat up the time.

Less than two years more. One, two.

And then the end.

The door opened, and Dr. Dawson came in.

He was holding a slide in his hand. The hum of conversation died suddenly. There was a rustling as the crowd turned to look at the Old Man.

He came in slowly, walking with dragging steps. He looked stunned. His face was blanched; he moved like an automaton.

David stiffened. Something was wrong, he thought. Something had hit the Old Man hard.

But what was it? What had the Old Man seen? What was on that slide?

The men in the room stared at the astronomer stupidly. They sat rigid, fixed in their seats, like men in a trance.

They, too, sensed that the Old Man was suffering from some kind of shock.

Instead of walking down the aisle and going up on the platform to explain what he had seen, he walked straight to David and wordlessly handed him the slide.

With shaking fingers David turned on the projector. Francis turned out the lights, and a funnel of blank white light hit the screen on the platform.

David inserted the slide.

And then they saw the face of Planet "Y."

But it was not really a face at all.

It was a leering, malevolent, staring EYE!

As the months went by the world robbed the big telescope of its nickname and gave it to Planet "Y."

After that they called it *THE BIG EYE*.

11. Long before it became visible the Big Eye leered malignantly from every rotogravure page and every magazine cover in the country and in the world.

It was a dead kind of eye, with a baleful stare, and it was bloodshot under a puffy eyelid.

And finally, in the late summer of the Year One, it became visible through small telescopes.

In cities all over the world sidewalk entrepreneurs did a bonanza business by mounting telescopes on street corners for a preview of the killer planet. The Big Eye became the biggest show in town.

It was still far off in the void, still remote, but getting nearer and bigger every day. Through the telescope it was about the size of a pea, but remarkably distinct.

And as the planet made its half rotation every four months the Big Eye became distorted and finally turned and looked away, presenting the back of its "eyeball," a nondescript pattern of shadowed ridges and mountains.

But it always reappeared, turning slowly on its revolving eyeball, till it again glared down with a fixed and fishy and knowing stare.

When it was full it always seemed to look directly at you, but, unlike the human eye, it never blinked.

When your turn came for the telescope and you looked through the lens, you saw the Big Eye and you were alone with it.

And when the man who owned the telescope finally touched your arm and said, "Next," it was as though you were coming out of a hypnotic trance. You felt weak and gone inside, and your hands and knees shook, and your clothes were wet with perspiration.

It was all very well for the astronomers to be dryly scientific about it. It was all very well to say that the blood-red color was only the reflection of the sun below the horizon, that the black eyebrow was a huge, curved volcanic mountain range, that the eyeball was a great round crater, that the iris was a darker depression within the crater.

They spoke of the topography of the Big Eye in terms of mountains, craters, rays, rills, crevices, ridges, furrows, walled plains, and shadows. They blandly made comparisons to the friendly and benevolent face of the moon, matched the elevations and contours of the Big Eye with the lunar craters of Tycho, Copernicus, Kepler, Clavius, Grimaldi, Archimedes, and the lunar Apennines.

The astronomers said that what you saw through the sidewalk telescopes was simply a dead planet.

But to you the Big Eye was very much alive.

And it did not deviate. It was right on schedule; it had a date to keep at an appointed time.

The Big Eye, although yet invisible to the naked eye, already had profound effects.

As it plummeted through the solar system it brought about certain natural phenomena. There were high winds, freakish changes of temperature; the tides became erratic; navigation instruments were becoming unreliable. Minor tidal waves were reported, and the number of earthquakes increased, although for the most part they were isolated to those countries already susceptible to subterranean shocks.

Seismologists assured the people who had returned to New York that there was no further danger. What had happened in November was a minor series of tremors, called foreshocks. There had been a small fracture in the bedrock under the city and a subsequent readjustment to a secure and stable base.

But the impact of the new planet was strongest upon the minds of those who lived under it.

In the first few months of the Year One there had been a wave of suicides, an interval of violence and lawlessness, a kind of mass madness. The crime rate had soared; rape and robbery were rampant. Statistics showed, however, that the number of homicides was almost negligible. Under the circumstances, life suddenly became a very precious commodity, and even hardened criminals and murderers showed a certain reluctance to take it.

Alcoholism soared, the demand for liquor far exceeded the supply, and the governments of the various nations all installed rationing systems. The streets swarmed with staggering drunkards and prostitutes. Respectable men and women of sound, churchgoing families, slept in strange beds and each other's beds.

There was so little time.

Yet as time went on the hysteria tapered off. People settled back and accepted the fact that they had to live under the planet, and there was nothing they could do to avert it.

Millions became ardent church- and temple-goers. Some were merely mending their fences for the next world just around the corner. But the vast majority found real comfort and peace in religion. Money became a drug on this kind of temporary market, there were no futures, and rich men gave their wealth away.

There was nothing the Lord loved so much as openhanded charity. It was a good hedge against the hereafter.

In the field of agriculture there was a little trouble at first. Farmers, who were now interested in enjoying the leisure which was the farmers' special dream, saw no reason why they should work from dawn to dusk to supply the needs of others. But the granaries were bulging, and experts calculated that, with only a minor effort on the part of farmers, there would be enough to last through the appointed time. The government buttressed this with emergency edicts, establishing harvest quotas by law.

Poverty began to disappear. At the end of the first few months of the Year One, not a beggar was seen on the streets of any metropolis in the world, not even in Shanghai, Bombay, Cairo, and other cities which had once swarmed with hungry supplicants. The various governments surprisingly discovered that they had all the resources it took to feed and clothe and otherwise take care of its people. It was only a question, to coin an old, old phrase, of proper distribution. Governments had no future to worry about, no more armies and navies to support. The national debt became a figure of speech. And although death was still certain, taxes were canceled.

Everywhere, in business and industry, the wheels began to slow to a stop.

But Government was active, and changing fast.

Politicians, having no re-election to worry about, suddenly became representatives of the people. In Washington the Democrats and Republicans almost immediately merged into a single party. The ordinary issues that had brought forth oratory and filibusters suddenly became obsolete. The Big Eye stared down impartially upon the sunny shores of California as well as the rock-bound coasts of Maine.

And this was only the beginning.

In July a world government came into being.

The Federation of the World, as it was called, took over the old United Nations setup on East River Drive in New York City as its headquarters.

The Secretariat skyscraper bordering Forty-second Street, the Library, the General Assembly Building, the giant office building on Forty-eighth Street once again blazed with light. The hedges on the terrace were clipped, the grass trimmed, the broken windows replaced, and the corridors scrubbed.

There was a tremendous dedication, with hundreds of thousands jamming the area. Batteries of huge searchlights blazed from surrounding skyscrapers, bathing the area in brilliant white light. The East River sparkled with many-colored reflections as one gigantic fireworks display after another boomed in the summer sky and exploded in glittering cascades.

A Supreme Council of the World was elected by the assembled delegates of every nation on earth.

The ex-President of the United States and the ex-dictator of the Soviet Union were elected to serve in alternating chairmanships.

There was no problem as to tenure, and the bylaws of the World Constitution held no provision for any re-election.

On the following morning the New York *Times* devoted its entire editorial page to the event. The lead editorial said in part:

> *Today a wistful dream nurtured by mankind for centuries has come true.*
>
> *World government is a fact.*
>
> *It is both wonderful and pitiful. It is wonderful in that we*

have lived to see it come. It is pitiful that we shall have it for such a short duration.

Under the glare of the Big Eye, world government had to come. It was inevitable, and natural, and practical. The moment the dramatic announcement broke from Palomar, it was on its way. In the past months we have watched the two great conflicting systems, capitalism and Communism, crumble, disintegrate. We have seen nationalism, isolationism, and all the other isms that separated state from state, man from man, go down into ashes.

And out of the ashes has risen one great universal system—worldism.

After a million years of ignorant infancy, man has finally shed his swaddling clothes. If the Big Eye is a tragic miracle, so, too, is the speed with which it has changed the pattern of our lives. As it swiftly began to shorten the celestial abyss between the earth and itself, it became a powerful catalyst, pushing the reaction forward with dramatic speed. In a few months it did what man in all the centuries of his history had failed to do.

Under the lash of fear, under the baleful glare of the Big Eye, men and nations both suddenly stopped being afraid of each other in their one common fear.

Now they are coming together in universal brotherhood.

The Big Eye will one day bring total darkness, but in the interim it has brought its own light. It has broken up, at one powerful stroke, the false gods invented by man—the legends, the superstitions, the errors and lies and prejudices and hypocrisies accumulated in the human mind for thousands of years.

The overwhelming tragedy is that the new idea has such a short time to live. But there is still another tragedy we cannot fail to note here.

The real tragedy is that we did not begin to create this new world back some fifteen years ago, when the first bomb fell on

Hiroshima. The tragedy is that all through the late forties and fifties, as the world broke asunder into two worlds, we failed to understand that the bomb was a kind of Planet "Y" itself, in its devastating threat to mankind.

Had we recognized the fact then, that the bomb was simply a man-made Big Eye, we might have begun our new Federation of the World in 1945 instead of today.

How could we have been so blind?

Why did we, beginning from the end of the last war, through the late forties and the early fifties, move apart into hostile and nationalistic and suspicious segments, instead of coming together as we have now?

Why did it take a celestial manifestation to bring us to our senses?

Why?

12. On the third of September, in the Year One, the Big Eye became visible to the human eye.

It appeared as a tiny pin point high in the heavens, shortly after dusk.

As time went by the pin point thickened into a dime, a penny, a quarter, then a half dollar, varying in color, like the moon. Finally it was a rotting, overripe tangerine hanging in the sky, and the Eye emerged from a shadowy outline to become sharp and clear.

And, like the human eye, it seemed to reflect mood and intent to the viewer.

Sometimes it was dead and expressionless and indifferent. At other times it was bloated and swollen and puffy, as though suffering from some kind of heavenly hang-over. It was capricious, too. It was sly; it flirted and beckoned. It smirked cynically; it leered triumphantly. Sometimes it was hard and threatening, malicious and mischievous, smug and angry.

It was never a shifty eye. It knew what it was about; it was a knowing eye; its purpose was plain and understood.

And the times when it was visible in the day or night sky, whether you saw it in America, or Siberia, or Australia, or Arabia, it never looked at other people elsewhere.

It always looked directly at you.

It was impossible to stare the Big Eye down. It followed you everywhere, like a conscience. And as it grew bigger and bigger it became heavier and heavier, so that your back and shoulders and head seemed to ache with its oppressive weight, and your feet dragged more slowly.

It was particularly vivid when the moon was invisible. Stray dogs howled and bayed at it in the night when it shone alone in the sky. But when the moon appeared with it and the two competed for supremacy, the dogs seemed confused and uncertain. They merely whimpered a little or stopped barking entirely.

At the end of the Year One the moon paled into a sickly white, and the Big Eye dominated the night sky.

It hung high overhead, tinting the night, so that it was never really night at all, but a kind of murky and oppressive sunset from dusk until dawn.

And it kept coming on, hurtling down, nearer and nearer, leering malignantly as it came.

As the calendar shortened, the Big Eye became bigger, bigger, and bigger, rounder and rounder, crueler and crueler, brighter and brighter, redder and redder. . . .

David Hughes and Joe Morgan, the Palomar spectrograph man, came out of the air-line terminal on Forty-second Street.

"Taxi!" yelled Morgan. "Hey, taxi!"

A Yellow Cab stopped short, its brakes squealing. David and his former roommate threw in their luggage, slammed the door, and settled back.

"First the New Weston Hotel on Madison," David told the driver. "We'll check in there—it'll only take a minute. Then you can take us to the Hayden Planetarium on Central Park West."

The driver nodded, and they began to move through a dense wedge of confused traffic.

It was late afternoon in December, and David's first trip to New York since the previous November.

A week ago the Old Man had received an invitation from Dr. Herrick, director of the Planetarium, to lecture on the Big Eye before a Science Council seminar of the world government.

Dr. Dawson had politely declined, for reasons of health, and had offered to send his first assistant and his spectrograph man to substitute for him. Herrick had accepted, and David and Morgan were on their way to confer with the director before lecturing the next morning.

The cabdriver was a small, bull-necked, bald-headed man. His picture framed in the rear of the taxi said he was Frank Leone. And although in the grimy photograph he glared villainously at them from beneath a sinister-looking cap, he turned out to be quite friendly and garrulous.

As he waited for the light at Lexington and Forty-second he turned and asked:

"Been out of town long, gents?"

"About a year," answered David.

"How's the big town look now?"

"Different. It's changed."

"You said it, mister. It's changed plenty."

David noticed that the driver was wearing an expensive overcoat and hand-stitched gloves. He looked more like a prosperous businessman than a taxi driver. A sign of the times, thought David. Only a year to go, what was the use of saving money? Buy the best, live high, eat, drink, and be merry.

Spend every dime, cash in the insurance, go to town, *live*.

He was willing to bet that Frank Leone's wife had a mink coat. He looked out of the window, and as the cab lurched forward with the light he saw that the streets were jammed with what seemed to be hundreds of thousands of people on the Lexington block between Forty-second and Forty-third.

And David noticed that practically every woman in the crowd wore a mink coat.

He turned to Joe Morgan, but Morgan was looking up through the glass roof of the taxi, staring at the towering height of the Chrysler Building. There was awe on his face.

"Look at that, Dave," he said. "Look at that. Not a pane of glass in a window above the first floor."

David had noticed the same thing when they had come out of the terminal. The upper stories of the surrounding skyscrapers were all geometrically lined with open, gaping, rectangular holes. Occasionally the sun glinted on a jagged fragment of glass which still clung to a window frame. They hadn't bothered to replace the windows after the tremor of last November.

"Sure," said the driver, Leone. "All these office buildings are ghost buildings. Most of 'em are shut off above the first floors; the elevators ain't even running. The business sections all over the city are ghost towns."

"Well," said Morgan, "it makes sense. These empty offices, I mean. Accountants, businessmen, they haven't anything to do any more. And take lawyers. No use in lawyers coming down to the office. No one's making any more wills, under the circumstances. There's no more building going on and no titles to work out. And as for contracts——"

"Yeah," interrupted Frank Leone, "who needs a contract now? You make a deal with a guy these days, you don't sign any paper. He takes your word, you take his word, you trust each other. Who wants to kill the other guy, when this damned thing up there in the sky is going to come down and blow us all to hell?" The driver threw on his brakes, bumped a big limousine in front of him. "That's why there ain't a courthouse open today in New York, from Brooklyn to the Bronx. The lawyers and the judges didn't have nothing to do, so they went home."

They inched ahead in the crush of traffic, and David noted that the insurance companies and the banks, too, were closed. The hedges against the future had been clipped at the roots.

But it was the crowd jamming up the sidewalks, barely moving in either direction, that fascinated both David and Morgan. This was a boom town, and the people had a boom look, the look of free spenders. They seemed to be on a holiday. David could see no one hurrying, hustling ahead, as they did in the old days, before the Year One.

But there was more to the crowd than numbers. It was a crowd with a mood.

In the old days, before the Big Eye, the people in a New York crowd looked sullen; they hungered for privacy; they fought and elbowed and resented each other.

Now the faces on the sidewalk looked different.

They looked almost happy, in a taut kind of way. They seemed to say, "Sure, the Big Eye is looking down at me, but it's watching you, buddy, and you, lady, and you and you, and everyone else in this crowd. We're all in the same boat."

David found that he was more relaxed himself, just being here. The tension of the thing in the sky was loosened a little. Palomar was lonely compared to this, and the Big Eye, when its gaze was full, had a trick of picking out its personal target more readily. It was more intimate because you were few in number.

Here, although it was still personal, you could in some measure share the impact with thousands of other people. You could, like cattle huddling together flank to flank under a thunderstorm, find a certain amount of comfort in the nearness of others.

However, David told himself, it was still daylight, and perhaps he had only the illusion of comfort, a temporary feeling of security, here in the bright sunlight.

But the night was coming, and then the Big Eye would hang in the sky, low and leering.

Then David heard Joe Morgan's awed voice.

"I never saw anything like this. The mobs jamming up this sidewalk. Where do they all come from?"

"From everywhere, mister," answered the man at the wheel. "From jerk towns, from the farms, from all over. This town is jammed to the ceiling. You're lucky if you can find a place to sleep. They're sleeping out in the parks, anywhere, no matter where it is. Every train, every plane, and every bus coming in are unloading 'em. I was reading in the paper they got ten million people right here in Manhattan right now, let alone the other boroughs."

"Back a year ago November, this town looked like a morgue," said David.

"Yeah. *Now* look at it!" Frank Leone shook his head. "It's murder just to drive a hack five blocks."

"Why are they all coming to New York?" asked Morgan.

"New York, Chicago, Detroit, it's all the same. People feel better when they're in crowds. The big cities are getting the play. They're all looking to escape, looking for entertainment, for a good time before they die, booze, shows, women. If you got nothing to do tonight, take a walk down Broadway and around Times Square. You'll *see* something there, mister."

As they turned off Lexington and moved west on Forty-ninth toward Park Avenue, Joe Morgan got back to the subject of the crowds.

"Seems to be a lot of foreigners on the streets," he remarked. "Asiatics and Europeans alike."

"Yeah," said Frank Leone. "Only nobody calls 'em foreigners any more. Last summer, when they opened up this here world government over on East River Drive, they let down all the bars of immigration. So they all started to come in—Chinese, Japs, Dutchmen, Russians, everybody. Guess they all figured the U.S. was dreamland, and they wanted to see it before the Big Eye got 'em." The driver grinned. "The first few days it felt kind of funny—like this wasn't the U.S.A. any more."

"And after that?" asked David.

"I dunno," answered Leone. "It was funny, how you got used to it. Nobody gave a damn where anybody came from any more, I guess. Same way in Russia. Me and the wife took a trip over there in September. Blew all our insurance policies in on it."

"How'd you like the Soviet?" asked Morgan.

"It stinks. It's all right to visit, but not to live in. Give me New York any time. But the people are all right, once you get to know 'em. And they don't call it the Soviet any more. Communism is a dead turkey over there. They tore off all the signs and painted over the walls, like they did here. But getting back to the U.S., it's funny how things change. Take the taxi business now."

"Yes?" asked David. "What about it?"

"We got a lot of guys driving hacks that used to be in the Red Army. The doughnut-and-coffee joints near the big hack stands are full of 'em. They drive like they're crazy, and I guess they are. When the big Irish cops around here argue with 'em, *they* go crazy." He grinned back at David and Morgan through the reflector. "Funny how times have changed. Before the Big Eye came I would have murdered any one of these Ivans if I could have got close enough. Now—some of my best friends are Russians."

"Look out, driver!" David yelled suddenly.

Frank Leone jammed on his brakes. The cab came within a foot of hitting three children crossing against the light at Park. The youngsters, their faces white and frightened, scurried for safety to the opposite sidewalk.

"Those goddamn kids," sweated Leone. "There ought to be a law to keep 'em off the downtown streets. Ten times a day I almost run 'em down."

"Where do all these kids come from?" asked Morgan. "School out or something?"

"Ain't you heard?" said the driver. "Every school in town closed the week after they found the Big Eye."

"No schools open?" David was surprised.

"Not a one."

"Seems funny," remarked Morgan. "I don't get it."

"Don't you?" The driver began to explain patiently: "Look. Take me, Frank Leone. I got five kids. In the old days, before that damned Big Eye came along, I worked nights, slept days. My kids got on my nerves when they came home from school; sometimes I used to swear at them. Now it's different. Now I can't see enough of 'em. A guy likes to get as much as he can out of his family at a time like this, wants to keep his kids home where he can be with 'em all the time."

As they turned on Madison from Forty-ninth, David thought of Carol, heavy with child, back at Palomar.

And he noted, as they turned, that a long line of people stood on Forty-ninth toward Fifth, waiting patiently to get into St. Patrick's Cathedral.

The cab drew up in front of the New Weston.

"What good is education for kids now?" Frank Leone concluded. "There ain't no future left for them to use it in."

They told Leone to wait. Then David and Morgan went into the lobby of the hotel.

The place was crowded with people looking for accommodations. David was grateful that Dr. Herrick had made reservations for them long in advance.

As the bellboy took their luggage Morgan asked where he could find the nearest drugstore.

"What's the matter, Joe?" David said.

"I don't know. Feel a little under the weather, I guess. Maybe I'm a little airsick or something. I never could take planes."

"Look," said David, "why don't you go upstairs and lie down awhile? I'll talk to Herrick alone and go over the routine for tomorrow morning."

"You're sure you don't mind?"

David shook his head. "No use in both of us going over to the Planetarium. I'll see you here at the hotel in a couple of hours."

At the Hayden Planetarium, David spent two hours with Dr. Herrick. They planned to present an illustrated lecture, with David doing the talking and Morgan showing the plates.

Finally, when David rose to go, the director said:

"David, you can't be very busy at Palomar now, under the circumstances."

"No. Planet 'Y' has made observation pretty difficult. Too much interference from its light. We'll probably close for good in a few months."

As Dr. Herrick escorted David out of the office he said:

"David, I wouldn't want to take you away from Dr. Dawson. But there's a position open to you on the staff here at the Planetarium any time you want it. Of course it'll be routine and unspectacular, but we expect to stay open here"—Dr. Herrick hesitated—"until a month or two before Christmas."

David thanked him and left.

When he got back to his room at the hotel Joe Morgan was just coming out of the shower and whistling.

"Feel much better now, Dave. An hour's nap did it. By the way, what are you doing tonight?"

David shrugged. "Nothing."

"Look, Dave." Joe seemed a little apologetic. "I made a phone call. There's a girl I used to know here in New York. I had some ideas about her at one time, but they never came true. But when I talked to her on the phone she sounded a lot different. I think the planet's changed her, and I'm going to find out." He hesitated. "I can make it for two. Like to come along?"

David shook his head. "Thanks just the same, Joe."

"Okay." Morgan shrugged. "I don't want to corrupt you, or anything like that, and you know how much I think of your wife. But with Carol the way she is, and with just a few months left, I thought you'd——"

"Sure, Joe," said David. "But right now I'm not in the mood. You go ahead. I'll just go out and wander around town."

It was seven o'clock when David left the hotel.

As he walked west down Fiftieth toward Broadway, he saw the Big Eye.

It had taken up its post just as dusk had come, and now it hung directly over the huge RCA sign atop the Rockefeller Plaza skyscraper.

It was a little bilious now, its color washed and diluted by the great glare of light thrown up from the amusement district beyond.

It followed David as he walked; it stared at him with a fixed and intent look, until mercifully the intervening buildings hid it.

A wind was blowing, a sharp, raw, and incessant wind, and it moaned and wailed through the windowless rectangles in the Rockefeller Center group.

But if the upper floors of the buildings were dead, the streets swarmed with life.

David had barely crossed Fifth Avenue when he ran into the crowds.

They were lined along the sidewalks, waiting to get into the theaters.

The small theater at the Plaza, once a newsreel house, had changed. Now it sported a giant marquee, and although the original sign still spelled "Newsreel Theater," the legend in lights on the blazing marquee told a different story:

HOUSE OF LAUGHS
ONE SOLID HOUR OF LAUGHS
THREE CARTOONS, TWO
FUNNY SHORT SUBJECTS

The signs on the outside lobby indicated the theater ran a continuous performance, twenty-four hours a day. They offered the balm that was box office:

FORGET THE BIG EYE
FOR AN HOUR
COME IN AND LAUGH

The crowd blocked the sidewalk; it lined up snakelike in a continuous line to the Radio City Music Hall just down the block; it spilled over into the street and on the other side of the street, where it was kept in check by ushers and police.

The faces of the people looked chalk-white in the garish light; they chattered incessantly, their voices high-pitched and shrill; they complained bitterly about having to wait so long.

The strange part of it was that David heard no one laugh.

Between Sixth and Seventh, just short of Broadway itself, he noticed a new and unfamiliar group of establishments.

On the second and third stories of the cheap hotels there were neon signs just above discreetly curtained windows.

They bore odd names like "The Careless Hour," "The Green Slipper," "The Mirror," "The Oasis," "Katie's," "Edna's."

And under each sign was a single and discreet word: "Hostesses."

David inched his way through the dense crowds until he came to Broadway.

Broadway was obscene in its incandescent brilliance.

Every marquee was blazing, every electric sign; the dense crowds moved in a great bath of white light. On the corner of Forty-sixth Street a huge spectacular showed an animated clown, laughing and dancing and jumping up and down, advertising a current comedy at one of the big movie houses.

The clown laughed and chuckled; his roars came from his illuminated belly and rolled over the street.

But only the clown laughed.

On the huge television screen, the same one where the old Camel cigarette sign had once been located, a network comedian kept up a fire of running gags, which instantaneously poured into the living rooms of ten million homes, coast to coast.

But on Broadway the gags fell flat.

Nobody laughed.

Yet the marquees indicated that every show was a comedy, every comedy a hit. The producers had learned early that a serious drama, no matter how artistic, would run no longer than a night.

The legitimate theaters were offering performances around the clock instead of just matinee and evening. They accomplished this by the use of rotating stock companies. When one company finished on the stage, there was an hour intermission, and then another company took over.

And everywhere the "Standing Room Only" sign was out.

David managed to travel two blocks. He was mauled, propelled by the thick crowd, crushed, shoved along. He found the experience physically exhausting.

Finally, almost in desperation, he decided on a movie and waited in line. And after a two-hour wait he entered the darkened movie house.

A light domestic comedy, a farce, was on the screen, and once inside the theater, it was different.

The people laughed in waves, they guffawed, they split their sides hysterically, shrilly.

Within the theater they sat under a starry sky devoid of the Big Eye.

The roof of the rococo interior was designed as a romantic heaven, splattered with tiny electric stars; it even sported a dull moon near the second balcony. This heaven was free, wonderfully free, of any foreign invader.

And so the audience laughed, and David laughed with them.

But when he finally came out on the sidewalk again he felt let down, depressed. The real sky was overhead again, and although the Big Eye was temporarily invisible in the wash of Broadway light, he knew it was there.

It was there and coming, closer and closer. . . .

It was midnight.

David came back to his room at the New Weston and found that Joe Morgan had not yet returned.

For a few minutes he puttered around the room aimlessly, restlessly, having no desire to go to bed.

The movie had provided him with a three-hour anesthesia. But now he needed more, something different, something stronger, to take the pressure off.

He thought of Carol and her swollen abdomen and the nights that his whole body had ached for want of her.

It began to ache now. . . .

He thought of the places with the neon signs, the curtained windows, the names, "The Careless Hour," "The Oasis," "Katie's," and the others, licensed and available, and the beckoning signs, "Hostesses" . . .

The phone rang.

The operator asked him to wait a moment, Palomar was calling.

Then suddenly Carol's voice came over the wire. She was hysterical, sobbing.

"David! David! You've got to come back right away!"

"What is it, Carol? What's the matter?"

"It—it's Mrs. Dawson. She had an automobile accident just after you left—died an hour ago. And Dr. Dawson's had a stroke!"

For three agonizing hours David waited in the hotel room until Joe Morgan returned.

Then they took a cab for the airport.

13. At San Diego, while Joe Morgan was getting the car, David phoned Carol.

"Mrs. Dawson was driving one of the station wagons, David," Carol explained tearfully. "The roads up here are slippery from the ice—and, well, the car turned over. She lingered for hours, and Dr. Wilk did everything he could. But it was no use."

At the moment David's mind couldn't concentrate on Mrs. Dawson. She was dead; that was gone and done with now. He was thinking of the Old Man.

"How about Dr. Dawson, Carol? How's he taking it?"

"I—David, I'm afraid. When he heard the news he had a heart attack—almost collapsed. Dr. Wilk ordered him to bed, but he wouldn't go. He insisted on staying at Mrs. Dawson's bedside—till —till——"

Carol's voice broke, and she was unable to finish.

David told her that he and Morgan were just starting out in the car, and she said:

"Better come right to Dr. Dawson's house, David. I'll be there—everybody on the staff is there now. And, darling, be careful when you get upon the mountain. It's beginning to snow hard."

The last few miles to Palomar were a nightmare of driving. The snow whipped in horizontally against the windshield, a relentless tattoo propelled by a screaming wind.

Finally, however, they plowed through the observatory road, up the incline, and stopped in front of the "Residence" where the Dawsons lived. The road and driveway were clogged with cars, and the house was brilliantly lit. As David and Joe Morgan slogged through the snow toward the door they saw that the rooms within were crowded with people, their shadows moving restlessly behind the snow-frozen windows.

It was just getting dark before David had a chance to talk to Dr. Wilk.

The colony physician had finally come out of the Old Man's room, and his face was grave as he answered David's anxious question.

"Dr. Dawson's in fairly bad shape at the moment, David. The shock didn't do his heart any good. He'll have to stay in bed—get a complete rest for a few weeks. That's the physical picture. But there's another one—perhaps even more serious."

"You mean—his *mind?*"

Dr. Wilk nodded. "We'll have to wait and see. He acted very strangely near the end."

David gripped the physician by the lapels of his coat. "What do you mean, Dr. Wilk?"

"It's a little early to say anything definite as yet. But I am quite positive, David, that Dr. Dawson has been out of his mind for the past few hours. Just after Mrs. Dawson died he said something very strange."

"Yes? What was it, Dr. Wilk?"

"He kept moaning that he had to stand there and watch his wife die, that he could have saved her, but there was nothing he could do."

He could have saved her, but there was nothing he could do. . . . David tried to analyze that, but it didn't make sense.

"What about Mrs. Dawson? Was she unconscious at the end?"

The physician nodded.

"And she never had a chance?"

"On the contrary, David, she did. She was suffering from shock, severe contusions, and internal injuries. But at the beginning she had a fairly good chance. The trouble was that she gave up—she didn't have any will to fight."

"You mean she didn't *want* to live?"

"I'm sure that was the case," said Dr. Wilk. "It's a phenomenon that we in the medical profession have noted recently in an increasing number of borderline cases similar to hers. We've always said that it's instinctive for a human being to fight for his life, to want to live." The physician hesitated. "But now I don't know——"

"You think the planet affected her somehow, Doctor?"

"Yes. My theory is that Mrs. Dawson knew, deep in her subconscious mind, that she had little time left, even if she did recover. And this militated against her fight to survive, broke her will to resist. Perhaps it's wrong to rationalize, but it's the only explanation I can offer. And as I said, our medical associations have several reports of the same thing happening elsewhere in the country. Patients who could have won through simply gave up."

"And you explained this theory to Dr. Dawson, sir?"

The physician nodded, then put on his hat and coat. "It's a great loss to Palomar, David. Emily Dawson was a fine woman. I don't know how Dr. Dawson is going to get along without her—for the remainder of the time we have left."

"Perhaps I'd better stay here with him tonight," said David mechanically.

"No," answered the physician. "That won't be necessary. I've already asked Francis to sit up with Dr. Dawson for the rest of the night. And in the morning I'll arrange for a day and night nurse."

When David and Carol went out they found it impossible to move the car in the deepening and drifting snow. And so, with heads down against the fierce, battering smash of the snow-needled wind, they plodded through the snow toward their cottage.

As he stumbled along, David thought bitterly, Why did Emily Dawson, why did *anyone* have to die now? Why wasn't there a moratorium on death under the Big Eye? To die now was a tragedy far deeper, more profound, than ever before.

Emily Dawson was near sixty; she was an old woman by calendar years. Under normal standards she was almost ready to go. But there were no longer any normal standards, and the calendar was different and brand new.

By the new calendar, in this, the Year Two, Emily Dawson had died a young woman, with almost half a lifetime left to live.

"David! David!"

David woke suddenly out of an uneasy slumber to find Carol shaking him. He opened his eyes to look up uncomprehendingly into her frightened face. Then, half drugged with sleep, he realized that the doorbell was ringing insistently.

"Someone's at the door, David," Carol whispered. "The doorbell's been ringing for over a minute. I can't imagine who it could be out in this storm now. It's almost one o'clock."

David, lying warm in bed, lingered a moment, hoping the ringing would stop. But it continued, became more insistent, more urgent than ever. Finally he cursed softly, got out of bed, put on a robe, and went downstairs. The storm literally shook the house, and he could hear the windowpanes rattle.

He wondered savagely what damned fool was out there in the blizzard at this time of night, pumping his doorbell.

He fumbled with the latch, flung open the door. The cold wind blasted a barrage of snow into the living room. David blinked at the impact, tried to make out the snow-coated face of the muffled figure in the doorway.

"Dr. Hughes! Dr. Hughes, sir!"

It was Francis, the steward. He came in, and David slammed the door behind him.

"Francis, for God's sake, what are you doing out in——"

"Dr. Hughes, it's Dr. Dawson. He's—*disappeared!*"

"*What?*"

Francis began to stammer piteously. "Dr. Hughes, it's my fault —it's all my fault. I'm afraid I dozed off for a little while in Dr. Dawson's library. When I awoke I went upstairs and looked into his room. He—he was gone!"

David seized the steward by the shoulders, shook him savagely. "Francis, are you sure?"

"Yes, sir. I went all through the house. I looked into—I looked into Mrs. Dawson's room—in the attic—in the cellar—everywhere. He's out in this blizzard somewhere, Dr. Hughes. My God, he's out in this terrible storm."

"Where? Where'd he go?"

"I don't know, sir. I don't know. But his clothes are still in his room. He must be in his pajamas—his robe. He's unprotected, Dr. Hughes. He'll freeze to death unless we find him. Lord, lord, he'll freeze to death! I didn't know what to do—where to look. I came straight here—straight to you. I was so upset—I even forgot to phone. Dr. Hughes, he's out in this blizzard. He must have gone out the back way. I don't know, I didn't hear a thing!" The tears began running down Francis's cheeks; he was on the verge of hysteria. "It's my fault, sir. I'm to blame. If we can't find him before——"

"Stop it, Francis!" yelled David. "For God's sake, stop it!" He went to a decanter, poured out a stiff shot of whisky. "Here, drink this!"

The steward took the glass with a shaking hand, spilled half the drink, managed to swallow the rest.

"Now wait for me here," David said to him. "I'll get some clothes on and be right with you."

He drew on his trousers over his pajamas, then shoes and a

mackinaw, rapidly telling Carol what had happened as he dressed.

"David," said Carol, "where on earth could he have gone—in this snow?"

"Not very far," grunted David. "But I've got a hunch he's gone to the observatory."

"The observatory? On a night like this? Why?"

"Don't ask me why. I don't know. It's just a hunch, and I may be wrong."

He raced downstairs, and together with Francis he plunged out into the storm.

The wind slashed at them, hammered them as they floundered through the drifts. They could see nothing before them; the murky white wall slanted in at them, blotted out their vision ten feet ahead. They saw no tracks in the snow, but that proved nothing. If Dr. Dawson had come this way ten minutes before, the snow would have already buried his footprints.

As David plowed along, his head bent against the screaming wind and his arm interlocked with Francis's, a nagging doubt began to seep through him. Perhaps the Old Man hadn't gone to the observatory at all. There would be no one there now, no work in progress, not on a night like this. Maybe he'd gone the other way, thought David desperately, down the road. There was no way of telling. They were just guessing.

The Old Man didn't know what he was doing; the loss of his wife, as Dr. Wilk had pointed out, must have driven him out of his mind. It was suicide to walk out in this damned blizzard with just pajamas and a robe. Even through his heavy mackinaw and mittens David could feel the numbing cut of the wind. If the Old Man had walked out just before Francis had awakened, if he had gone to the observatory, there was still a chance. If not . . .

He yelled at Francis to hurry, but Francis was unable to hear him over the banshee yell of the wind. The steward was gasping for breath, staggering through the snow like a drunken man, exhausted. David released his arm and stumbled forward, fighting the drifts. Like feathery straight jackets, they tried to hold him, they clung and wrapped themselves around his legs, they tried to trip him and tie him down.

And then David was in the observatory yard. The squat building loomed suddenly in front of him, like a fat gray ghost leaping up from the drifts. He scraped his hands against the rough wall, moving slowly, trying to find the door. He cursed as his fingers encountered nothing but wall. Finally, after a long minute of exploration, he found the door just as Francis came up.

The door was open. They went in, slammed the door shut against the storm, and stood gasping in the foyer, swaying in their exhaustion.

The lights were on in the foyer.

"Come on, Francis!"

David plunged ahead up the wide, curving staircase, out into the circular corridor, raced past staff quarters, the computing rooms, the darkrooms. The breath sobbed from his tortured lungs as he ran up the stairs to the mezzanine.

Finally a last short flight of rubber-covered steps and he plunged out into the main rotunda of the observatory.

Then he stopped short and stared.

The dome was open!

Stupefied, he pointed upward as Francis came panting up the steps. The wind was howling down through the open dome in an icy blast. The snow was coming in; it was snowing inside the observatory itself. The white particles slammed down gustily, as though propelled by a high-powered gun, filtering down on the floor itself, and feathering the upper part of the telescope so that a faint lace of white on the shell was already visible.

"He's here!" yelled David to Francis. "The Old Man's here, somewhere. He's opened the dome to the blizzard. It couldn't have been anyone else. He's mad, Francis, stark raving mad. But even so, he wouldn't do that unless——"

The echo of David's voice ricocheted through the dome for a moment and then clipped short. Numbly he stared into Francis's chalk-white face, and in the steward's eyes saw the same dawning suspicion, the same awful horror.

With a single accord they broke and ran for the automatic elevator leading to the upper deck and the loading bridge.

The elevator seemed to whine up and up forever. Finally it stopped, its door slid noiselessly open, and they burst through and onto the wide ring-shaped deck.

The aerial platform running to the top of the telescope was gone!

That could mean only one thing.

The Old Man was up there.

He was up there at the top of the telescope, perched in the cistern of the observer's cage, exposed to the icy blast of the blizzard slamming down through the open dome.

Somewhere in the shock-twisted depths of the Old Man's mind he had chosen this fantastic way to commit suicide. Fantastic to everyone else, perhaps, but quite logical to Dr. Dawson. He had built the telescope, it was his life. He had spent many years of his life up there in that dizzy place, bundled in heavy furs. He knew how cold it could get up there.

David ran over to the panel where the push-button control for the aerial platform was located. As he yanked open the metal door the thought throbbed through his mind, *How long?*

How long had the Old Man been sitting up there, waiting to die?

He pressed the control button, peered up at the four slender rails arching up and curving into the darkness of the dome. But nothing happened. The monel-metal platform stayed at the top of the telescope.

The Old Man had locked the controls at the top.

David slammed the panel door shut, went back to where Francis was standing.

"What are we going to do now, sir?"

"You'd better go down and phone Dr. Wilk, Francis."

"Yes. But you——"

"I'm going up to the top by way of the handrails and get Dr. Dawson."

The steward paled. "Be careful, sir. It's dangerous now. Those rails might be slippery and——"

"I'll make it all right, Francis. You go ahead."

Outside of the flying platform, this was the only method of getting to the top of the big reflector. The handrails and narrow steps went straight up, like the ladders in the engine room of an ocean-going vessel. Finally they led to a steep iron platform on the back of the girder carrying the flying platform. It was a dizzy ascent, and with the rails wet, as they were now, it was dangerous.

David gripped the handrails, climbed gingerly, carefully, conscious of the hazard. As he went up, higher and higher, he found that he could not raise his face upward toward the dome. The storm coming straight down through the dome blinded him by its fury, slashed his face in a pin-point attack, forced him to lower his head.

He remembered stupidly, now, that neither he nor Francis in their excitement had thought of the obvious thing—to close the dome before he began his climb. The blizzard came straight down, sucking through the open dome in a powerful downdraft, and once or twice he swayed under its force and hung on desperately.

But finally the precarious steps began to level off. He was high up in the soaring steelwork now, running over the abyss, almost blinded by flying snow.

Then David was looking down into the cistern of the observer's cage.

The Old Man was sitting there in his usual place, in the little revolving seat before the instrument board.

He was sitting there, stiff and rigid, like a grotesque snow man.

The snow whipping down upon him from the open dome had covered his bowed head with a white fez. It stuck to his face, powdered his robe and pajamas, and had already drifted up above his slippered feet on the steel floor.

Looking down from his dizzy, wind-swept perch above, David Hughes knew that he had come too late.

The Old Man of the Mountain was dead.

Two weeks later, California Tech, the university administering Palomar, closed the observatory.

David wired Dr. Herrick at the Hayden Planetarium, accepting his offer to work in New York.

And then Carol's baby was born.

It was a girl, and they named her Emily.

14. In the last four months the Big Eye was visible both by day and night.

It did not seem to get any larger now; its approach seemed to slow. It seemed simply to hang in the sky, waiting. Now the planet was pursuing the earth, moving in the same direction, as the earth swung around its orbit to the other side of the sun.

In September the astronomers, after extensive calculations, announced that the catastrophe would occur at exactly 8 P.M., Greenwich time.

In New York and on the Atlantic seaboard, zero hour would be 3 o'clock in the afternoon.

The Eye would be in full glare upon the earth, and the end would come out of a daytime sky.

On the first of October, the Hayden Planetarium closed for the duration.

At dusk David closed his desk and gathered together the few personal effects he wanted to take back to the apartment.

He found it difficult to concentrate on what he was doing; his eye kept straying toward the window.

The Big Eye swam in a red bath high over an apartment building across the park. It would stay that way until the sun sank deep enough behind the western horizon so that the first stars would just begin to twinkle.

Then it would emerge from its bath, huge and heavy and frightening, and dominate the sky, and the stars would disappear.

For a full minute David stared at the Big Eye, unable to turn his head away.

It looked particularly malevolent at the moment. Its leer was confident and assured; its message to David was familiar and personal and intimate.

"Damn you," David suddenly blurted out hysterically. "You big red bastard, you'd like to end it right now, wouldn't you? If you had *your* way, you wouldn't wait until Christmas!"

He went to the window and viciously yanked down the blinds. The room darkened in semi-gloom, and for a moment he experienced overwhelming relief, the throbbing cleared in his head.

But then he fancied that even now, with the blinds shut, the Big Eye was still looking into his office. The reddish light was seeping in through the blinds, through the cracks and crevices, through the solid wall itself. And now the office was tinged with a weird reddish light; it reflected from the glass top of his desk, from the framed pictures, from the paneled walls.

In a kind of feverish desperation he took his hat from the rack, flung open his office door, and hurried down the corridor, through the adjacent Museum of Natural History, and finally out of the door and onto Central Park West.

The Big Eye hit down on him like a blow of a hammer. Now, in the dying light, it was beginning to take shape. He could already see the familiar leer pushing through the reddish haze.

It etched the sky line of the east side in sharp relief, and the trees in the park stood black and stark against the light. It slanted down on the road and sidewalk and ricocheted up into the eyes of the pedestrians. It glinted from automobile windshields and the glistening chrome on the radiators.

There was nothing soft about it, like the set of the sun. It was harsh and brutal and direct and unfiltered.

David hunched his shoulders in his topcoat, put his head down, and got into his car at the curb.

At Eighty-third Street he stopped at a newspaper stand. The man in the small booth was smiling broadly under the peak of his frayed cap.

"Paper, mister?"

The owner of the newsstand drew a dirty finger across the headlines of the stacked newspapers.

"Good news for a change," he said. "Me—I can't wait for tomorrow night."

The headlines were the same in all the evening newspapers—the *Journal-American*, the *Post*, the *World-Telegram*, the *Sun*.

They were big and black and bold across the front page, and they said simply:

CLOUDY, RAIN TOMORROW NIGHT!

Cloudy and rain. That *was* big news, front-page news. Cloudy and rain meant that the Big Eye would be blotted out for a merciful evening. It meant that the nightly pressure would be off for a few precious hours, that they would not feel the direct visual and physical lash of its stare, even though they would still sense it.

Tomorrow night the streets would be crowded with people, drenched with rain, maybe, but laughing, exhilarated, buoyant in their relief.

Cloudy and rain. An eyelid closing over the Big Eye for just a little while, a little wonderful while, as it slowly revolved toward its full phase.

Cloudy and rain.

David grinned back at the man in the newsstand, bought a paper, and scanned the lead story. The weather forecasters were almost positive of overcast weather and even held out hope for an extra day of clouds or rain.

David reached his apartment building and walked into the lobby. Tom, the parchment-faced elevator man, greeted him with a grin as he opened the elevator door.

"You heard the news, Dr. Hughes?"

"Just a few minutes ago."

"I hope they're right," said Tom anxiously. "I sure hope they haven't made a mistake this time. They've been wrong before, Dr. Hughes, these weathermen."

"They'd better be right, Tom," answered David grimly. "They'd better be right."

When he came into the apartment Carol was in the kitchen, feeding the baby. Emily's curls were still wet from her bath; there was a smear of gelatin dessert on her mouth.

She gurgled and held up her arms to David.

He picked her up, swung her high in the air, and she laughed and squealed.

"Piggyback!" he said, grinning. "Piggyback!"

He held her arms around his neck, so that she hung like a sack of flour down his back, and ran into the living room. Then he lifted her clear over his head, and his daughter laughed delightedly, wriggling like a bug in his upstretched hands.

"Airplane," he told her next. "Airplane ride!"

He carried her through the living room, pressed her tiny nose against the cold windowpane, carried her into the bedroom, ran around the crib, flew her into the bathroom, dipped her deep toward the bathtub in mock ferocity.

"Dear," he heard Carol call from the kitchen, "please bring the baby back. She hasn't finished her supper."

Then as she laughed and squealed he carried her back into the kitchen. . . .

The same old wonderful ritual.

Later, when their daughter was ready for bed, he brought forth the pièce de résistance.

He picked her up and swung her back and forth, back and forth, across the bed. There was a spark of fear in the baby's eyes as he dropped her on the soft bed so that she bounced.

And then the child laughed and laughed and held up her tiny arms to David to do it again.

Finally he kissed her good night and gave her to Carol to tuck in. And there were tears in his eyes.

The same old wonderful ritual, until Christmas.

Later David Hughes lay on his back, sleepless.

The Big Eye stared through the window like a great round Peeping Tom. It was like living with your own hangman, he thought, month after month. You saw your death before you; it followed you, peered over your shoulder, hung over your head, shone through your window, like this.

Men had been executed before, he thought, but the execution had been reasonable, civilized, merciful. The condemned man never saw the chair or the noose till he was ready for it.

David turned toward his wife.

"Carol," he whispered. "Awake?"

Her hand fumbled for his in the darkness. "What is it, darling?"

"I can't sleep."

"Neither can I."

"Carol, can't we do something about that damned window? The way that thing shines in here every night, it's enough to drive anyone crazy. It's like having a third party in our bedroom every night. Why can't we get those blackout curtains that everyone else seems to have?"

"I've already ordered them, David. But they're hard to get. There's been a run on them—everybody wants them—and there are so few stores open any more. I've almost finished making drapes."

He reached over on the night table, picked up a cigarette, lighted it. They shared drags for a minute and then he said:

"Carol, are you afraid of what's coming? Are you *really* afraid?"

She was silent for a moment. Then she answered:

"I don't know, David. I was for the longest time, but now I don't know. I've thought a lot about death, and I keep wondering what it'll be like. A flash of flame? A whirling in darkness? And after that, what? How long will death be?" She hesitated. "I don't know. I guess we're like children, David, asking how long the night will be when we go to bed, because we love the daylight in which we play." Her hand tightened about his. "Darling, I think if I feel anything at all now, it's regret. Not so much for you, not for me, but for the baby."

He said nothing, and Carol went on:

"I keep thinking, David, our baby sleeping there in the crib, she'll never have a birthday party of her own, or go to school or a movie, or eat a sundae, or wear an evening gown, or have a boy friend and fall in love, and have a husband and children of her own. She'll never even have a Christmas, David, not really."

The baby whimpered in the crib.

"Oh, David!" Carol began to cry.

He rose and padded over to the crib in his bare feet and picked up his daughter. She clung to him sleepily as he took her to the bathroom. Then he carried her over to the big bed and placed her between himself and Carol.

And so they finally slept, the three of them, close to each other.

But the Big Eye, looking at them through the window, was wide awake.

In the fall of the last year the Big Eye appeared nightly as a great flaming, coppery-red sphere in the sky.

The effects of the new planet's intrusion into the solar system were gradual and cumulative.

Japan suffered tremendous earthquakes, so that its entire remaining population was evacuated to the mainland of China. Much of California was abandoned for the most part, although the shocks were not as serious. Seismologists listed earthquakes in Alaska, Lisbon, Calabria, Chile, and many other places already susceptible to disturbances in the earth's surface.

The tides were erratic and no longer could be charted. There were tidal waves in the Philippines and in the Caribbean. Acapulco, Mexico, as well as Cape Lopatka, on the southern tip of Kamchatka Peninsula, were completely inundated. The sea level rose in some coastal areas, fell in others. In the islands of Polynesia and the Coral Sea there were spectacular volcanic eruptions.

Landslides were a daily occurrence in the Swiss Alps, in the Himalayas, the Rockies, and many other mountainous areas.

All over the world the temperature dropped progressively, degree by degree, and the Big Eye loomed bigger.

In New York there had been no summer. June, July, and August became early spring or late fall, thermometer-wise.

But the most significant changes were man-made.

In the last year, goaded by the driving and demanding leer of the Big Eye, men had made some long-time dreams come true.

They had stopped making atomic bombs and instead were making atomic bullets, as tracer detectives and interbody projectiles. From the Oak Ridge laboratories, which once gave the world the most painful problem of the age, came a steady stream of radioactive isotopes.

And in August of the last year they had discovered a cure for cancer.

This was only one of the many other great achievements in the field of medicine.

By using radioactive isotopes as a means of prying open the once bolted door to the inner processes of life itself, by probing deep into the inner mysteries of the human body, they had found quick and positive cures for most of the myriad diseases of the bones, heart, tissues, nerves, and other organs, diseases which once had taken a great toll of human life.

This, the golden age of atomic medicine, was not without irony.

In the last year the *Journal* of the American Medical Association calculated that the life span of man had increased twenty years and that new medical techniques had progressed to a point where man could normally expect to live a hundred years.

The article was interesting in a wistful kind of way.

The final year had also ushered in another golden age—the age of practical atomic power.

At the Hanford laboratories in the state of Washington, which, in another era, had made plutonium for atomic bombs, the nuclear scientists had released a seething storm of neutrons from spontaneous fission in a huge atomic pile. Later they had applied this power to run ocean-going vessels, locomotives, and other great fuel-consuming machinery. The heat which was generated as a by-product from the pile was piped to great cities and used in huge central heating systems. Coal, gas, and oil became unwieldy and expensive, antique fuels to be laboriously torn from the earth. City planners drew up blueprints for generating plants whereby the householder would receive all the power he needed for a fraction of the cost he had heretofore borne.

The blueprints were pretty to look at and breath-taking in their concept. But no one thought of translating them into the practical phase. Under the circumstances, file and forget.

The Year Two was a year of peculiar phenomena in a hundred different ways.

The death rate hit a rock-bottom low.

To be sure, some people died by accident. Some were drowned, or killed by falls, or hit by vehicles, or struck by lightning. Some died in the now frequent earthquakes or tidal waves. And some still died of natural causes, despite the great advances of medicine.

But not a man, woman, or child died through war. And no man died in violence by the hand of his neighbor. Not a Jew was murdered, not a Negro lynched. Not a single person died of hunger, not even in India or China. Neither did any man, woman, or child suffer death because of exposure, or lack of medicine or medical attention.

There were no strangers left in the last year. No man held himself aloof from his neighbor on grounds of religion, caste, color, or environment. The Big Eye was blind to these differences; it was not socially selective; it was completely impartial.

Its clientele was not restricted.

In the fall of the final year, in the cities and towns and on the farms, men waited to die.

A special commission of the Federation of the World, called the World Conservation Commission, planned and enforced just enough productive activity to maintain economic life until midnight on Christmas.

Not a hammer or saw was heard anywhere, and only a few wheels turned, of necessity. The spindles and machine shafts of the factories became quiet gray forests of steel, and cobwebs grew in the gears and belting of drill presses, lathes, milling machines, and shapers.

Farmers sat on their porches at the time of the autumn harvest and looked idly across their weed-grown fields, unplanted in the spring.

There were no longer any profits to be calculated, any reserves to be accumulated, any investments to be made, any new business to anticipate. There were no bills to be sent, no debts to be collected nor credits advanced, no taxes to pay for next year, no accounts receivable.

There was simply one big Account Payable.

The world still spun on its axis, but the surface was almost motionless.

And the only sound heard upon it was the sound of prayer.

The Big Eye fattened to a great luminous globe and filled the heavens day and night and kept coming on and on. . . .

And at last Christmas came.

15. For some deep and illogical reason people everywhere observed Christmas in the usual fashion.

It was the last day of their lives.

Yet they were stubborn, they were perverse, they insisted on following the traditional ritual step by step.

They played at life up to the very end, desperately going through the motions as though the future were forever, finding a kind of comfort in it, in these, their last few hours.

Everything in the apartment looked the same, as it might have on any other Christmas morning.

The wreaths were on the windows, the stockings hung over the fireplace. The tree was in the corner, glittering with many-colored lights, topped by a star, speckled with silver tinsel. And beneath the tree the gaily wrapped presents.

A silk robe for David, a new wallet, a solid-gold tie clasp, an initialed cigarette lighter, a half dozen ties, a pair of fleece-lined slippers, a new electric shaver.

A jeweled wrist watch for Carol, a new handbag, a Paul Revere sterling silver bowl for the whist table, three handmade nightgowns, a new fur coat. A huge fluffy rabbit for Emily, a pair of golden-haired twin dolls.

It was warm and cozy in the room, and the snow was falling outside and piling on the sills against the frost-fingered windowpanes. The last Christmas was a white Christmas.

There was the opening of the presents, the warm kisses, the embraces, the tears. There was the last breakfast, and the last careful ritual of dressing, and the last walk to church. There were the last hymns, and the sober faces, and the heads bowed in prayer, and the last sonorous sermon, the last story of Bethlehem.

It was the final day of their lives, but it was still Christmas.

There was the last dinner, turkey and stuffing and mince pie and coffee and brandy and all the fixings.

They went through all the motions with a kind of hysterical intensity, even to the salutations of "Merry Christmas . . ."

But the other part of the traditional greeting, the rest of the salutation, the "Happy New Year," was conspicuously missing.

And the clock ticked on toward three, as on any other Christmas.

It was very much the same as it had always been, yet so very different: the carols they would never sing again, the sermon they would never hear again, the tree they would never adorn again, the stockings they would never hang again, the good wishes they would never give again, the presents they gave but would never use.

It was not a Merry Christmas, and there would be no Happy New Year.

It was a pathetic kind of Christmas.

And yet it was comforting too.

At two o'clock the bells began to ring.

Slowly they rose in volume, opened their brassy mouths, swelled the cold night air with a somber and mournful symphony.

It was very near the end.

Carol stirred in David's arms.

"David."

"Yes?"

"It's time to go."

They had decided to go outside, out in the street, to die. They were going out into the open, under the sky, where they could watch the Big Eye. Already from their apartment they could hear the hum of a crowd below, like the buzz of a great swarm of bees far away.

It was easier to die outside, where they could see their executioner. Waiting for the end in the apartment was too much like dying alone. It was easier out in the street among other people, thousands of others, millions of others, packed close for warmth, for courage, for comfort, for anonymity.

It had always been easier to die en masse than alone.

They were silent for a moment there in the bedroom. They heard Emily whimper once in her nap, and then it was still again.

Still, except for the ticking of the clock on the dressing table.

And David thought: This is the last time, this is the last time I'll hold my wife in my arms like this. Soon, the last kiss, the last warm embrace, the last touch of her hand and the thrill of her skin, the last sound of her voice, the last scent of her hair, the last long look in her eyes. The last, the last of everything. This is how it is to wait to die. A poignant, rending, unbearable awareness of the last in everything, because it *is* the last. Funny, he thought, I have no fear. Only regret. Regret for what I have now, and what I shall soon lose. I haven't had enough of what I have. Yes, that's it. That's what I want and can't have. More daylight. More life, more living. More Carol, more Emily, not the last, the absolute, final last, but more, more, more. . . .

Tick-tock, tick-tock, tick-tock, tick-tock . . .

And Carol thought: In an hour it'll be over. And I'm not afraid, I'm not afraid, I'm not afraid. As long as David is close to me, and the baby is in my arms, I'm not afraid. I don't know. Maybe it's just because I don't believe it. In an hour I'm going to die, and I don't believe it. Maybe death is unbelievable, even to the dying. Something that happens to everyone else but not to you. Funny, about the way it feels, about going out to die. It's like leaving on a long trip. Yesterday I cleaned and scrubbed the apartment from top to bottom. Crazy-clean for the hereafter. Can't die with an untidy house. And this morning I made the beds. Can't die with the beds unmade. And I washed the dishes. Can't die with dirty dishes in the sink, even if there'll be no one around to eat from the clean ones. And I drew the blinds and fluffed the cushions in the living room and turned off the electric stove and defrosted the refrigerator. Just as though I were going away on a long trip with David and the baby and would return someday. Everything but pack the bags. But we'll never be back, we'll never be back again. I won't be back, and David won't be back, and the baby won't. The baby. Emily. I hope she sleeps in my arms, that she's asleep when it comes, when the Big Eye comes, in an hour. I wonder what she would have been like, what she would have grown up to be? Would she have grown to be sweet, and generous, and lovely, and beautiful? And the husband she'd never have, who would he have been, and what? Rich and handsome and intelligent? And the children she might have had, the grandchildren I might have had, David and I. What would they have been like? I'll never know, we'll never know. Still, I'm lucky, I'm lucky. I've had something out of life. Daughter, lover, wife, and mother. But I want more, more, more. This is the last, the very last, the last hour. And I want more, more, more. . . .

Tick-tock, tick-tock, tick-tock, tick-tock . . .

"It's time to go," she whispered to David. "It's time to go out there with the others. David, David, David, it's time to go."

"All right, darling."

They kissed, and embraced, and wept. Then they rose and went into the other room, where Emily was sleeping.

She was lying there, her face buried in her own curls, resting on her elbows and her knees, her buttocks arched up, as she had lain in the womb. The blankets were half off, and she clutched a doll in her two tiny fists, and the huge bunny rabbit was at the foot of the crib.

For a long time the two of them stood by the crib, looking down, watching their sleeping child by the reddish light of the Big Eye filtering through the blinds.

And then David said: "Carol, let her stay here. Let her sleep."

"No, David." Carol's eyes were wet, and the tears were in her throat. "No, David, no, no!"

"She'll never know," he whispered. "She'll be sleeping and she'll never know. Maybe it'd be better for her that way."

"No, David, no. Not alone. Not like this. Not away from me. I'll hold her close in my arms. She'll sleep. She'll go with us, David. All together. You couldn't leave her here alone. You *know* you couldn't."

"No," he said. "I guess I couldn't. It was—just that she looks so warm and happy and wonderful now—here—in the crib." He spoke brokenly now. "I—you're right, Carol. If we walked out of the door without her I'd have come back for her."

They watched her for a moment more. And the clock sounded loud in the silence:

Tick-tock, tick-tock, tick-tock, tick-tock . . .

Hurry-hurry, hurry-hurry, hurry-hurry, hurry-hurry . . .

"Wake her up, David," whispered Carol. "Wake her up now."

He reached out his hand, touched the child's cheek. She whimpered and then turned on her back and lifted her arms toward David. He snatched her up and pressed her close, so that she was warm and sweet against him, so that his tears stained her sleep-blushed cheek.

Carol dressed the baby warmly in a long-sleeved shirt, sweater, overalls, and snow suit.

Finally they were ready. As they opened the door they heard the insistent sound of the clock:

Tick-tock, tick-tock, tick-tock, tick-tock . . .

David hesitated on the threshold, stopped, and gave the baby to Carol.

Then he walked into the bedroom, and the clock stopped ticking.

After that he returned and closed the door behind him, and they went down into the red afternoon.

It had stopped snowing, and now the Big Eye shone down balefully upon the frozen city.

It was low and directly overhead, and it seemed to hang like a heavy stone on an invisible thread, filling the winter sky.

It reddened the snow and the faces of the people as they turned upward, and glared back at itself in the waters of the rivers and the sea and in the darkened windows of the cold skyscrapers.

It had a gaunt and hungry look as it waited voraciously to spring upon and devour its prey.

It was fifteen minutes to three and almost time.

There was no sound but the mournful, funereal ringing of the bells.

No vehicles moved, no horns blew, no trains roared in the paralyzed city.

There were the bells and the people, thousands upon thousands of them, thronging the sidewalks, jamming the streets, choking the park in a solid mass of silent and waiting humanity.

From the churches and temples, illuminated by the pale flicker of candles, came the wail and lamentation of prayer.

Every face was turned upward toward the Big Eye, the faces of men, women, and children, and the stamp of death was upon every one of them. There was no fear, no hysteria, only silence and resignation.

The glow became redder, the Big Eye bigger, the bells louder.

And then it was three o'clock.

The people, with a single accord, dropped to their knees in the snow and bowed their heads and prayed and waited.

The bells stopped ringing, and it was still.

A minute passed.

The Big Eye hung suspended in the sky and looked down, as though delaying a little to savor the moment.

Five minutes passed—and then ten—and fifteen.

And still the Big Eye hung in the sky.

At last a great sigh spread through the kneeling crowd, a kind of convulsive shudder. Heads that were bowed turned upward with a kind of wild, unbelieving hope.

The people started to whisper, and the whisper spread and rustled through the mob and went from one to the other, like a rippling electric shock.

Then someone shouted hysterically:

"Look at it! Look at the Big Eye!"

The shout traveled like wildfire; it was contagious, almost instantaneous; it became a wild roar, a bedlam; it possessed the crowd and gripped them and shook them, and a sea of faces turned up to look into the sky.

It seemed to them, and they swore to it afterward, that the Big Eye had stopped leering, that it had for the moment smiled.

The people knew that it would not strike, that God had stayed His hand and deflected the Big Eye and given them life again. And the people cried and wept and shouted:

"A miracle! A miracle!"

It was Christmas, and they had been given a miracle.

They stayed on their knees and prayed.

An hour later the flash came from the Harvard Observatory, the official clearing center for all astronomical data.

The planet, Planet "Y," the Big Eye, was passing on into the eternity of space, away from the earth. The astronomers professed bewilderment. They could not account for it: the Big Eye had betrayed their calculations and their charts. In time, perhaps, they might have a logical explanation for this extraordinary phenomenon.

But the people knew that it was Christmas and that God had given them a miracle.

They knew He had been pleased with what they had wrought in the last two years, the new and better world they had made.

As the crowds began to dissolve and move homeward, as the bells rang in deafening clamor, as the people laughed and shouted and prayed and wept and embraced each other, amid the roar and clamor and the wild hysteria, David Hughes heard the calm voice of Dr. Dawson on that night in the Old Man's study, when he had first known about the Big Eye:

"I can only say this, try to console you with this, David. You must have faith—faith in a miracle—another miracle—a miracle of redemption."

16. The world had been caught short by the miracle. It had not expected any future and had not prepared for it. Only by the most drastic measures and by strict rationing of food supplies was it able narrowly to avert a global famine.

As the months passed into the year 1963 the Big Eye grew smaller and smaller.

As it spun off into the void its circumference shrank, and the Eye itself began to blur in its outline.

It no longer hovered directly overhead and followed people about, bowing them down with its weight and paralyzing them with its baleful stare.

Yet people knew that it was still watching them, that it would be watching them long after it had disappeared into the sky.

They had seen the miracle, and they knew that the Big Eye, wherever it was or would be, would always be watching them.

And the effect of this knowledge upon them was profound.

There were pessimists who predicted a return to the old patterns, the old folkways and mores, the old way of life. It was all over now, they said; the predatory instincts of men would come to the surface again; they would rebound from their idealistic stupor and be themselves again.

It was bound to come again, they said. The world government would slowly disintegrate, and nations would build up the fences they had torn down. There was profit to gain now, and power, and prestige. Men would go back to the luxury of hating each other again, indulging in their pet prejudices, reviving their favorite whipping boys again.

A Jew would become a dirty Jew again, and different-from-us; a Negro, a lousy nigger again, and different-from-us; a capitalist, a fat, blood-sucking son of a bitch again, and different-from-us; a Communist, a goddamn atheistic Red, and different-from-us. There would be wops and spicks and greaseballs and squareheads and Chinks, and all of them different-from-us.

It had to happen that way, the pessimists said. The Big Eye was going away, and now the sky was the limit again.

There'd be customs again, and passports, and tariffs and identification cards, and classifications, race, color, creed. There'd be restricted areas and selected clienteles, and they'd build new railroad tracks where they had torn up the old ones, with a right side and a wrong side. There'd be cliques and cartels and monopolies and black marketeers and labor racketeers and profiteers all over again. The rich would get richer and the poor poorer, as they did in the good old days.

The instincts of men ran pretty deep, and they were very tenacious, the pessimists said. In time they would again rise and assert themselves. And one day, they even predicted, men would contrive to go to war again.

But somehow the people did not listen to the pessimists.

They had seen the miracle, and they remembered, and they were grateful.

And they started up the machinery again and went right on living in the same old new world they had fashioned, after the Big Eye had first been seen at Palomar.

It was October of 1963, and David sat in the Old Man's study at Palomar.

Three months before, California Tech had reopened the Observatory. They began negotiations for a new director and in the interim offered David the post of chief research astronomer until the permanent appointment was made.

David had accepted the offer and moved back to Palomar with his family.

Now he turned to the task of sifting through Dr. Dawson's voluminous papers and personal memoranda.

David had spent a few hours each day opening the bulky manila envelopes in the files, sifting out the notes and correspondence, and segregating material for the observatory library.

He went through folder after folder, reading, fascinated. The correspondence was, in effect, a biography of the Old Man's life. His student life at Harvard, then as a young professor, his career on the *Astrophysical Journal,* his invasion of the National Academy of Science when still a young man, a brilliant child in a learned and aged society.

There was much of his trips abroad and his awe at viewing Galileo's telescope in the museum at Florence. He had written in a letter to his wife how he had wanted to look through Galileo's little telescope, and the authorities had flatly refused him the privilege. Then an Italian astronomer, Abetti, had interceded and persuaded the museum people to go along. An so the Old Man had carried the telescope, like a priceless diamond, to the Arcetri Observatory. And there he had fixed it to the equatorial mount.

"I waited for the night to come, Emily," wrote the Old Man. "It seemed years—centuries—before the sun went down. But then at last the stars came out one by one. If I ever lived for any moment, my dear, this was the moment. I cannot describe my sensations when I grasped the same tube that Galileo had grasped. My hands rested where his hands had rested—my eye was against his eyepiece, where his eye had been. And then I saw what he had seen —three hundred years ago.

"There it was, Emily, high in the south, the same Jupiter the old master had seen on that first voyage of man through the void of astronomical space. And the four moons, a string of bright diamonds, hugging the mother planet close, just as Galileo had seen them. Clear—and wondrous—and beautiful—and mystic. I have seen Jupiter a hundred times, Emily darling, through every kind of telescope, but just then I felt the same awe that Galileo must have felt. I felt that I had seen Jupiter for the first time. I felt uplifted and humble at the same time, and I think I even wept."

There was more. The Old Man's battle with industrial tycoons and wealthy patrons of the sciences to put up money for Palomar. The skeptics, the critics, the men who said the 200-inch reflector couldn't be done and called it a crazy dream. The faith that turned the dream into the biggest telescope in the world. The heart-breaking technical problems—the eternal grinding of the great lens, interrupted by the war in the forties; the problems of the mount and the supports.

And finally the dedication in 1948.

As David took up the last big folder, marked "Current," a slip of paper fell from it and dropped on the floor of the office.

He leaned over, picked it up, and was about to insert it back into the folder. But something about it caught his eye. It was a piece of scrap paper, and on it were rough drawings and notations.

Probably something the Old Man forgot to throw away, thought David. It didn't seem to belong with these letters, these documents.

Then he stared at it, and his mouth dropped open and the room began to spin around.

He read it again and again.

The discovery began like a whisper, then swelled up and burgeoned out through his brain and mushroomed through his nerve centers and grew and grew, louder and louder, until it was like the beat of a hammer inside his skull, until he trembled uncontrollably.

After a long time, in the haze of his reeling mind, he thought of Dr. Ellender. Ellender, his old professor, Ellender at the Harvard Observatory, *he* would know!

Ellender had been one of the astronomers the Old Man had called in on that fateful conference before they had announced the coming of the Big Eye.

Ellender would know the truth.

He stuffed the scrap of paper into his pocket, got Carol on the phone.

"Pack my bag, Carol," he said. "I've got to take a plane to Boston right away!"

Dr. Ellender looked at the scrap of paper on his desk for a long time.

It was a diagram in pencil of the Big Eye—of Planet "Y"—and the earth.

And underneath the Old Man had written in crooked lines, almost as though he had been doodling:

> *Planet "Y" and earth. Closest Christmas, 1962.*
>
> *Cosmic clash close—close, but not quite.*
>
> *Lie—hoax—hoax—will it work? Must work—world at stake —must work—must. . . .*

Ellender sank heavily back in his chair.

"Then you know, David," he said finally. "Then you know."

David nodded.

"Where did you find this piece of paper?"

"In a file of Dr. Dawson's correspondence, sir. It must have been put there by mistake."

"Yes," said Ellender slowly. "We were sure we destroyed all data. In fact, we burned all our notations and diagrams—the true ones—that night."

There was silence for a while. Ellender's gray eyes searched

David's, his eyes probing deep. He saw the demand in the younger man's eyes, the burning desire to *know*.

"Sit down, David," he said finally.

Ellender lit a cigar very deliberately, waved out the match, and dropped it in an ash tray. Then he leaned back in his chair, fingering the piece of paper on his desk, as though searching for a way to begin.

"I'll have to tell you, David," he said. "I'll have to tell you the whole story now. You know something now, but not enough. In this case—a little knowledge is a dangerous thing." Ellender paused a moment. "Later on, when I've finished, you'll know why."

"Yes?"

"Back in the beginning, back in November of 1960, I received a phone call at the observatory at Harvard. It was Dr. Dawson calling from Palomar. He told me of his new discovery and asked me to come to Palomar at once. Naturally, this was sensational news. I dropped everything else and took the first plane out that I could get."

"Then you didn't know about the path of Planet 'Y' when he phoned, Dr. Ellender?"

"No. Not then. It was only when we gathered at the conference that night that Dr. Dawson broke the news. It was then we learned that Planet 'Y' would just miss crashing into the earth on its heavenly journey. Dr. Dawson insisted on our checking his calculations to make sure that he was right, that it *would* miss."

Dr. Ellender fell silent for a moment. Then he put down his cigar and said quietly:

"It was then, David, that Dr. Dawson asked for our collaboration in a gigantic hoax."

David leaned forward, his eyes riveted on Ellender's immobile face.

"You mean, to misinform the world—to tell people that Planet 'Y' and the earth *would* meet?"

"Yes. I'll never forget Dr. Dawson then, David, as he stood up and began to speak. His eyes blazed, and there was the look in them

—well, of a prophet. He told us that this was our chance, the only chance to save the world from destroying itself. It was a heaven-made opportunity, he said, to save men from their own folly, from blowing themselves up with atomic bombs." Ellender's face was rapt. "We listened. We sat there without stirring, and listened. Dr. Dawson went on. He pointed out that this, this objective, was worth everything, the complete sacrifice of our scientific integrity, everything. Our duty now was not to truth, but to humanity. We who sat there, we astronomers, knowing what we knew, had the power to save the world. It meant that we had to lie to the world and deceive it. It meant that we had to enter into a great conspiracy."

"I see."

"Of course the proposal stunned us. In effect, we were being asked to participate in a great and colossal lie. But then Dr. Dawson pointed out that we, as scientists, could not afford to let things slip out of our hands this time. We could not afford to make the same mistake as the nuclear scientists who had failed to weigh the social consequences of their discovery and had given the atom over into irresponsible hands. War was imminent. The first bombs might drop at any moment. We had to act fast. And we did."

Now, out of the mist of David's memory, came something Dr. Dawson had said to Professor Kellar that night at the Big House. Now it was clear, now it added up. He heard the voice of the Old Man again:

"Professor Kellar, I am an astronomer. My worlds are universes. I use giant telescopes to study them. Should I then condescend to turn to a microscope and study the microbes on my own pitiful planet? The answer is yes. And again, yes. Perhaps I am lacking in nobility, in the pure scientist's approach that the truth is the thing, and damn the consequences. But I believe our first responsibility is to the people with whom we live."

David heard Ellender as he went on:

"And so we released the joint announcement that there would be a cosmic clash on Christmas Day of 1962 the date when the two planets would be nearest each other. We knew the consequences of such an announcement would be staggering, its effect shattering. We knew that there would be suicides, that few if any children would be born. But on the scales, the cost in human life was trivial compared to that of an atomic war."

David stirred. "How did you know some research astronomer— some man who wasn't present there that night—would not rise to dispute your calculations on the basis of his own?"

"We took a chance on that, David," answered Ellender. "And it was a desperate gamble. But the margin of difference was so small —almost infinitesimal—that even a crack research astronomer might have doubted his own figures. And we counted on Dr. Dawson's prestige and our own to add weight to our conclusion. As it turned out, we were lucky."

"And so you kept the secret within the group? You didn't extend the conspiracy to anyone else?"

"No. We entered a solemn pact, David, that we would tell no one, not even those close to us, not even our immediate colleagues, not even our own wives. That is why Dr. Dawson did not tell his wife of the lie we had created, and that is why he did not tell you. We knew that if the truth of our hoax ever got beyond our own small circle it would somehow leak out and spread, and that would be the end. A secret like this, we reasoned, was too big, too important, to hide for very long. Its possession, under the pressure of the Big Eye, under the stresses and strains it would bring about, would be almost unbearable. Only we would know it, we decided that night, only we would live with it. And when we died, it would die with us."

Now David remembered the Old Man on the night Emily Dawson had died. Dr. Dawson knew, and he might have saved his wife by assuring her that there was a future to fight for, and live for, but he had kept silent. He had kept silent and watched her die, and it had been too much for him. And so he had gone to the top of the telescope to die. But even when his mind had gone, he had kept the secret and died with it.

Dr. Ellender was watching David steadily. Finally he rose and began to pace the floor.

"Well, David, now you know. Now—you know everything. You discovered our hoax by accident, and now you are one of us."

"Yes."

"Now," continued Ellender, "we have seen an exciting new world come to pass in the last two years. Now that the Big Eye is passing away, almost every second woman on the street is bearing a child; a new generation will be born. Our hope is that as the elders die out the old concepts of greed and power will die with them, while they are still under the influence of the miracle. Then the new generation, trained in the concepts of this new world, and never knowing any other, will take it on from there."

Ellender turned to the desk, picked up the slip of paper, and handed it to David.

"Well, David, that's all," said Ellender quietly. "I ask only this of you. Say nothing of our conspiracy to anyone—not even your own wife. Take what you know to the graveyard, as we will. Let the people go on believing that they have seen a miracle. If they ever find out the truth they will be disillusioned. They will go back to building atom bombs, to their prejudices and ancient fears, to wars and the same old destructive insanity. Let them believe that they were saved from the Big Eye only by divine will. Let them believe that they have been given a last chance—to make good. Let them have their miracle."

David nodded. He shook hands with the shaggy, gray-eyed man and then walked out along the corridor to the observatory door.

As he stood on the threshold his eye strayed up toward the heavens.

The Big Eye was still there, but it was a pin point now, and very far away.

Slowly David Hughes reached into his pocket, took out the piece of paper, tore it into shreds, and threw the fragments into the wind.

Then he walked out into the night.

Help Your Children Be Self-Confident

Help Your Children Be Self-Confident

Curtis Booraem, John V. Flowers, & Bernard Schwartz

PRENTICE-HALL, INC., *Englewood Cliffs, N.J.*

Help Your Children Be Self-Confident
by Curtis Booraem, John V. Flowers, and
Bernard Schwartz
Copyright © 1978 by Curtis Booraem, John V. Flowers,
and Bernard Schwartz
Printed in the United States of America
Prentice-Hall International, Inc., London
Prentice-Hall of Australia, Pty. Ltd., Sydney
Prentice-Hall of Canada, Ltd., Toronto
Prentice-Hall of India Private Ltd., New Delhi
Prentice-Hall of Japan, Inc., Tokyo
Prentice-Hall of Southeast Asia Pte. Ltd., Singapore
Whitehall Books Limited, Wellington, New Zealand
10   9   8   7   6   5   4   3   2   1

Library of Congress Cataloging in Publication Data

Booraem, Curtis D.
  Help your children be self-confident.

  Bibliography: p.
  1. Assertiveness in children.   2. Self-reliance
in children.   I. Flowers, John V., joint author.
II. Schwartz, Bernard, joint author.   III. Title.
BF723.A74B66   158′.1   78-16705
ISBN 0-13-386219-4

CONTENTS

I.
THE NEED FOR SELF-CONFIDENCE TRAINING

Anyone who has strolled down the aisle of the child-care section in a bookstore knows that there are many opinions about what children need from their parents in order to develop optimally. Among the thousands of books on the subject of child-rearing, there are certain "shoulds" of parenting that are most commonly emphasized.

The one most often stressed is that parents need to communicate to their children that they are loved and accepted—this in order to give children the foundation in life of belonging, of being wanted and being protected.

Second, parents are called upon to establish a balance between freedom and constraint with regard to the child's activities. There is no consensus as to where that balance lies,

1

The Need for Self-Confidence Training

but it is agreed that while children need the opportunity to explore, to try out, to initiate behavior, they also need parents to monitor and limit that decision making.

Various manuals on child-rearing emphasize that parents should be good listeners and communicators, should provide a stimulating "learning" environment in the home, should discourage narrow and stereotypical sex-role behavior, should provide opportunities for frank and age-appropriate instruction in such areas as sex, divorce, and death.

All this parents and teachers are called upon to provide. Yet there is still more that children need: they need to learn assertive social skills as an alternative means of dealing and interacting with people. It is as important for children to develop competencies in these abilities as it is for them to be provided with love or any of the other "needs" of childhood. Without these skills, the chances of their succeeding in life are greatly reduced.

To demonstrate the present lack of training in these skills, consider the following:

PEOPLE ARE NOT TAUGHT OR ENCOURAGED TO MAKE REQUESTS

Over 50 percent of students in an introductory psychology class admitted they were afraid to visit their professor's office to ask for clarification of an idea or an assignment. Several students were afraid to visit the college registrar to have a grade of F removed for a class in which they have never enrolled.

Obviously, a student who is unable to make contact with a teacher has less of a chance to get information which will be helpful on tests or in writing papers. He is also in no position to question the validity of a grade he has received. On the other hand, students who feel comfortable in seeking out the help of teachers or other students, even though they may be no brighter than the nonassertive individual, will earn higher grades. These individuals feel that they can affect their environment, that they are not just passive recipients of whatever the universe might offer them. In the long run, therefore, they will investigate far more alternatives for their future than a nonassertive individual who learns to respond to what comes along but does not take an active role in making things happen.

> At a college counseling center, it was reported that several students complained that they could not study or sleep because their roommates disturbed them continually. One student's grades had dropped significantly. They had been afraid to tell their roommates about this because they didn't want their roommates to be displeased with them.

It is clear that these students had not learned to make requests of other people. Their fear of being rejected by the roommate is most likely based on the fact that they did not know how to ask for things in ways which minimize the likelihood of making the other person hostile or resentful.

> In a study of American consumers, it was found that 20 percent of those who had purchased new products were dissatisfied with the items' performance. However, of those 20 percent, only one person in fifty had even bothered to contact the store or individual from whom he or she had purchased the product.

Again, we have an example of people not protecting

their best interests through the process of information gathering or request making.

Request-making skills are essential in interpersonal relationships—for initiating contact with an individual, for clarifying the goals of a friendship, for arranging times and places to meet, and so on. Requesting in this area is also very difficult for many people to do. There are numerous clinical examples of individuals who, totally lacking in request skills, spent part or all of their lives alienated from others.

> Steven was an intelligent and good-looking 27-year-old graduate student enrolled in a social skills course. He disclosed to the class during a practice session that he had never asked a girl for a date because he was afraid to do so. From further discussion, it was clear that somehow Steven had made it through adolescence without so much as a rudimentary knowledge of the principles of getting someone's attention, making eye contact, or initiating interaction.

Children must be taught and encouraged to make requests so that in school, with friends, and in intimate relationships, they are not afraid to ask for what they want.

PEOPLE ARE NOT TAUGHT OR ENCOURAGED TO REFUSE

> Mrs. J., a housewife, was very meek when it came to saying "no." She was therefore a salesman's dream. She once bought not one, but two, sets of encyclopedias within one week. The salesman of the second set had a response for every situation. When Mrs. J. told him that

she had just bought a set of encyclopedias, he asked her how many children she had. She replied that she had two daughters and a son. The salesman then talked about how terrible children are these days and how it would certainly be better to get each his or her own encyclopedia so as to avoid their fighting if they needed the same volume at the same time.

Mr. R. is a successful businessman, but found that his relationship with his wife was deteriorating because he was away at work for longer and longer periods. It was not that he wanted to be at work more than he wanted to be at home. He just did not know how to say "no" to his boss when he was asked to take on a special assignment or take over for someone who was sick.

Mr. and Mrs. D.'s marriage was in difficulty because neither person knew how to refuse the other. Each felt obligated to do exactly what the other requested, leaving neither person the freedom and time to be alone or pursue separate activities.

Sally, a teenager, was a member of a group of high schoolers who were regularly using drugs. She wanted to avoid drug taking but still wanted to participate in many of the group's activities. Since she did not know how to refuse while maintaining her friendships, she continued using drugs and was subsequently arrested.

Arthur's cousin was visiting from the East. The visit had turned into a permanent residency. Arthur did not wish this to continue, but his cousin cleverly kept postponing the date of his leaving.

However great the anticipated pain of making a refusal may be, the consequences of not doing so are even more dire:

wasting time on activities which are uninteresting or even harmful; being taken advantage of by employers, students, relatives, neighbors; losing money and performance efficiency because of unneeded purchases or substandard products. Clearly, part of a child's "curriculum" at home and in school should be directed toward teaching the skills of making refusals.

PEOPLE ARE NOT TAUGHT HOW TO GIVE OR RECEIVE POSITIVE EXPRESSIONS

On a given day at school, the average child will receive from five to ten times as many negative statements as positive ones. These expressions come from his peer group, from teachers, administrators, even bus drivers.

The result of this situation is that school is not a very positive experience for most children. For many youngsters the ratio of positive to negative statements does not improve much at home; in some cases it is worse. Even in homes where the parents are fairly positive toward the children, there is often a constant flow of criticism and teasing between siblings. Parents and teachers therefore need a means to increase the incidence of positive interaction for children.

> Mrs. M. came to marriage counseling complaining that her husband was not "giving her enough." What this phrase really meant, it turned out, was that he never paid her any compliments. In talking with Mr. M., the therapist found that he considered saying such things as, "It's really nice being with you tonight," or "You look pretty," to be corny and even unmanly.

In this case, we see how the ability to request and the ability to give positive statements can overlap. The therapist further found that on the rare occasion that the husband did give a compliment, instead of responding appropriately, his wife discounted the comment. This reaction illustrates another skill that children and adults often need to be taught—the ability to receive positive statements.

When John would compliment Connie, it was very difficult for her to accept the compliment. She would say things like, "You don't really feel that, you're only saying that to make me feel good." Pretty soon John got so tired of defending his position that he stopped giving praise altogether.

In a relationship where there is no positive feedback, the people soon lose contact with one another. How is one to know what is pleasing to the other unless there are some verbal and nonverbal expressions to use as a guide? Without knowing why, the individuals in such a relationship soon stop doing and saying positive things to each other because nothing seems to evoke a significant response.

Often parents neglect to say positive things about their child's behavior. They communicate only when behavior becomes undesirable or inappropriate. When they respond to such behavior with negative messages, it is as if all of the positive behavior that preceded is forgotten.

Charlie had brought home good grades throughout junior high school. His parents' typical response was merely to sign the report card and give it back to him. One semester, when Charlie's grades fell somewhat, his parents had a lot to say. Up to that point, however, his positive behavior had been ignored.

PEOPLE ARE NOT TAUGHT HOW TO GIVE OR RECEIVE NEGATIVE STATEMENTS EFFECTIVELY

Expressing disapproval to another person is very difficult for many people. As a result, people frequently feel frustrated and powerless to do anything about their problems, be they at home, on the job, or in day-to-day affairs.

Donald, a regular patron of a rather expensive restaurant, never would complain about how his food was prepared. If he asked for a medium-rare steak and he got medium-well done, he would eat it without saying anything. One day he decided to send the food back to the chef and explain that the meat had not been cooked as he had requested. To his surprise, the management paid his bill. They were grateful for the honest feedback which they felt they needed in order to provide the best service.

There is a tendency for people to feel that negative feedback, even when justified, is something to be avoided like the plague. In reality, as this story illustrates, expressions of dislike can be another way of helping people to grow and improve themselves, if delivered appropriately.

In the following case, Rachel expresses a negative message to her husband. However, because this couple had not learned to handle this type of expression, the conversation erupts into a battle.

Rachel was feeling that her husband was bored with her, and one night said to him, "It really makes me angry that you watch so much television." His reply was that if she was more fun to be with, he wouldn't watch it so often. She then complained to him that she would be more fun if he was a better manager of the household affairs.

What happened in this case, as in so many others where a negative message is in order, is that Rachel's initial statement was not phrased in such a way as to elicit a problem-solving or cooperative response. This example demonstrates the difficulty people have in accepting negative statements.

Children must be prepared to deal with criticism and other negative feedback which they might encounter. They must learn alternative responses other than counterpunching or withdrawing. They must learn to expect negatives as a natural part of an active and productive life.

Craig, a salesman, regularly performed demonstrations of his products to a group of prospective buyers. His boss casually mentioned to him after one of his demonstrations that he had done a good job, but not quite as good as the week before. This comment started a psychological slide for Craig, who now felt that he was not growing and was not talented enough for advancement.

Criticism was for Craig the great dread of his existence. He perceived it as an attack against his own value as an individual.

Being oversensitive to negatives can interfere with normal social behavior also:

The Need for Self-Confidence Training

Kelley was very easily aroused to strong feelings of jealousy by the slightest attention paid to his wife. She had never given him any reason to suspect her of being involved with other men, but he could not stop himself from flying off the handle at the merest glance or bit of attention that she might receive.

This person perceives his wife's attention getting as a negative thing (which, of course, is only *his* interpretation), and he has no way to deal with it other than to fly into a rage and cause embarrassment to himself and to his wife.

When a person has not learned to feel comfortable expressing negative reactions, often the feelings of helplessness which accompany this passivity can erupt into an act of violence. It is as if the person can no longer tolerate the long accumulation of silent acceptance and so finally reacts to a minor occurrence with an outburst that is out of proportion to that situation.

Charles Whitman was shot and killed after he terrorized and murdered students at a Texas University by shooting at them from a tower atop the school library. Research of his childhood revealed that he had never engaged in a violent act in his life. In fact, he never made negative expressions until one day a minor incident triggered this brutal massacre.

Often in bureaucracies and in large institutions there is no outlet for negative expressions. This setting often leads to outbursts of aggression which, on the face of it, would seem unwarranted.

In reviewing aggressive incidents which had led to military men being confined to the brig, it was found that many of the cases involved the striking of a superior after some relatively minor criticism or embarrassment. What was not so apparent was that, for the persons who committed the aggression, this final incident followed a long catalogue of such episodes and the fuse had finally blown.

Many job environments are sources of minor but continual pressures and negative comments. Frequently, the individual who has not learned ways to handle these messages will blow up and enjoy temporary satisfaction. However, the relief is often short-lived when the individual must deal with the consequences of his explosion.

School is another place where stresses build up because of lack of training in handling negative input.

Marsha recounted the incidents leading up to her dropping out of college. First her roommate had complained that she was not neat enough. Then she found that the computer had placed her in a class for which she had not enrolled. The next disturbing occurrence was her math instructor embarrassing her when she asked a question, stating that if she had read the assignment she would have understood the problem. Finally, she missed a B by one point on a mid-term. She had learned no way of handling these negative experiences.

It should be clear at this point there is a tremendous need to teach children the skills necessary to avoid the countless problems like those outlined thus far. There is no guarantee, of course, that a child who has developed assertive abilities will always experience success in getting what he wants. But certainly he has a better chance of succeeding than does the child without such training.

The Need for Self-Confidence Training

There is a larger issue related to the development of these skills: the issue of raising children to be effective participants in a democratic society. Children who learn to make requests, to refuse (or attempt to refuse), and to give accurate feedback, both positive and negative, to those around them are more likely to become better and more informed citizens than those who leave the thinking to others.

In addition, it is important that children's education equip them with the necessary tools to succeed in life. The ideal of "the pursuit of happiness" will remain unrealized if children are not effectively prepared for adulthood. This preparation must involve more than just academic skills. Parents and teachers are now advised to acknowledge the emotional aspects of a child's development as well as the cognitive. Furthermore, extensive research has borne out the fact that related to both cognitive and emotional development are the abilities to be assertive in social interaction, and that there is as fundamental a need to instruct children in these abilities as in the other developmental areas.

Certainly there are advantages to a society which places high priority on raising questioning individuals—people who seek information and who do not placidly accept everything simply because it comes from an "authority." But these advantages also accrue to the individuals themselves within that society; such individuals will have a better chance to get the most out of their lives. This reciprocal process of improving the individual and thereby improving society can best be accomplished through a process of training beginning in childhood. The evidence thus far shows that children and adults with such training do better in every area of life. In school the child with assertive skills will do better than other children with equal intelligence. They ask more questions of more people to get the information they need. In addition, because they know when and how to refuse, they are not as likely to be influenced to act contrary to their better judgment. Thus they are able, for example, to withstand group pressure to go out the night before a test instead of studying.

Such individuals also excel in the work world. They get their ideas across better. Their opinions are credible because they do not always agree with everything that is proposed. Furthermore, their relations with other people at work and home are more satisfactory. They communicate their needs and desires more honestly. They compliment and disagree freely. They will not sacrifice so much for another individual that they end up being resentful and frustrated at not doing what they wanted.

So in every sphere of involvement, the individual who can interact effectively with his environment is more productive and satisfied. Such a person has many tools at his disposal for coping with a myriad of situations and pressures. The unassertive individual has far fewer alternatives in life. In fact, there are basically only three alternatives to assertive behavior.

The first of these options is *passivity*. A person dealing with situations in this way simply does nothing, except perhaps to physically leave the environment. In school, this type of child does not initiate social contact, he often sits in the back of the room and never raises his hand to answer or ask a question. He waits for friendships to come to him, and often the ones he gets are those he would rather be without. Because of his behavior, he receives very few rewards in the academic or social process at school. He is a high risk for dropping out because school is something which, from his point of view, happens to other people, not him. Teachers are aware that the percentage of such children in their classrooms is higher than many people imagine. These children are lost in the shuffle. The cost to society for their loss is great, because these children often become the lonely, alienated and uninvolved adult who frequently falls back on drugs, alcohol—even prostitution— as a means of dealing with his or her problems.

On the job, this person is not heard from often and is

therefore not sought out for advice and suggestions. He gets passed over time and time again. In their adult relationships with others, since passive people have not learned to ask for what they want, the quality of their interactions often depends on how good a mind reader or how generous the other person is.

Passivity over a long period of time can lead to a second form of response: *aggression.* As we have seen, sometimes the frustration of not expressing oneself can suddenly erupt into an act of violence. In other cases, children have learned from an early age that aggression is one way to get results. Sometimes they may learn this from their parents.

> Mark was brought to the child guidance center for his continual aggressive behavior at school. When the mother was asked whether Mark exhibited this same behavior at home, she responded that he and his brother were always raising hell around the house. When questioned as to what she did to try to restore order on these occasions, she replied that she always grabbed the whip with which she trained horses and switched them with it until they decided to stop.

These children were learning that the more powerful violence is, the more effective it is in controlling others. Violent activity can be learned from and reinforced by friends, television, and siblings.

The costs to society for producing aggressive individuals are even more ominous than the consequences of passivity. There is a direct link between the aggressive child and the criminally violent adult. Often these people have learned no other way of getting what they want in life; their environment has taught them to act in aggressive ways to obtain their ends.

In his relationship with people, the aggressive individual

tends literally to scare people away. By his behavior, he cuts off any possibility of intimacy. He may have many superficial friends, but the friendships are short-lived because few people will expose themselves to either verbal or physical punishment for very long.

The aggressive individual tends to develop a response pattern which is impulsive. That is, he doesn't learn to think things through first and then act. Instead, he is prone to act immediately and often destructively. This type of person is also at a disadvantage when undertaking long-term projects or goals. In his personal relationships, in school, or at work, he wants what he wants when he wants it. He just isn't willing or able to work now for a future reward.

The third nonassertive response to situations is *passive aggression.* A person who behaves in this way gets back at others through subtle and indirect means. Being late is a common example of this phenomenon. With such behavior, one can punish others by making them wait or worry. In the long run, of course, the person who is late often punishes himself, as people come to consider him unreliable and are not willing to depend on him.

Passive aggression can also take the form of sarcasm.

> Mrs. L. asked her husband how he liked the wallpaper she had just put up in the bedroom. He replied, "Not bad, I hope you still like it next year." She then tried to "straighten out" his communication by asking, "Are you saying you don't like it, or are you saying you don't trust my judgment?" He then backed off by saying he really did like it and was only teasing.

Many relationships are full of such examples of hidden "negatives" indicating that the people are not comfortable in stating directly to one another what is bothering them. Sar-

The Need for Self-Confidence Training

casm not only hurts relationships but usually prevents a person from getting what he wants. If the husband in the above example was concerned about his wife's changing the wallpaper after one year, he could have expressed that viewpoint more directly. Then additional steps could have been taken to try to work out a satisfactory agreement. No steps can be taken to solve anything when a person is teased about his behavior, the typical response being counterteasing or other defensive reactions.

Other passive-aggressive individuals act in such a way as to thwart another person's objectives.

> A student asked a professor to write him a letter of recommendation. The professor did not think much of the student and obliged him with a highly negative and critical evaluation.

In this case, instead of directly telling the student that he could not write a favorable recommendation, the professor seized the opportunity to attack the student in a behind-the-back fashion.

An individual who engages in passive aggressive behavior finds that others mistrust him. People feel that they cannot count on him for honest feedback, that his outer behavior is no indication of how he really feels. Obviously such a person does not do well in relationships or in groups which must work together harmoniously.

For some time now professionals have been helping people avoid the traps of passive and aggressive behaviors through the teaching of assertive skills. Thus, individuals who have had trouble in meeting other people have been taught how to make "requests" so that they can meet the kind of people they want. Aggressive individuals have been trained to get what they want without having to resort to violent behavior.

They have also been helped to make "refusals" as an alternative to the storing up of resentments which can lead to aggressive outbursts.

Assertion training has become a widely used and successful tool of "therapy." It has been both used with individuals and taught to large groups of people in search of alternative means of interaction. It has been applied in prison settings and in mental institutions.

A large percentage of adults who are taught these approaches are able to apply them successfully in their lives. However, in many cases the training is "too little too late." Often the anxiety of changing one's behavior after a pattern has been established for many years is too great. Sometimes the deficits in learning are immense and what is required is years of reeducation. Intervention or preventive teaching at an earlier age was what was required. It is for this reason that attention became focused on teaching assertive skills to children. When children are taught these skills they do in fact use them in their day-to-day life in and out of school. They will stay after class to ask their teachers questions about an assignment; they are not afraid to ask for what they want from friends, brothers and sisters, and parents. They will speak up and not merely do what the group wants to do. They can handle the fact that they are not perfect but make mistakes. They know that people like to be thanked and appreciated for what they do.

In the course of utilizing their assertive abilities, children develop a more positive view of the world and of themselves. No longer is the world a place where things only "happen" to them. Instead, they have learned to make things happen. This character trait is often called self-confidence. In school, the self-confident person is often a leader. He therefore perceives the school experience as a positive one, as one in which he derives status and a feeling of involvement.

Self-confident children also tend to be calmer than chil-

The Need for Self-Confidence Training

dren who are not as sure of themselves. They seem not to be as anxious about their environment because they feel they have some control over it.

Moreover, self-confident children are more willing than other children to take risks and try new things. This particular characteristic is related to every aspect of life, be it social, academic, or vocational. The person who tries new things learns a great deal from his attempts, whether they succeed or fail. In fact, these people view failures as simply steps along the way to learning. They do not perceive a mistake as an indication that they are not competent or worthwhile. Because they are willing to continue to practice a particular skill rather than give up at the first blunder, they often go on to develop expertise in that area. Consequently, there is a positive cycle of achievement which begins with self-confidence then leads to experimentation and risk taking, which lead to further skill development leading to more self-confidence. The child who is afraid to try new things because of the threat of failure cannot, of course, learn from what he doesn't try.

In addition to self-confidence, the development of assertive abilities is also highly correlated with self-esteem. Assertive children think well of themselves most of the time. They tell themselves good things about themselves when they do good things. Because of this tendency to "self-reinforce," they are not totally dependent on other people for approval and validation.

In summary, children who have been taught assertive skills by their parents and teachers have profited immensely in their development. There are myriads of situations in which children can utilize these abilities, enabling them to enjoy their childhood years more fully while at the same time preparing them for the stresses and challenges of adulthood. The specific techniques which have been used successfully in training children are presented in the following chapters.

2.

REQUESTS, REFUSALS AND POSITIVE AND NEGATIVE EXPRESSIONS

This chapter deals with two main issues. First we will discuss the specific skills which children need in order to behave assertively, and second, the techniques for teaching these skills will be presented.

The first step in learning assertion is to understand clearly the difference between assertive and nonassertive interactions. An assertive behavior is one in which the person is exercising his rights to ask for what he wants, to refuse what he does not want (with children in authority situations, this right is limited to attempting to refuse), and to give honest feedback to others. In teaching children to employ these "rights" one must emphasize that those with whom one interacts have these same rights, that, in fact, the best assurance that others will treat you in a dignified way is to give them those same freedoms that you desire. This means requesting what one wants without resorting to undue pressure; responding to the requests and feedback which others give in a clear and straightforward manner; expressing honest feedback without being malicious or hurtful.

Learning all of this is real work, for either an adult or a child. Parents and teachers must therefore emphasize to children that behaving in this fashion has definite rewards; that individuals who learn to ask assertively get more than those who don't; that those who refuse to do what they don't wish are not pushed around by others; that those who can give as well as take positive and negative messages are respected and trusted. These ideas must be demonstrated to the child in word and in action.

In each of the social skill areas there are clear distinctions between assertive and nonassertive behaviors. Understanding these distinctions is vital to the learning of assertive alternatives.

REQUESTS

An assertive request is appropriate when an individual wishes something of another person. It is posed as a direct question, thereby increasing the likelihood of eliciting an immediate reply. An assertive request is not merely a statement of desire, such as "I would like to go out to dinner." It must be followed by a question: "Would you take me?" or "Are you free to go along with me tonight?" Often the question itself is preceded by a statement of feeling or self-disclosure; "I'm exhausted from working all day. I would really like to go out to dinner. Will you come?" Though asking something of a person may seem to be a rather simple task, many children do not choose this direct route. Instead, they employ a wide variety of nonassertive reactions when placed in situations where they desire something.

A fourth-grade class of students were asked to tell what they would do if they were walking past a ball field where a group of children were playing and they wanted to join in the play. Only three of thirty children said they would react with a direct request. The following are some of the reactions which the other children proposed:

Passive
Most Passive
> "Walk away"
> "Stand there for five minutes and then leave if not asked."
> "Stand there and look like you want to play."
> "Tell someone that it looks like fun." (hinting)

Least Passive
> "Tell someone that you would like to play."

Aggressive
Demand
> "I would tell them to let me play."

Threaten
> "If you don't let me play, I'll tell the teacher."

Passive to
Physical Threat
> "Tell someone you want to play, and if he doesn't let you, beat him up."

Passive-Aggressive
> "Stand there and if they don't ask you to play and the ball comes to you, tell them they can't have it back unless they let you play."

From these examples it is obvious that children are not at all masters of making direct requests. It is also apparent that aggressive reactions often follow a passive attempt at getting something.

REFUSALS

Children need to be taught that they have the right to say "no" to other people's *requests*. (Notice the emphasis on the word "request." More on this in Chapter 3.) It is also important to help children differentiate between the use of "reasons" and "excuses" in making refusals. If, for instance, a person is asked out and would like to go but has a prior commitment, then "being busy" is a *reason* for not going. If, however, the person does not wish to accept this invitation even if free, then saying that he is busy is an *excuse*. It is advisable to avoid making excuses because they leave the door open for further requests when the situation changes. In this case, another request for a date might be asked the next day.

Children are often uncomfortable in making assertive refusals to their peers. (They are very good at making aggressive refusals, as will be shown.) A group of 9-year-olds was asked what they would do if a friend asked to borrow their bicycle and they did not want to lend it. Only 15 percent responded with an assertive refusal. The following are some of the nonassertive ways in which the children responded to this request:

Passive
> "Loan the bicycle even though not wishing to." "Make excuses such as, 'I'm not allowed to.'" (In this case, the child did not want to loan the bike—even if permitted by parents, so it is an excuse, not a reason.)

Aggressive
"Tell him he's not a good rider."
Passive-Aggressive
"Say you'll do it and then not be home when the kid comes to pick it up."

Assertive responses, on the other hand, are direct and honest. "No, I never lend it to anybody," or "No, I'm using it this afternoon," (as long as this is the real reason for not lending it) are possible examples. Note that the latter response leaves the door open for future requesting, whereas the first statement is more final.

Refusing someone raises the possibility of that person being hurt or resentful. Thus it is important that children be taught the skill of "softening" a refusal. One does not have to be tactlessly blunt to get one's point across. Children need to be taught to acknowledge the other person's feelings through the use of buffering statements, such as, "I know you really want to use it, but I just don't lend it out." This kind of response does not imply that the person is backing down. It merely demonstrates that he does not wish to hurt the feelings of the requester. It must be pointed out to children that no matter how hard one tries to avoid it, occasionally a person's feelings will be hurt when his requests are denied. This is to be accepted as something natural and is not to be construed as a reason to change a refusal into an acceptance.

SENDING AND RECEIVING POSITIVE AND NEGATIVE EXPRESSIONS

Sending Positive Messages

Children in our culture are not encouraged to say positive things to one another. However, this type of behavior can be

Requests, Refusals and Positive and Negative Expressions

learned by children if it is modeled and rewarded by authority figures and one's peer group.

Anyone who has seen Little League competition knows that there are distinct types of teams. If a team is well coached, the teammates are expected to give supportive statements to one another throughout the game. "Nice hit," "Good try," "Next time you'll win" are a few of the positive expressions one might hear. On the other hand, there are teams whose main purpose, it seems, is to annihilate the personalities of its team members through a continual barrage of disparaging remarks. "Boy, are you lucky today," is the closest thing to a compliment on that type of team. Attention is more often paid to mistakes than to positive behavior. The sad fact is that the majority of children are more often exposed to the negative condition than to the situation which focuses on supportive and positive behavior.

A group of thirty 9- and 10-year-olds were observed as they chose up teams for baseball. Only four of the children who were chosen said anything approximating a positive message after being selected. Most said nothing at all. One stated that he wouldn't play because he wasn't chosen first. Several mentioned that they would rather have been chosen by the other team. The positive messages included nonverbal responses such as a pat on the back or a handshake and verbal statements such as "Thanks, man, I like being on your team."

Often children (and adults) are so uncomfortable giving positive statements to others that they can do so only by mixing the compliment with a sarcastic remark such as, "Thanks, Jerko," or "Is that all you can lend me?" which take the edge off a straight compliment, so that, heaven forbid, one doesn't appear to be too friendly or grateful.

Receiving Positive Messages

Children fare rather poorly in handling compliments on those rare occasions when they are actually praised or thanked for something other than being "such a cute child." In our society the "aw, shucks" attitude is the one most encouraged as a response to positive expressions. When a fourth-grade class was asked to write down what they would say or do if someone said that they liked what they were wearing, only six students gave assertive responses such as, "Thanks, I'm glad you told me that," or "I'm glad you like it, I made it." The majority stated that they wouldn't say anything. Others suggested that the child must want something from them or they wouldn't say something like that. Many children challenged the compliment by saying things like, "I don't like it so much," or "It's kind of old now." This type of response has the effect of actually punishing the praiser because it contradicts his statement. People who react thus soon find that no one compliments them because the comments seem to be unappreciated.

Sending Negative Messages

It might seem that sending negative messages is something which children do with great facility. The fact is that though they do communicate negatively to one another at a high rate, the messages are not assertive. An assertive negative statement is specific and does not attack the individual, just the bothersome behavior. For example, calling someone names (adults are not above this either) is not giving an assertive negative message. However, "I don't like it when you cut in line," or "I don't like it when you keep interrupting me while I'm working on my homework" are assertive examples, because they stick to the issue and they focus on the feelings of the person who is being bothered rather than on the personality of the botherer.

There are many children who will not stand up for themselves and complain, regardless of how irksome someone's behavior might be to them. Children may tolerate being hurt, angered, or made anxious without signaling a reaction of any sort. Their faces are impassive, with the result that others do not know what effect their behavior is having on them, and do not much care, since no direct communications have been uttered.

Other children may go so far as to look bothered. Their eyes may be downcast, their faces tight, their eyes angry or watery. These messages may help their cause, somewhat, but they are not clear enough to really effect change in someone else's behavior toward them.

The most common negative communications are aggressive in nature, either verbal or physical. Calling a person a name or combination of names, ranging from attacks on ancestry, race, height, weight, size of bodily features, and the like, are the focus of most verbal attacks. Physical aggression has many possibilities also. Parents and teachers are all too familiar with the particulars.

Receiving Negative Messages

The first step in accepting negative feedback assertively is to decide whether or not the criticism is justified. If the person decides that he has done something which warrants the comment, then the assertive response is first to admit the wrong, and then to buffer that statement with a related positive statement about oneself. This is very similar to the process of delivering a negative remark with a buffer, only in this case the buffer is made for the sake of both the criticizer and the person who is being complained about. In this way both parties are reminded that though a mistake has occurred, the transgressor has other positive attributes. For example, a child who is chastised for being late to an appointment might say: "I know I'm late, I should have allowed myself more time. I usually do and so am usually on time."

Sometimes a child has engaged in objectionable behavior for some time. It would be unreasonable, of course, for a child who is frequently late to state that he is usually on time. In this case, the child is taught to admit being late but then to say something positive silently to himself. One child who frequently left his lunch at home learned to admit fault without blaming other people for rushing him, as he had done previously. He would say to himself, "I do have a problem forgetting my lunch, but I do remember lots of other things like people's names and homework assignments." In this way he cancelled some of the negative statement about himself.

Children (and adults) tend to respond to criticism with an aggressive response known as counterattacking. Counterattacking is quite simply shifting the guilt to something or someone else. "I got an F on that test because you made me go to bed early the night before the exam," or "You don't know the answers to some of the questions yourself, so how do you expect me to know them," are some examples. It is crucial that children learn that such responses typically lead to a lengthy discussion of the matter, often ending in emotional outbursts with no resolution of the problem; however, when one admits having erred, the discussion is usually shorter and centers on ways of preventing the behavior from recurring. It must also be realized that admitting wrong is effective only the first time or two with a particular behavior. It is not to be treated as a way out of having to change a habit.

There are times when a child is clearly not in the wrong and therefore not deserving of the negative message. An asser-

Requests, Refusals and Positive and Negative Expressions

tive response for the child in this case is to simply state that he did not do what he is accused of. He should not elaborate further until it is clear to him that the accuser understands this. The reason for his making sure that the denial is clearly heard before proceeding further is that often it is not really heard the first time. For example, a mother complained to her child that he left the TV on all night. The child told her that he was positive he turned it off before going to bed. (He does not add information such as, "Maybe somebody else came in later and turned it on," or "Johnny told me he was going to watch a late show, so maybe he left it on.") The parent then stated, "You kids always forget something."

The parent, being upset, had not really heard the child's response. Therefore, it was necessary for the child to return to the original issue, that he did not leave the television set on. It is important for the child's sake that he do this; otherwise he may get caught up in the emotionality of the parent, who in this case has gone from the present problem to an historical review of all the forgetting that her children have done throughout the years. A statement which returns to the original issue will head this off. Thus, an assertive response to "You kids are always forgetting something," would be, "That may be, but *I* did not leave the set on last night." What tends to occur after a restatement such as this is that the person who is upset returns to the original theme and may, in fact, ask for help in solving the problem.

Occasionally a child may not have enough information to decide if he is guilty or innocent of a charge made against him. He should then request the information he needs in order to come to a decision. If, for instance, two children had divided up the yard work and a parent complains to one child that the job was done sloppily, it is necessary to find out what particular part of the job was not acceptable before admitting to or denying the mistake. If the part of the job that was done "sloppily" was that child's responsibility, then he should admit it and seek to correct the situation. If, however, the job was not his, he should clarify the fact.

WHAT TO DO WHEN REQUESTS, REFUSALS AND EXPRESSIONS FAIL

In addition to learning the distinction between assertive and nonassertive responses, a child also needs to develop competencies in following through when an initial assertive response does not gain the desired goal. These follow-up responses are divided into *defensive techniques* (used when trying to refuse or when being confronted with a negative expression), and *offensive techniques* (used when requests are not heard or acknowledged, or when sending negative messages). It is important that children learn not only when to use these techniques but also with whom they are appropriate.

DEFENSIVE TECHNIQUES

In our culture the term "defensive" has many connotations, mostly negative. We tend to view being on the defensive as the worst possible situation to be in, and one in which the other person has the upper hand. The fact is, though, that people living active lives are going to be asked to do things they do not wish to do and are going to encounter people who, rightly or mistakenly, may be upset with them. We feel awkward at being placed in these positions mainly because we think that somehow we should be able to avoid such situations, rather than as seeing them as a natural product or our day-to-day living. The defensive position is weaker than the offensive one only if a person feels ashamed or guilty in making a refusal or denial. Once these responses are seen as one's right, the tendency to feel the underdog in the situation is greatly diminished.

Time-Out

This is the first defensive technique which should be taught. It is employed in a situation where the person is not sure whether to accept or deny a request. Rather than make a decision which may later be regretted, the assertive response is to terminate the interaction for a determined period of time. Thus, after a surprise phone call from someone asking for a date, an asserter might say, "This is something I want to think about; I'll call you back at five o'clock; is that a good time for you?" It is inappropriate not to set a time for a checkback, or to be vague about the issue of when you will decide, such as saying, "I'll think about it and maybe give you a call." Such responses get one off the hook for the moment, but often people who say such things never get around to calling back and the person who made the request is ultimately more resentful than if a direct answer one way or the other had been given.

Broken Record

When one is under pressure from a request or a negative expression, the broken-record approach helps keep the situation from getting out of hand by redirecting the conversation to the key issue rather than letting it drift to those issues that are peripheral or more general.

The technique involves the use of a key phrase such as "but the point I wish to make is. . . ." This phrase may have to be repeated at various intervals until the message has been acknowledged. The following is an example of how this technique may be used to reiterate the desire to make a refusal.

Child A: Will you bring some of your records when you come to the party tonight?

Child B: I don't bring my records to parties; they always end up getting ruined.

Child A: Yeah, but we really need them, couldn't somebody watch them?

Child B: I know it would be nice to have them, but I just don't take my records to parties anymore.

Child A: But you have the best record collection.

Child B: You may be right, but the point is, I just don't do it.

This example demonstrates how the broken-record technique helps the child to stand his ground in making his refusal. Included in his repeated refusals are statements which acknowledge the content of his friend's statements. Later in this chapter we will discuss methods of softening the blow of a refusal or negative statement.

Broken record may also be employed when one is placed in the position of having to affirm and reaffirm one's innocence of a charge. This was illustrated earlier in the case of the parent who accused one child of leaving the TV set on. He had to remind her that although he had previously left the television on, he did not on the occasion she was referring to.

Broken record can also be applied when sending positive feedback. In this case it is an offensive technique, since the asserter is initiating the interaction:

Lorraine called Pattie to tell her how much she had enjoyed lunch with her that afternoon. Pattie continually discounted the compliment by saying things such as, "I thought I talked too much and didn't allow you much of an opportunity to speak," and "I wasn't in too good a mood." Lorraine used the broken-record technique in reiterating that she thought Pattie was excellent company. She re-

Requests, Refusals and Positive and Negative Expressions

peated this until it was acknowledged by Pattie's stating, "Well, that is nice to hear, thanks."

It commonly occurs, when one is making a request of someone else (offensive situation), that the person being asked attempts to dodge or sidetrack the issue. Broken record is useful in such cases also, as the following example shows:

Parent: Remember, the yard needs to be done today.
Child: But I have a date tonight and I won't be able to finish the job and still have time to get dressed.
Parent: I understand that, but the yard is to be cleaned up today.
Child: How am I going to get it all done in time?
Parent: You're going to have to work that out, but I expect the yard to be done before you go.

In this case, the parent felt that the child had been warned long enough in advance about the yard that there was no reason to back down on the issue. Therefore, when the child raised questions and complained, the parent acknowledged the child's dilemma but then reiterated the original statement.

What if the side issues raised in the course of a discussion are important? In this case it is advisable to let the person know that this is something that should be dealt with but that there is an earlier point which needs to be clarified first. One might say, for instance, "I want to talk to you about that, but first we need to settle whether you will help me move this weekend." Just as in the case of time-out, it is essential to keep one's word and check back on the issue that has been postponed.

The broken-record approach is one which children can be taught to use with their peers. When dealing with adults, children should attempt to redirect the conversation through a request instead of ordering a return to the key issue. Thus, instead of a child saying, "I would like to settle this first and then go on to that subject," it is more appropriate to say, "Is it all right if we clear this up first and then talk about that issue?" Phrasing the desire as a request lessens the possibility of the adult becoming hostile toward the child and this approach is therefore worthy of special emphasis in social skills training.

Clipping

When a person is under attack (receiving a negative expression) and the attacker seems to be highly emotional or vague and general about his complaint, an initial response may be used which helps the attacker to regain some composure. As this occurs, the complaint usually becomes more specific and can then be dealt with. The technique is to give a minimum response such as yes, no, that's right, or I disagree (and sometimes to say nothing when it isn't even clear who is under attack).

> A grocery store owner was tired of having youngsters come in and browse through his comic book selection without ever buying any of them. Curt, who did purchase comics sometimes, was examining the new arrivals when the owner yelled to him, "I'm tired of you kids coming in here and rummaging through all the magazines when you have no intention of buying them."

Instead of responding with a denial such as, "I do buy comic books in here," an appropriate response is to say, "That's not true," or "I disagree." This type of response, known as "clipping," forces the accuser to back off a little and ask questions to get more specific information. Having been asked for clarification, the "accused" now has a chance to make his views heard. In this case, the grocery store owner went on to ask: "What do you mean, you disagree? Are you telling me that kids don't come in here and read my books without buying them?" The assertively trained child would then respond, "No" (another clip). After this the grocery store owner most likely would ask, "Then what do you mean?" The child then has a chance to explain precisely what it was he disagreed with. At this time it would be effective for the child to state that he, unlike some other children, did in fact buy comics at the store.

Negative Assertion

This technique is employed when the asserter is under attack (negative expression) and knows he is wrong. Negative assertion involves admitting one's error and then immediately shifting to a positive self-statement following the admission. There seems to be a natural tendency for people to defend themselves when criticized. Often in these defensive tactics one uses excuses to appear innocent. However, offering such excuses often escalates the hostility of the person who made the initial charges. Saying something positive about oneself following the admission helps to balance the negative statement, thus leaving a better impression with the accuser and oneself. In the following situation, defensive-negative assertion was effective:

> An 8-year-old borrowed his older brother's baseball glove without asking. The brother was quite irritated at this and stated, "I really don't like it one bit when you do that; I might have needed it for a game." The 8-year-old responded appropriately in saying, "Yes, I know it was wrong for me to do that; I usually ask because I know that's important to you."

OFFENSIVE TECHNIQUES

These techniques are useful in making requests, in gathering information, and in softening refusals and negative statements.

One could utilize the time-out reponse as an offensive technique in a request situation as well. For example: A fifth grader asked a friend to help her with a term paper. The friend replied that she would and asked what specifically she could do to help. The requester could not think just then of what assistance she needed, so she stated that she needed to think it through a little more and would bring it up again the next day after class.

Children may use the time-out approach with adults by changing the response into a question. That is, instead of saying, "I really need to think about it for a few minutes, I'll tell you at dinner," a child might say, "May I think about it for a few minutes and tell you at dinner?" Also, it is essential that children check out with the adult (particularly a parent or teacher) whether the request they want to consider is really a request or whether it is really a demand that they do something; many adults request things of children when they have no intention of accepting a negative response. Children instinctively check this out when they ask the question, "Do I have to?" Obviously, a time-out is unnecessary if the child has no choice in the matter.

Free Information
Children, particularly those who have moved to a new area, often need help in making friends. Too often children and adults settle for friendships which they have not really chosen but have developed by accident, for convenience, or at the other person's initiation. The free information technique is

Requests, Refusals and Positive and Negative Expressions

designed to teach children how to actively pursue social relationships and not merely allow their social world to be determined by chance or by others. This technique is the most
complex of the offensive methods and is taught in three phases.

PhaseI/Am I interested in this person?

In order to determine whether one has interests or qualities in
common with another, effective interviewing techniques
should be employed. Some of the best (and worst) interviewing
occurs daily on television talk shows. One of the primary determinants of an effective interview is the type of questions that
are asked. Some questions tend to elicit substantially more
information than others. Questions which succeed at getting
people to talk freely are called "open questions." These questions tend to begin with the words *what, why* or *how*. Examples
of such questions are "What do you like about performing?"
"How did you get started collecting books?" "Why do you
suppose there is so much violence today?" and so on. "Closed
questions," on the other hand, are those typically responded to
with one or two words. These questions may be appropriate in a
courtroom or on a newscast where specific answers are sought,
but they do not help in getting persons to open up about
themselves so you can get to know them. Examples of this type
of question are "Where did you go to school?" "Do you like
fishing?" "Have you lived here for a long time?" Closed questions may be useful, however, as a means of determining
whether to ask further questions about a subject. For instance,
one might ask a person what he or she does for a living. After
this closed question, an appropriate open question might be,
"What kinds of things do you do as a _____?"

After gaining information about a person's likes and dislikes, the next step is to probe further into areas which are of
common interest. That is, if the child being questioned states

that he likes to draw, and the interviewer does also, he should then ask further open questions about that subject.

Phase II/Is this person interested in me?
Up to this point the interviewer is simply gathering information for the purpose of assessing whether or not this person is worth getting to know. In the second phase, the interviewer tries to determine whether the other person seems interested in him. In order to do this, one should begin to share information on subjects which had been mentioned in the earlier part of the conversation. For instance, if the responder had mentioned an interest in the desert, one might then share one's own experiences or feelings regarding the desert. This might lead to a mutual sharing of information about the subject. However, if one's sharing of a common interest does not lead to interested responses on the part of the other person, then another previously mentioned common interest should be brought up and elaborated on. If there is still no response to this second attempt, then either the person is not much interested in listening to other people, or he is not interested in continued contact. In such cases, the assessment should be to look elsewhere for a friend. If, however, sharing a common interest does initiate further discussion of the subject, then there is a good likelihood of a relationship developing.

Phase III
In the third phase, the focus is on whether the responder takes the initiative and begins to ask some open questions. If this occurs, then it is clear that he is interested in knowing more about the person.

These three stages sound complex, but with practice they are handy and effective guides in assessing the value of a potential relationship. Teenagers particularly can use help of this sort as they begin to date.

Reinforcement Sandwich

This technique is employed in situations where the asserter is afraid that a request or a negative expression might overly distress the responder and he wishes to lessen the likelihood of such an occurrence.

Offensive negative assertion, employed when delivering a negative message to someone, involves presenting a positive expression before or after the negative statement. This is done both to soften the negative expression and to increase the probability that the recipient will clearly hear the message, with minimal upset. This technique, of course, requires considerable practice, since many people state that they cannot think of anything positive to say when they want to criticize someone.

Children need to learn that giving negative statements is helpful in that one feels better getting bad feelings out in the open. However, if there is a concern about jeopardizing the friendship because of the statement, then one must take into account the recipient's feelings.

This technique was appropriately used by a 10-year-old, Estévan, who did not appreciate his friend making jokes about his ethnic background. His friend did not realize that this was a sensitive point with Estévan and, in fact, had other friends who didn't mind this type of kidding. In using a reinforcement sandwich, Estévan stated, "I really like you as a friend, but when you joke about my background in front of the other kids, it embarrasses me and I would really appreciate it if you didn't do it, because I don't want it to mess up our friendship."

A teenage girl employed this technique in asking her friend not to share information about her dates with other girls.

She said to her friend, "I really like telling you about what goes on when I go out on a date, but I don't like your telling other people about it, so please don't do that so I can feel good about our friendship."

A child may wish to use this technique to soften the blow of a refusal which he has made to a friend's request, when the request seems to be an important one. This may be accomplished through the use of such statements as, "I really do care about our friendship, but I really would rather stay around the house this weekend; thanks for asking me," or "I really appreciate your asking me to go to the concert with you; I don't care for that type of music, but I would like to do some other things with you." Unless this type of information is communicated, the child who has made the request might feel that there is no point in inviting that person anywhere in the future.

A child should indicate a desire for future contact only if he really wishes it, however. If not, statements such as "Thank you," or "That was nice of you to think of me" are appropriate.

NONVERBAL BEHAVIOR

There is more to a message than the words one uses. Research has clearly demonstrated the importance of looking and sounding assertive while delivering assertive statements. A person who looks like a doormat is going to get walked on, no matter what is being said. Likewise, the King Kong approach will either scare people away or cause counterattacking even if the actual words used are not aggressive in nature. People with effective nonverbal behavior are more convincing in their presentations and are therefore more successful at getting what they want. The discussion of nonverbal assertive behavior will be divided into two parts. The first section will examine the six components of assertive body behavior, the second part is concerned with the use of the voice in assertive messages.

ASSERTIVE BODY BEHAVIOR

Eye Contact

A message will have more impact if one looks people in the eye when speaking to them. Though some individuals overdo this component of assertive behavior, to the point of actually staring while speaking, most people are extremely passive at eye contact. Often people begin an interaction with eye contact and then look away at the decisive moment of making a request or negative expression. As a result, the message loses potency at the very instant when it is needed the most. Thus the receiver can rather easily dismiss the statement. With eye contact, the receiver is less likely to be distracted from hearing the words. Those who practice eye contact have reported that not only does it help them to feel more confident and assertive, but in addition, when they are delivering negative statements, their aggression and the perceived aggression of the other interactor are often reduced.

Research on this subject indicates that aggression increases when negative messages are delivered without eye contact. The reason for this is that when eye contact is avoided, the interaction is depersonalized and the resultant cold, distant atmosphere can very easily lead to hostile or aggressive behaviors. On the other hand, eye contact communicates that the interactors are dealing with one another as people, not objects.

Children learn, early in life, that it is difficult to lie when looking someone in the eye. The credibility of adults, also, is increased when messages are delivered with eye contact. This is true whether the message be a request, refusal, compliment, or criticism.

Distance

Messages delivered from within two to four feet are most apt to be considered assertive and will therefore be more potent. If one moves in too close, his action can be considered aggressive. At distances greater than five feet it becomes increasingly difficult to maintain an assertive posture. In the famous experiments performed by Stanley Millgram in which students were directed to electrically shock others when they made mistakes on a word drill (the students were unaware that the shocks were never really administered), it was found that the students were more likely to obey the experimenter when the order to shock the person was delivered face to face, than when the order was delivered from a distance or through a telephone.

The way in which the distance changes between two people during a conversation also affects the power of the statements being made. Backward movement, such as leaning back or stepping away of any kind, weakens the messages being sent. A gradual and slight amount of forward movement increases the power of a statement. However, too rapid a forward movement may convey an aggressive attitude.

Thus, for emphasis, one may move in slightly to improve the eye contact. Also, at closer distances one is able to use touch (discussed later in this chapter) as part of the communication.

Posture

The way one carries oneself can be an indicator of an assertive or nonassertive message. A rigid, tightened carriage and facial expression convey aggression; a person standing with head bowed and body rounded forward is waiting to be either blessed or beaten. The assertive person displays a somewhat relaxed and loose posture. The two sides of his body act independently of one another, not symmetrically. Aggressive behaviors (both hands clenched) and passive actions (both hands in pockets) are replaced by single-sided motions (one hand gesturing, the other in a pocket).

Assertive people move their hands when speaking. However, their use of gestures is selective: they are used mainly for emphasis of significant points. Gestures are most effective when made in synchrony with the words being spoken, heightening the impact of the words. These gestures become an "additional voice" in driving home the message.

At a very young age, children will employ gestures to indicate strong feelings. A familiar example is a child jumping up and down, shouting "I want to play." This ballet is so organized that he lands just as he says the words. Children can be taught that the hands can help make one's point effectively and that one needn't leave the ground to be assertive.

In teaching children to use gestures as part of their communications, it is necessary to help them discriminate between those which may be appropriate with their peers and those which are acceptable with adults. Pointing, for example, is effective with one's friends, but is not advisable when dealing with parents or teachers.

Touch

This is one of the most powerful of the nonverbal communicators. Like gesture, touch accentuates the statements which it accompanies. It can be used effectively with requests, refusals, and positive or negative messages, and should be timed to coincide with the main point being made. In the case of a request, a touch can be used to increase the listener's attention. In making a refusal, a soft touch can lessen the feeling of rejection. Touching is, of course, a very natural response when sending a positive or complimentary message.

Our culture is a relatively "touchless" society. Most of us have at one time or another brushed against or bumped into another person while in an elevator or other close quarters. Even when the extent of the touching is ever so slight, it is our custom to apologize for the invasion of personal space. In many countries people feel much more comfortable about being touched in similar situations. In such countries touch is considered an integral part of communication.

Nearly all children enjoy and respond to being touched by people whom they know and trust, and they can be encouraged to employ touch in all appropriate encounters. Watching a Little League game, one can see how a model can influence a child's use of touch. If the coach models "touching" as a supportive response at times, such as when trying to calm a pitcher down, then the other players will begin to emulate similar responses.

Facial Expression and Head Movement

One must be careful that the facial expression agrees with the message being sent. For instance, a person who smiles when delivering a negative statement is diluting his message by saying two things at once: I don't like the thing you are doing, but I do like something (what it is that is liked is left up to the imagination of the receiver of the message). Some people who inevitably smile while delivering a negative statement feel that, in doing so, they are helping to soften the statement. The fact is that they are not softening it, they are cancelling it. The impact of the message is: one step forward, one step backward. We have already talked of a more effective way to buffer a message—offensive negative assertion, in which one makes a positive supportive statement and then follows it with the negative statement.

Another "expression" which can augment the effectiveness of a communication is nodding the head when making a positive expression and shaking it when refusing or sending a negative message.

USING THE VOICE ASSERTIVELY

Volume

Many people speak very softly while complaining bitterly that other people don't hear them or don't take what they have to say seriously. Others speak very loudly and don't understand why the responses they receive often include counterattacks or avoidance behavior. As with eye contact, it is essential that volume remain at an assertive level until the main points have been made. Often people begin a request or other expression at an appropriate level of volume but then slowly fade as the key issue approaches.

Latency

Latency refers to the time interval of silence between the termination of one individual's statement and the initiation of the second individual's statement. Long latencies are perceived as passive behavior. Short latencies or interruptions are usually perceived as aggressive.

It is common for a person to feel confused or anxious after receiving a negative statement. In order not to appear passive and therefore vulnerable to attack, it is important not to let too long a silence intervene before responding (three seconds is a rough guide).

Affect

Affect is the transmission of emotion or feelings that accompany a verbal message. It is the affective component of a message that signifies whether the person really cares about what he is saying. Affect is communicated through all of the previously discussed nonverbal body and voice variables.

An additional indicator of emotion is the level of intensity expressed in the voice. When this intensity is too high, the tendency is for the responder to discount the statements being made. "This person is too upset to know what he is talking about" is the feeling transmitted. On the other hand, a statement made flatly without any feeling will convey the message that what was said was not of much import. If a request is made in this manner, chances are the response will be a negative one. The level of intensity can be determined by changes in the pitch and speed of the voice. Pitch should also be changed to indicate concern. One can learn much about voice modulation by listening to the news on radio or television. Newscasters learn to raise the pitch in their voice to indicate dramatic aspects of a story. If one were to hear the same news without voice modulation, the events would seem far less interesting and important.

Using voice modulation too often, of course, diminishes its effectiveness. People will not respond positively when all matters, small and large, are presented as if they were of great importance.

In summary, combining some or all of these nonverbal components of message with the verbal content make for a powerful assertive communication. Additionally, the person who employs nonverbal behaviors not only has a stronger impact on others, but also feels more assertive himself. The reason for this lies in the kinesthetic or neuromuscular feedback which he is receiving from his body posture, gait, gestures, eye contact, intensity of voice, and so on. This feedback increases one's confidence and is thereby an aid in making a poised and relaxed presentation. This attitude, in turn, increases the likelihood that the message will be well received.

REHEARSING ASSERTIVE SOCIAL SKILLS

Thus far we have enumerated the skills which children need to learn in order to behave assertively. But how are they to learn these behaviors? Whenever a subject is taught which has performance as its ultimate goal, the training must include opportunities to practice the desired behaviors. This is true whether the subject be spelling or hitting a baseball. Of course, some introduction to the new skill is appropriate, but it is important that at regular intervals the new information is tried out and then assessed for accuracy. In the case of spelling a new word, one might look at the word (introduction to new information), try writing the word or saying it to oneself without looking (practice), and then check to see if the word was written correctly (assessment). In the case of hitting a ball, one would be instructed in the holding of a bat (new information), then the ball would be thrown and struck at (practice), and finally, the success of the swing would be judged on the basis of contact or lack of contact with the ball (assessment). In practicing a skill such as hitting a ball, there are some additional requirements. Unless one has a pitching machine, there is a need for someone to throw the ball and to point out the performer's mistakes. Also, this practice would not be initiated in the middle of a crucial game with the bases loaded and two outs in the last inning; that is, a safe environment must be available for effective practice.

All of these components of learning a new skill—presenting information, practicing with others in a safe environment, and assessment—are indispensable in the learning of social skills. Practice of social skills has been shown to be of the greatest importance in promoting assertive interactions. Several studies have been undertaken to determine whether mere knowledge of assertive behavior would lead a person to put that knowledge into action. The results of the studies indicate that although people had changed their attitudes about assertive behavior (they now approved of the idea of making requests, refusals, and expressions), only a small percentage of the subjects were actually acting any differently than before instruction had taken place. These subjects were compared with a group who not only had been exposed to the new information on social behavior, but also had had several opportunities to rehearse this behavior in front of other "students" with supportive, as well as critical, feedback. Those in the "practice group" not only had attitudinal changes, but had incorporated the new behaviors into their real-life social interactions.

Behavioral rehearsal works for several reasons. One is that practice affords a person the chance to think through what he wants to say; then when the time comes to make the statement in the real situation, he is likely to feel more confident than when responding on the spur of the moment. There is also a chance in behavioral rehearsal to prepare for several alternative responses from the person to whom the message will be addressed. Also, such preparation reduces anxiety about the situation, and so helps to develop a sense of confidence. Another reason for the effectiveness of practice is that if a person knows a skill very well when calm, he will be able to perform that skill successfully even when nervous.

Requests, Refusals and Positive and Negative Expressions

Many of us who as children experienced the trauma of having to play a piece at a piano recital can recall the terrifying feeling that the mind had gone totally blank and was unable to remember a note of the music. Somehow, though, the fingers did the job and the song was played (of course, not always perfectly). It was the endless hours of practice that paid off in overcoming the anxiety. Through rehearsing, the behaviors had become almost automatic, independent of thinking. In performing social skills the situation is similar. It can be quite anxiety-producing to try a new piece of behavior in real life for the first time. However, if the practice has been well executed, the words will somehow come out even if the mind seems slightly blank.

Unfortunately, children are taught many subjects without being given a chance to apply their knowledge actively. Language instruction is a case in point. Many students who have had two or even three years of instruction in a foreign language cannot express themselves at all when meeting someone who speaks that language. Why is this so? The rather simple explanation is that the learning included only passive memorization of vocabulary lists and verb conjugation charts. Having had no actual chance to practice using the language, the student finds when traveling abroad that his years of study enable him at best to read a menu or train schedule.

In the case of learning social skills, the person who leads the practice sessions is called the trainer. The job of training children varies somewhat, depending on whether it is done by a parent or teacher. However, in either case, the trainer: (a) helps the child to formulate his goals clearly; (b) structures the role-play to maximize learning; and (c) gives feedback to the child following practice.

Goal Clarity

Before one can practice (behaviorally rehearse) a new social skill, it is first necessary that the goal of the practice be clearly stated. Typically, people begin discussions of problems by stating them in rather vague and general terms. The trainer helps to focus in on the problem until it is specific enough to be practiced. For example, one child stated that he did not think he was very popular. To this his parent responded: "What kinds of things happen to a person who is popular?"

Child: Oh, kids ask you to do things with them or they come over to your house after school and play—things like that.
Parent: Is there a particular child who you would like to invite to your house?
Child: Sure, there's Kenny, he's a real neat guy.
Parent: Do you think you could ask him?
Child: But I never get a chance to talk to him. He's in a different class and he's always with other kids.

Thus, the parent was able to pinpoint a behavior which would help the child achieve his broader goal of wanting to be more popular. This was accomplished by asking questions which would help to give a clear definition of what the child meant by "popularity." Once the definition was clear, the parent was able to direct her child to taking the first step toward being more popular, namely, offering a classmate an invitation to play after school. It may occur that if the child succeeds in becoming a friend of Kenny's he will then feel more popular. On the other hand, he may feel he needs to meet still other children or that he needs to change in some other way before he can become "popular." In either case, positive steps toward his goal have begun by focusing on a specific problem.

Once the goal has been clarified, it may be necessary to do some problem solving before proceeding to behavioral rehearsal. In the previous case, the parent had suggested that her child ask the schoolmate over to the house. The child responded to this by raising the problem that he wished to make this invitation privately and that he had little opportunity to do so. To help the child overcome this obstacle, the parent tried to elicit some possible solutions from the child.

Parent: That seems to be a problem then, not having a chance to speak to Kenny alone. What do you think you could do about that?

Child: Maybe I could wait for him after school.

Parent: Any other ideas?

Child: Maybe the best thing to do would be to call him up. I don't have his number though. (The problem has now moved from how to talk to Kenny alone to getting his phone number.)

Parent: How do you think you might get it?

Child: I could try the phone book; I know what street he lives on.

Parent: Could you also ask at the attendance office, if that doesn't work?

Child: Yeah, I think so.

Helping a child develop the skills to think and work through problems is one of the most important things parents and teachers can do. True, it is easier, in terms of time and energy, just to offer solutions without allowing the child an opportunity to suggest and attempt reasonable alternatives to the problem at hand (a reasonable alternative is one with a high probability of success). Encouraging problem solving on the part of children is more work, but it pays off in the long run, because once the skills are learned, children become much more independent in dealing with their own problems. People who counsel adults comment that all too often their clients do not have the skills to attack problems in a systematic way. Such people were rarely given opportunities to solve problems when they were children, so the more complex issues of adulthood often seem overwhelming. Of course, problem solving should not become so complex that the child might want to throw up his hands in frustration and decide that the goal just isn't worth the effort. Therefore the parent, as in the case above, should offer suggestions when they appear to be needed. The point is to allow the child input into his own problem situation.

Role-Play

After the goal has been specified and obstacles to the goal have been dealt with, it is appropriate to rehearse the interaction if the child appears anxious or uncertain about his ability to say what he wants.

The parent or teacher helping the child with this problem begins by asking the child what it is he thinks he might say to start the interaction. It is important that the child be coached to use the approximate words he would use in the real situation and not to narrate what he would do. Instead of saying, "I would tell my friend how I felt about it," the child should imagine that he is talking directly to his friend and therefore say something like, "I didn't like it when you told me in front of the other kids that you thought I was stupid."

Now the child is ready to try this first statement with another person playing the responder. (Chapter III explains more about what to do if there are no other children available.)

Requests, Refusals and Positive and Negative Expressions

After the first line is practiced, the role-play stops immediately for feedback.

Once the child is happy with his performance on the first line, he may decide that he doesn't need to go further into the dialogue. In some cases, there may be several lines which need to be rehearsed.

Examples of each of these situations follow:

Situation 1/One-Line Practice
This is the most common of the rehearsal types. Most assertion problems require getting started.

Dave is fearful of asking questions in class, thinking he might appear stupid.

Trainer: What would you like to say to the teacher when you don't understand something—say a math problem?
Dave: I would ask him to go over the solution again.
Trainer: What words would you say to him?
Dave: Mr. Adams, would you go over that problem again?
Trainer: Okay. Now, would you choose someone in the group to play Mr. Adams and try saying that same thing to the person you choose? (Dave chooses his friend Gene.)
Dave: Mr. Adams, would you go over that problem you just explained once more?
Trainer: That was really good. How did you think you did?
Dave: Pretty good.
Trainer: Do you want to do it again, or do you think you can do it in class now?
Dave: I think I'd better try it once more.

Dave and Gene then rehearse the line again and keep doing so until Dave feels comfortable with the line. Each time, the trainer praises Dave for either doing it well or for trying and also attempts to get Dave to say something positive about his performance.

Situation 2/Two or More Lines to Be Rehearsed
Let us say that when Dave is asked whether he wants to try the first line again he says so, but that he is concerned that the teacher will not respond very positively to his question. In this case the trainer asks Dave to tell Gene (who is playing the teacher) to respond the way he anticipates Mr. Adams will.

Trainer: What do you think Mr. Adams would say?
Dave: He always says things like, "You must not have been listening" or "I shouldn't have to repeat the explanation."
Trainer: What do you think you could say to him then to get your point across?
Dave: I don't know.
Trainer: You could restate your request by telling him, "I was listening, but I still didn't get the explanation; would you repeat it please?" Will you try that?

The trainer encourages Dave to use the broken-record technique of returning to the central issue. In addition, Dave is instructed to deny assertively that he was not listening. (Only, of course, if it is an incorrect accusation.) In addition, this example demonstrates what the trainer should do if the child does not know what to say. The approach, in this case, is to make a suggestion that the child might consider, such as, "You might try . . ." or "Maybe you could. . . ." These are better than statements which direct or tell the child what he "should" do.

Feedback
After each line of practice, the child should be reinforced with praise. Even if some mistakes have been made, the most im-

mediate feedback to the child should be a positive statement about his behavior. "That's a good start," "You're getting the hang of it now," are ways to compliment the child yet keep the door open to further practice. One can single out a strong point of the performance and then suggest that the child work on a different aspect of the message. For example, a child who was very stiff and rigid physically but who spoke clearly and articulately could be told: "I really liked the way you said that. Do you want to try it again and take a deep breath first, so you can relax a bit?"

The primary reason for beginning the feedback to the child with praise about his performance is the power of positive reinforcement. Before we discuss the nature of reinforcement, we first need to reexamine the purpose of the behavioral rehearsal. If one is concerned only that the child learn assertive social skills and never use them again outside of the practice situations, there would be little need for reinforcement. Obviously, though, our goal does not end with the dress rehearsal. What we want is that the child transfer his learning into the real world, that he become adept at actual performance.

The way to accomplish this is to reward the desired behaviors. Praise is one of the most powerful of the rewards or reinforcers. Praise does not have to be overly dramatic to be effective. Children, as well as adults, know when praise is not realistic. Therefore, early attempts at a new skill should be praised somewhat, but room should be left for more intense and comprehensive praise as the person develops higher levels of competency. In this way, praise maintains its potency. In addition, reinforcement is most effective when it occurs immediately after a behavior occurs. The longer the delay between the completion of a response and the reinforcement, the less likely is the behavior to recur.

Of course, in the real world, efforts do not always meet

with a positive response. In fact, in the unpredictable area of social interaction, a well-rehearsed response may not only fail to elicit the desired response, it may even be punished. A 10-year-old who had been coached to give compliments when appropriate, told a classmate that he liked the speech he had given in class. To this the student replied, "What do you know?" To this the first child replied that he certainly knew enough to know a good speech. He maintained his dignity in the situation, but his initial compliment certainly had not received the predicted response.

Similarly, one is likely to encounter failure in making requests of others. What children need to learn in using their social skills is that the "effort" is worthy of praise, not just the outcome of the effort; that it is admirable to stand up for oneself and attempt to get what one wants without denying others their rights; that even in the face of a flat refusal to what one wanted, the important thing is that the person tried hard. Athletic coaches often (though not unanimously) advocate the "it's not if you win or lose, but how you play the game" attitude. Too many coaches of young children adopt a very different attitude which, because it is anxiety-producing, defeats its own purpose. This is the concept that "winning is all that is important." In social relations, we advocate that "doing" is all-important. Children need to be taught that the outcome is something which we don't have a great degree of control over, any more than we could decide to hit a home run on the next pitch.

All we can do is enable children to practice social skills so that they can make the best presentation possible. Once a child has developed competencies in social skills and has been rewarded for using them, it is natural that he will employ them in his day-to-day interactions. Because he asks more often for what he wants, even though he may fail frequently, his total number of successes will be higher than those of a child who does not make his desires known. The situation is analogous to that of a baseball player who has a .300 batting average, that is, one who gets a hit only three out of every ten times he is at bat. This is considered quite a good average. Of course, the more a person is up, the more chances he has to improve his average. The hardest thing in playing a sport like baseball is to keep a positive attitude on the occasions that do not result in success. How does one accomplish this?

Obviously, no one is going to say, "Nice strikeout" or "Nice double play" to someone who has ruined the team's chance to score a run. What both children and adults need to do in these cases is *reinforce themselves in some way for the attempt they have made*. The effects of such self-reinforcement cannot be overemphasized. We are able to accept failure much more easily if we praise ourselves for the effort and if we remind ourselves that we have succeeded previously and that if we keep trying we will succeed again.

Throughout life, praise, money, and other reinforcers often do not occur at the moment an action is completed. What does one do to keep himself going until he finishes that term paper, or gets that job, or receives his diploma? He must become a good friend to himself and remind himself of how well he is doing as he completes portions of a task. In doing so, he becomes less reliant on the responses of others, because he is an effective reinforcer of his own appropriate behaviors.

Self-reinforcement is not something new. We have long been aware that children learn to praise themselves for doing what their parents or teachers have told them to do. One 4-year-old, for instance, was overheard saying to herself, "Now be a good girl and clean up the room." In training children to use assertive behavior, essentially the same process is involved. After a child has finished rehearsing a request, refusal, or expression, the child is praised by the trainer in a general way and then asked, "What did you like about what you did?" If the child cannot think of anything about which he is pleased, the trainer can remind him of some part of the performance which was good, or can mention that just doing the practice takes nerve, that it isn't easy. What is crucial is getting the child to *state verbally some positive remark about his own practice.* For example, after the trainer states that the child's eye contact was good, it is appropriate to ask the child if he is aware that his eye contact was effective.

We have already mentioned that our society does not encourage giving positive statements to others. This is even more true of saying positive things about ourselves. By showing a child that it is all right, even good, to self-reinforce, we increase the likelihood that he will feel comfortable in praising others also.

The value of self-reinforcement has been explored in several studies which very clearly show that those who learn to praise themselves for their actions weather the storm of failure and continue to ask for what they want, whereas those who receive only external reinforcement (praise from others) do not make as many attempts in the real world and are more affected by failure than the self-praisers.

3.

PARENTS AS TEACHERS OF ASSERTIVE SOCIAL SKILLS

If parents model assertion, their children are more likely to behave assertively. However, there is more that can and should be done. For instance, parents who want to encourage their children to play an instrument would do well to play and enjoy music themselves. But in addition, to ensure the development of musical abilities, they should allow the child time and space to practice his instrument and should praise the child's musical skills.

In the same vein, a child needs to feel that at home he has the time, space, and encouragement of his parents to use assertive skills.

Parents as Teachers of Assertive Social Skills

REQUESTS

Almost from birth, it is natural for children to make numerous requests of their parents. Even before the infant can speak, he attempts to "ask" for what he wants through crying or by using body language such as reaching toward his parent when wishing to be held. Acquiring language allows the child to greatly expand the quality and quantity of his request making. Words give him the ability to specify his desires in a way that was not previously possible. Learning the word for an object enables a child to ask for that thing effectively when he wants it. No longer does he have to limit his desires to those objects which are present in his environment and to which he can point. Through the magic of language, he can ask his parents to bring him anything in the world at large.

While expansion of his power may be very exciting to the child, his parents may become dismayed at the never-ending number of requests being thrust upon them. It is no wonder that many parents take steps to limit the request making and question asking of their children.

The problem for parents, then, is to somehow maintain their sanity and yet not discourage the tendency of children to ask for and receive what they want. Obviously, parents cannot accede to their child's every wish, nor would it be good reality training to do so. However, one can deny a child his desires without implying that asking for things is in itself bad. "No, you may not stay the night at Bruce's house, you have too much homework this week" is an appropriate refusal which simply deals with the issue at hand. On the contrary, replies like "Why are you always asking to do things away from home; can't you find something to do around here?" punishes the child for making a request.

Teachers and counselors frequently remark on the great

number of children who rarely seem to ask for anything. In some cases, this may be the result of their parents' providing them with everything without their having to ask at all. In the majority of cases, it is the result of parents who have too often punished the child for his natural tendency to seek gratification through request making. With such children, it is necessary to reestablish the request pattern by reinforcing question asking as much as possible.

Even if a parent cannot grant a particular request, some positive statement should be made in the reply. For instance, if a child wishes to buy a new toy that the parent does not wish to purchase, a response which denies the request yet reinforces question asking is: "Richard, that is too much money for us to spend right now, but I like it when you ask for what you want, and sometimes you will get things by asking me for them." Only through praise of question asking (plus granting their requests whenever possible) can a child "relearn" request making.

Request making is for the child a symbol of his being able to exert some control and influence over his environment. If he learns that asking for things is more effort than it is worth and, in fact, often gets him in trouble, then he will give in and develop an attitude of, "You take what you get in life." Certainly children should not feel that "to ask is to receive," but they should not lose the belief that they have at least the right to try to do the best they can for themselves without denying others their rights.

REFUSALS

As with requests, a child does not initially have to learn to refuse. We have a natural tendency to avoid what is not pleasurable to us. As part of the socialization process, however, we learn that we have to do things which we would rather not do, that on many occasions, we are not allowed to say "no," that somehow others bigger and more powerful than us think they know better and boss us around no matter how vehemently we protest. Parents, of course, must make demands on their children. The key problem for parents with regard to refusals is to not develop a child who is so obedient that he unlearns the ability to refuse in situations where he does have that right, as with his friends or classmates.

The extent of unthinking obedience was dramatically illustrated in an experiment by Stanley Millgram. He told the subjects it was their job to teach a person to remember a list of words, and that in order to expedite the learning process, they were to deliver an electric shock to their student every time a mistake was made. In reality, of course, the shock machine was not hooked up and the student merely acted as if he were being shocked. (He was behind a screen, so the subject would only hear the screams when the shocks were supposedly delivered.) What was so troubling was that 70 to 80 percent of the subjects would continue the shocking regardless of the student's protests and, in a number of cases, even when the student pretended to have fainted due to the intensity of the shocks.

There are several things parents can do to ensure that children retain the ability to refuse. One is to differentiate clearly for the child what things he has to do and what he can refuse if he wishes. Many parents think they are *telling* their child to do something when in reality they have *requested* that it be done. When the child says "no" to the request, the parent then gets mad and punishes the child. An example of this is the question, "Would you like to go to your grandmother's with us on the weekend?" If the child says "no" when the parent did not really mean to give a choice, the child may then be surprised to hear: "Well, you have to go, anyway. You know how happy your visit makes Grandma." This response is, in effect, a punishment, because it takes no account of the child's reply. When any behavior is punished, the likelihood of its occurring again is decreased. Thus, punishing a child for refusing a parent's request discourages further refusing.

It may sound ideal to raise a child who never refuses to do what is asked of him. The problem is that a child needs to be able to say "no" to other children when they wish him to do things that he doesn't want to do or that might get him in trouble. If his only experience in making a refusal is punishment, he will not be able to stand up for himself. Thus, the parent who expects his child to go to his grandmother's on the weekend (and will not take "no" for an answer) should simply tell the child that this is something he will have to do.

In addition the parent who wants his child to learn to say "no" should not only avoid giving choices when they're not really meant, but should always be on the lookout for situations where choice making is appropriate. Mealtime is one place where children might be allowed some practice at refusals. Some appropriate questions at this time are "Do you want more food?" or "Do you want to set the table, or clear it after dinner?" The latter question offers the child the choice of refusing one thing for another.

Offering children choices is another way of helping them to practice making refusals, because in order to choose one alternative, they must say "no" to the others. Situations where parents can offer choices include deciding what to play, choosing the type of instrument to take up, selecting an elective course to take in school, making a decision to invite a friend to dinner, and so on. Parents must be careful, in offering alternatives, that either choice is acceptable to them. For example, stating, "If you do that one more time, you will have to go to your room" offers the child the choice of stopping the undesired behavior or suffering the penalty of having to go to his room. When the child makes the wrong choice from the parents' perspective, they are doubly mad at him. This is not fair, because they are the ones who offered the child the choice in the first place. Choice giving, therefore, is appropriate only when either behavior is a positive one. When one is trying to get a child to obey, threats are never a clear message to the child and therefore not always effective. It is much better to help children learn to make choices between two positive behaviors than between obeying or being punished.

What happens when a child attempts to refuse to do something his parents have decided he should do? Again, there is less likelihood of this occurring if parents do not make requests of their children when there is no choice in the matter. In such cases, a clear statement or demand is the appropriate communication. Children who are given real opportunities to make choices are less apt to challenge clear directives from their parents.

RECEIVING POSITIVE MESSAGES

One would think that children receive compliments quite frequently at home. The fact is that, in many households, a child's positive behaviors are often overlooked or taken for granted, whereas his shortcomings are broadcast regularly. Praise and physical affection should be a regular part of parent-child interactions. Of course, children should not be praised out of proportion to a particular behavior. One parent was so continuous and lavish in praise for every attempt the child made on the basketball court that, if he once didn't receive that praise, he felt he had done something wrong.

Children are very accepting of praise until they learn that one "should not get a swelled head" or be "conceited." After this has been drummed into a child's head for eight or ten years, a child may even learn to feel bad or guilty about his achievements. He may pass them off as resulting from luck or as not being all that impressive. He becomes self-conscious about excelling because achievement always entails an attempt not to look overly proud of himself. Children who have lost the ability to accept praise often discount the compliments which others give them, through statements such as, "I could have done better." In these cases, the parent should insist that the child receive the compliment by getting the child to reinforce himself verbally about the behavior. Thus, if a child who is complimented for his ball playing replies that he should have done better, he could be asked, "Maybe, but don't you agree that you did do well in catching that fly ball?" Sooner or later the child will get the message that it is okay to say good things about himself.

It is a premise of those involved in social skills and self-confidence training that, in order to feel good about oneself, one must be able to say positive things about one's own behavior. Perhaps some wish to call this arrogance, but we are confident that this type of arrogance is invaluable in helping a person to value himself and thereby be able to value others.

SENDING POSITIVE MESSAGES

Most children freely give affection to their parents. In the early years, the affection tends to be of a physical nature and, as the child matures, verbal messages of appreciation dominate.

There is no correct amount of positive interaction. What

is crucial is that the child's attempts at sending positive feelings to family members be appreciated. Often children choose inopportune times to express these feelings. Mother is busy and an enthusiastic child runs to give her a big hug. The tendency is to shoo the child away with the admonition, "Can't you see I'm busy?" or "Not now, honey." While parents in such cases needn't drop what they're doing to accept their child's expression, they can show that the thought was appreciated through such statements as "I can't work when you hug me, but I really like it when you show me that you like me."

Obviously a childs environment will determine to what extent he will engage in sending positive messages. If a child grows up with criticism being the main mode of interaction he will model that same approach with his friends and family members. A more fortunate child is one whose parents freely praise one another, and who seem to seek out the positive behaviors of other people as opposed to focusing on the negative. These more pleasurable acts are also easily imitated by the child. Everyone knows people who seem to see the good in everything and those who focus on the ugly and depressing. It is often the case that these tendencies are traceable to parental behaviors. There is a Hindu legend which nicely sums up the subject of seeking out and praising the good:

> In India there was a holy man who had a powerful orientation to the positive in life. One individual, who wanted to test the holy man, arranged to have the decaying carcass of a dog placed on a path that the sage frequently traversed. As people walked by the dog one could hear complaints and negative statements of all kinds. When the holy man approached however he stated, "Look at the beauty and strength of those teeth which survive even after death."

If one is encouraged to notice the good in others, and in life, then positive messages will naturally flow forth. One occasion which sets the stage for a positive message is after having been shown an act of kindness. The assertive response in such situations is to go one step beyond saying "Thank you," and instead personalize the message. For instance if a child had received some help from a friend on his homework, he might say, "I really appreciated your taking the time to come over and help me." The key phrase in sending a positive message is "I really liked it when you . . . or I really appreciated it when you. . . ." This personalization of a thank you has a great deal of power and encourages the continuation of friendly acts.

RECEIVING NEGATIVE MESSAGES

This is one of the most difficult interactions between individuals. The goal for parents is to model the appropriate response to criticism or disagreement. Thus, one seeks to accept the blame for "wrongdoings" without counterattacking and also without undue self-deprecation. The child can learn a crucially important lesson from such modeling. He learns that it is all right to err from time to time and that such mistakes do not inevitably lead to fighting or guilt; that neither of those alternatives are constructive. What is constructive is the admission of fault and the resolve to do better in the future.

The ability to accept disagreement on matters of personal taste is also likened to receiving negative messages. Surely the reader can recollect occasions where such disagreements between couples led to intense bickering. Sometimes the issues are so trivial it is hard to believe anyone could get worked up over such a matter. When an individual expresses a difference

Parents as Teachers of Assertive Social Skills

in opinion over a movie for instance, there is no reason to interpret the difference in taste as a personal attack. People are simply different and have different likes and dislikes. Instead of viewing differences in taste as a threat, one can actually learn to appreciate how others perceive things by being willing to discuss or at least hear out the other person. A child can learn to be intolerant of any ideas differing from his own, or he can learn to be open-minded and flexible in his thinking. To a great extent his parents behavior is a key ingredient in determining which of these patterns he will develop.

SENDING NEGATIVE MESSAGES

Parents who are concerned that their children develop self-confidence will attempt to convey the idea that it is important to let other people know when they have done something which is bothersome. The child needs to learn that not only do other people have the right to criticize and disagree with him, but that he too has the right to criticize what he perceives to be hurtful behavior.

One way parents can encourage such behavior is to listen to their children's stories about their daily encounters with friends. If there is an occasion when the child might well have taken a stand but did not, the parent can suggest that the child make an assertive statement the next time something similar occurs. For example, if a friend had borrowed a child's book without asking and the child simply ignored it but decided that he wouldn't talk to that friend for awhile, the parent could suggest that it might help to tell the child, "I didn't like it when you borrowed my book without asking." The parent should stress the importance of the direct action instead of the other approach where resentments smolder and more damage is done to the friendship.

Parents of course can model this direct style also in their relationships with one another and with the children. Instead of pouting or being verbally (or even physically) abusive to one another they can make a direct statement of their dislike of the behavior. No one can argue with you when you say you did not like what they did. However, when one attacks the individual through name calling or put-downs this only paves the way for an escalated and counterproductive argument. The idea of simply telling people that you did not like something they did is so remarkably simple, and yet it is an infrequently used communication. When friends, couples and even employers use such an approach however, the quality of those relationships improves dramatically.

MODELING

At school, Glenn never asked questions of the teacher when he didn't understand a key point. Nor would he stand up for himself when other children violated his rights, such as cutting ahead of him in line. During a parent-teacher conference with Glenn's parents, it became apparent that Glenn had "learned" to model passive behavior in social situations. Glenn's father stated that he, too, had been afraid to interact with his teachers and that, to this day, he had the same difficulty in communicating with his employer.

This case demonstrates the power which a parent's example exerts on children. Before children can even speak, they are learning about how they are expected to behave. This "learning" does not take place formally through lecture and quiz. It takes place through observation of the people who are most important in the child's life. The way in which a child's parents speak, the way they walk, the amount of time they spend watching television, and the way in which they relate to one another all set the stage for the child's future behavior.

These early observations have tremendous significance because the child, having limited experience, cannot envision alternate modes of behavior than those of his parents. He sees how they behave and assumes that this is the way things are done.

Thus, parents are models whom a child observes to gain an understanding of what is appropriate behavior. When it comes to social skills, the child very carefully notes his parents' behavior. He sees how they relate to each other and thus learns how males and females should interact. One frequently sees males who are passive in their relationship with their wives, having learned this behavior from their fathers. Just as frequently one sees females who have learned to complain continually about their husbands in the same way their mothers complained about their fathers. Generally, children will model the same-sexed parent. However, in families with several children, a child may model the parent of the opposite sex if an older child has already strongly identified with the same-sexed parent.

The way in which parents handle conflict is also modeled for the child. Children whose parents fight aggressively, that is, through physical or verbal attack or by breaking household items, will tend to emulate that behavior when confronted with conflict in their own relationships. On occasion, a child from such a violent background will react in the opposite direction and become extremely passive in his social interactions. He develops a "peace at any price" attitude. He avoids conflict if at all possible. He gives in at the slightest sign of displeasure on the other person's part so as not to precipitate the battles with which he was all too familiar as a child.

The child also sees how his parents respond to authority figures and thereby learns how he should respond to powerful people outside the home. There are many opportunities for children to see their parents interacting with authority figures. Unfortunately, many parents unknowingly are modeling high degrees of aggressive behavior which may affect the child's dealing with authority figures.

> Lloyd was with a group of his friends one day as a policeman drove by on his motorcycle. The group of children, at Lloyd's instigation, began shouting insults at the policeman. Needless to say, this action got them in a great deal of trouble. In a discussion of the affair with Lloyd, it came out that his father was in the habit of muttering some obscenity every time a policeman went by. Lloyd was simply mimicking behavior which he had seen many times.

Research has shown that we tend to model some people more than others. People who are rewarded for their behaviors are likely to be imitated. People who are seen as powerful or of high status will tend to be imitated. Those people whom we perceive to like us in some way will tend to be copied. Thus parents are prime targets for children to imitate, since they are perceived to be powerful people whose behavior is often rewarded by others in the family.

While some parents respond aggressively when dealing with authority figures, others model passivity. Thus a parent who comes home and discusses the fact that he cannot tell the

Parents as Teachers of Assertive Social Skills

boss "no" about having to work overtime, or that he is afraid to ask for a day off for an important reason, is modeling passive behavior to the family.

Sometimes deferring to authority is the appropriate behavior for a parent. For instance, it is a rule in one family that the children cannot come to the dinner table without shoes when the grandmother is visiting. The children are told that this is done to avoid upsetting their guest, not because the parents are afraid.

The child observes how his parents relate to their friends and thereby learns how to deal with his peers. This area of parental behavior has a tremendous effect on the child. The parents' social skills can be of great benefit to a child who is attempting to meet and make friends and to have positive, meaningful relationships.

Children who have observed their parents welcoming a newcomer to the neighborhood learn that it is appropriate to be friendly and to initiate contact with an individual. Many children have the good fortune of having parents who model appropriate ways to develop and maintain relationships, such as having dinner parties, planning outings with family friends, attending the social functions of church or other groups. Such parental behavior provides the child with alternatives for meeting people which he can use in adolescence and throughout life. In addition, such occasions allow the child the opportunity to see his parents making requests, refusals, and positive and negative expressions. People who have effective social skills have typically been raised by parents who had these abilities and provided their children with ample opportunities to observe and participate in a variety of social situations.

Parents are the most important influence on their children's general attitude toward others. Whenever children accompany their parents, they are learning about how one is supposed to treat fellow humans. Such lessons occur daily. When we take children to restaurants, we teach them how to treat service personnel. Are we grateful to be seated anywhere or do we request to be moved to less noisy or crowded areas? When a dish is not cooked as requested, do we leave the food untouched and then "pay back the waiter" by not leaving a tip?

A child may view his parents acting unnecessarily hostile toward gas station attendants, waitresses, postal clerks, and so on. The lesson to them is that it is all right to order such people around without considering their feelings. Children will either emulate this behavior themselves (to their parents' embarrassment) or become totally passive in an attempt to avoid becoming like their parents. Similarly, the way in which one drives his car can be a means of instilling passive, assertive, or aggressive behavior in children.

> A seventeen-year-old boy was referred to the youth court for repeated incidents of driving recklessly and racing on public streets with members of his club. The father in this case had had his driving license suspended on two different occasions for excessive speeding.

EVALUATING YOUR CHILD'S SOCIAL SKILLS

How can parents determine to what extent their children are assertive? There are several avenues by which parents can gather information about their children's social skills.

Talking to and Listening to Children

Many parents are anxious to know about their children's lives. However, the questioning procedures they use to gather in-

Parents as Teachers of Assertive Social Skills

formation are often intimidating. Instead of employing "open" questions, which lead to more elaborate responses, children are often asked questions which require only a quick "yes" or "no." Instead of asking a child, "Did you like school today?" (closed question), a better approach is to ask the what, when, where, and how questions. "What kinds of things did you do in school today?" "How did it go on that math test?" Children, at first, may not really believe that you are interested in what went on, so don't be discouraged by a child who responds to the question, "What did you do in school today?" with an "Aw, nothing." Such answers need to be followed by other open questions which demonstrate to the child that the parent was sincerely interested in the day's activities. By listening to and talking to children, parents will very often become apprised of problems the child may be having in the areas of requesting, refusing, or expressing positive and negative feelings.

> One 14-year-old, Marianne, complained to her parent that her girlfriend borrowed clothes and returned them all dirty and wrinkled. The two girls had an arrangement whereby they expanded their wardrobes by loaning one another certain articles. Marianne always returned her friend's clothes in a good state and wanted her clothes treated the same way. The parent, in this case, helped the child to make the request, "I want to continue switching our clothes, but I will only do it if you return my things in the same condition as when you borrow them. Will you do that?"

To well-practiced adults, the solution may seem obvious. However, many children have not learned how to confront their friends with such statements. Instead, they simply stop calling or talking to the person, or they may complain to other people about the behavior but they take no action toward resolving the problem.

Sometimes when something is wrong the child may send a message to the parent through nonverbal behavior.

One child, who was generally good-natured, came home from school and appeared to be upset and sad. The parent asked her: "Is something wrong? You seem to be kind of down?" The child (as many children will do) at first responded that nothing was in fact wrong. The parent, not wanting to pressure the child, but at the same time desiring to let the child know that an ear was available, stated, "It's hard when things don't go right and you certainly don't have to talk about it, but I might be able to help with it."

This kind of statement lets the child know that his parent is receptive to hearing about his problems, but that there is no obligation to share information if the child does not wish to do so. More often than not, children are willing to ask for help if the person they are dealing with does not solve the problem totally for them, but simply helps with suggestions and with "role-playing" of the appropriate responses.

Observing Children

Sometimes parents can discover a problem in their child's social skills through observation. What does the child do after school and on weekends? Is he afraid to phone his friends to ask them to go places with him? Does he know what to do when salesmen come to the door? When he's playing with his friends, does he speak up and express his ideas or does he tend to avoid relationships with other children?

Darren's mother had observed repeatedly that, when called by a particular child, Darren would offer excuse after excuse for not playing with him. Following up on

Parents as Teachers of Assertive Social Skills

this, the mother discovered that Darren did not want to play with the child, but was afraid of two things: first, that he might hurt the child's feelings and, second, that other children might not want to play with him if they thought he was mean. The mother then suggested that Darren make the statement, "I'd rather not have you call to ask me to play. I'd rather call you when I want to play, is that okay?"

In this way, Darren was given permission or the "right" to his own feelings about who he wanted to play with. He was, in effect, told that he can and should control his own environment without being hostile or negative in his behavior toward others.

Another parent noticed that her child Barbara was easily bossed around by the older children in the neighborhood. If they told her to run an errand for them, she did so. If they told her to do chores for them, she did this also. After becoming aware of this, Barbara was coached to "refuse" such statements and was helped to see that she did not have to gain the friendship of the children in this way.

Many parents experience the age-old problem of children choosing friends who are seemingly not "good" influences on them. In many cases, what has happened is that these friends have not been "chosen" at all. Rather, the child has been accepted or chosen by a certain group and, though not totally enjoying their companionship, he does not have the social skills or confidence to initiate other relationships. Unfortunately, many well-intentioned parents try to get their children to seek other friends by downgrading the qualities of current friends. "What do you like about them? They're a bunch of troublemakers," are two of the complaints parents have been known to make. The results of such attempts at moving the child on to other relationships is often the reverse. The child comes to the defense of the friends who are being attacked and, although he may not convince his parents, soon the child has talked himself into believing that his friends are some of the world's finest inhabitants.

Therefore, rather than take on the child's friends, parents are advised to talk to the child about the kinds of things he likes to do and the qualities he likes in friends. Often, these qualities will be totally lacking in the child's current circle of acquaintances. At this point it is appropriate to ask the child if he knows about anyone in class or school who seems to have similar interests. If there is such a child, the parent can then coach the child in techniques for initiating contact with that person. In this way, the parent is helping the child to *expand* his social world, not to replace his old friends with new ones. This approach has been much more successful in helping children to make new, more productive friendships.

School Reports
Grades can often be a clue to a child's ability to be assertive.

> Michael, age 14, would continually disrupt the class during presentations by the teacher. It was found that he did this only when he became frustrated at not being able to follow the teacher's lesson. He therefore always started off by paying attention, but when he got confused, *instead of raising his hand and asking for clarification,* he would talk to and bother other children.

When Michael learned how to ask for help in understanding the teacher, he became less frustrated with school and was not a classroom problem any longer.

Parents as Teachers of Assertive Social Skills

Cynthia's problems with school (she was failing in several classes) were related to her inability to say "no" to her friends. They were in the habit of cutting class, often going to one girl's house where the parents were absent, and taking drugs. Cynthia had done very well in school up to this, her last year in high school. She really wanted to finish with a good record but didn't want to be ostracized from her group of friends.

When Cynthia was taught how to refuse assertively, she realized that she could still have her friends without having to go along with all of the behaviors in which they were involved. Thus she was able to finish her schooling without further problems.

Often more helpful than grades are the comments which teachers make about children. If the only thing the teacher has to say is that the child is a very good child who stays out of trouble, then the parent needs to ask further questions about the child's classroom behavior. Does he ask questions in class when appropriate? Does he answer the teacher's questions or does he let other children be the ones who respond? Does the child play with other children at lunch and recess times? Too often the "good" child in class is one who does his work and then disappears into the woodwork. This child gets through school with academic skills and abilities, but his forays into the social world are minimal.

Aggressive behavior can often be related to poor social skills. Teachers will often make note of this, citing that the child tends to "blow up easily" at other children or cannot tolerate any teasing. The child who gets into fights is usually one who does not know other ways to give negative expressions or does not know how else to respond to the negative behaviors of others. It is not enough merely to tell a child not to fight.

Children also need to know what they "are to do" in situations where a negative expression of some sort is appropriate.

> Allen, age 8, complained that every day at recess children continually ran through his four-square game. Not being the most patient of children, he took to picking fights when this occurred. Allen had no conception of other alternatives he could use that would be more effective in keeping children away from his game, as well as keeping him out of trouble. His teacher taught him to respond with statements such as, "Don't chase through my game when I'm playing" or "Please play somewhere else or I'll get the teacher." Allen thus learned that he could stand up for his rights without physically assaulting other children.

WHY CHILDREN BEHAVE NON-ASSERTIVELY

We have been talking about the various ways of determining the existence of deficits in children's social skills. How do these deficits develop in the first place? There are three main sources for the development of assertive problems.

Educational Deficits

When children have not been privy to examples of assertive behavior by their parents or other significant models, there is little likelihood that they will develop assertive skills themselves. Thus, if parents are hesitant to speak up and voice their opinion in various social settings, to request that they be treated in a dignified manner, to refuse the things they have the

Parents as Teachers of Assertive Social Skills

right to refuse, then their children also will tend to be hesitant to make their presence felt in given situations.

Cognitive Interference

Sometimes children adopt beliefs or values which cause them to dismiss assertive responses as an alternative behavior in a given situation.

> Diana, who was 12, was unable to ask her teacher to slow down and repeat explanations of problems. In a discussion of this, it was determined that Diana had learned from her parents that, "There are many children in the class and you should not bother the teacher, because if all the children asked questions then nothing would ever get taught."

In dealing with this situation it was necessary to convince Diana that school is for learning and that sometimes in order to learn it is necessary to ask questions of teachers. This conflicted with what she had "learned," and so before Diana could change her behavior she had to believe differently about the rights of children in the classroom.

> Rudy moved into a new town and after a few months felt quite lonely and wanted to meet some new children by joining a local youth group. His parents believed that it was proper etiquette to wait until one was invited before approaching "strangers." Their own behavior was to wait until the new neighbors came to introduce themselves rather than initiating contact on their own.

Rudy needed to examine his right to meet new people without wasting time by waiting for others to initiate contact.

Only when he dealt with his parents' unassertive belief could he then begin to practice the appropriate behaviors necessary to make new friends.

PRIOR PUNISHMENT OF ASSERTIVE BEHAVIOR

People often become anxious when called upon to perform a behavior which is unfamiliar to them. This is true in practicing assertive skills, whether the deficit results from lack of education or from the beliefs which the child has about the particular behavior. Even more intense anxiety may be caused when the situations call for behavior which the child has engaged in previously but for which he has been punished or ignored.

> Keith was a rather aggressive first grader who rarely expressed himself in class, refusing to participate at sharing time or to answer when called upon by the teacher. At home Keith had learned that "children should be seen but not heard." He therefore did not think he had the right to express himself; his experience had been that speaking up can get one in a lot of trouble and that it was better to keep one's mouth shut rather than risk punishment or being ignored. In working with Keith, the critical issue was to convince him that people really did care about what he had to say. As he began to change his viewpoint about people being interested in him and as he began to express himself verbally, his aggressive behavior markedly decreased.

It is not uncommon that the extremely shy child is one who is terribly anxious about expressing himself. Furthermore, in these extreme cases, the anxiety is nearly always attributable to a history of punishment of assertion at home. Because of the high degree of anxiety, one finds that a great amount of reassurance and practice are necessary in changing the behavior of such children.

HELPING CHILDREN PRACTICE ASSERTIVE BEHAVIOR

Regardless of the source of the assertive deficit, children need to practice (role-play) assertion in order to overcome their problem. In order to help them do this, parents should follow the coaching procedure described below:

Goal Clarity

Ask the four W questions: what, when, where, who. The purpose of this step is to get the child to describe the exact situation where the problem has, does, or will occur. Try to determine exactly what the problem is. Is it always a problem, or just at certain times in certain places with certain people?

Help the child to specify his goal. Break down larger goals such as "popularity" or "good grades" into more specific behaviors, such as meeting two new classmates or getting at least all B's on his report card. Ask the child what it is he really wants to occur. Questions such as, "What would it take for you to feel that you are popular?" or "What do you mean by good grades?" will help lead the child to a specific definition of his goals.

Role-Play

The next step for the trainer is to ask the child to state what it is he thinks he should say to another person in order to achieve his goal. If the child needs help in formulating his words, the trainer should *ask* if the child would like some help with the statement. The approach throughout the role-play is to ask the child for his ideas and not to offer suggestions without first checking with the child.

After the child has agreed on what he should say, the next step is to "act out" the situation. To do this, the parent pretends to be the person with whom the child will actually be interacting later. It is important that the parent try to make the practice environment as much like the real situation as possible. If, for example, the problem is one of calling on the phone to ask for a date, then the parent should turn his back to the child and pretend to be speaking on the telephone. If the parent is supposed to be a teacher, then it is necessary to find out from the child what kinds of facial expressions this teacher tends to have and how the teacher typically responds in such situations. The key issue is to make the practice situation as much like the real thing as possible.

Feedback

Practice is meaningless unless it is followed by evaluation. The trainer's role in this regard is twofold. The first is to reinforce. The parent asks the child, "What did you like about how you did that?" If the child says something positive about his performance, the parent responds in agreement. If the child says that he does not think it was very good, the parent emphasizes that it was a good start. It is important that the child be praised by the parent and by himself for some part of the rehearsal. As we have mentioned, self-reinforcement is an important aid in encouraging assertive behavior; external reinforcement (reward from the outside world) is intermittent at best, whereas one can always pat oneself on the back for attempting a difficult behavior.

After the reinforcement part of the feedback, the second

function of the trainer is to encourage improved performance. The parent can first ask the child if he thought there was something he could do to make the communication better. If the child suggests something, the parent can ask, "Do you want to try it again, doing it that way?" Parents themselves can suggest ways of improving a role-play, but again, this suggestion should always be formulated as a question. "Do you think your voice was loud enough?" "Do you think it would work better if your hands were out of your pockets?" "How do you think it would work if you looked in my eyes when you said that?" When there are several suggestions to make, only one or two should be mentioned after each role-play. Otherwise, the child will be overwhelmed by the number of items about which he needs to be aware.

The importance of the role-play cannot be overstated. People can be totally convinced that they have a right to make a request or to express refusal, but without practice the belief remains only that, and action is never taken. Often children and adults will object to the role-play as being silly because it is not the real thing. Years of research have shown, however, that if a person can learn to "rehearse" a situation comfortably he can reduce his anxiety considerably, so that by the time he performs the behavior in the real world, self-confidence has dramatically increased and the communication is performed with much less discomfort than would otherwise be possible. It is helpful if parents emphasize this fact in preparing children to role-play assertive problems.

The following example illustrates how a parent helped a child deal with an assertive problem through role-playing:

Dion, age 10, was never able to play after school or join an activities group such as Cub Scouts, because it was his responsibility to take care of his younger sister in the afternoon while his mother worked. Finally, when Dion was in the fifth grade, his mother quit work and he wanted to join the Scouts. He mentioned this to a group of his peers, and one stated that it would not be of any use for him to join because he was so far behind in all the things he needed to know in order to be a Scout. Dion told his father about this and stated that he did not know what to do.

Goal Clarity

Father: What do you want to tell your friends about joining Scouts?

Dion: I want to find out who I could talk to to see if I can join. But what if they say that it's useless to try?

Role-Play

Father: Do you think you could say, "That may be true, but I'd like to ask in order to find out for sure. Who should I talk to?"

(Notice the suggestion is put to the child as a *question*. Throughout the role-play, the trainer always questions and suggests, rather than telling the child what to do.)

Dion: Yeah, that sounds good.

Father: Good. Do you think it would help if you practiced it with me to see how it goes? I could pretend to be your friend and you could ask me.

Dion: Okay, but you don't act mean, like Tommy.

Father: I'll try to act the way he would. First, just tell me what you think you want to say without acting it out.

Dion: I'm going to say, "I want to find out who I need to talk to about joining Scouts," and if they say that it won't matter,

I'll say, "That may be true, but I'd like to find out for sure."

Father: Are you ready to try that, with me being Tommy?

Dion: I want to know how to join Scouts and see if it's not too late. Who should I ask, Tommy?

Father (as Tommy): "Well, it won't make any difference, because lots of kids want to join and you have to know stuff before they let you in."

Dion: "Yeah, but I want to ask someone anyway."

Feedback

Father: Hey, that was real good. (Giving positive reinforcement for the rehearsal.)

What did you like about the way you did that?

(Before proceeding to suggestions for improvement, it is important to elicit a statement of self-reinforcement for the try.)

Dion: I guess it sounded as if I wasn't scared to find out, that I just really wanted a chance to know.

Father: Right. (Reinforcing the child's self-reinforcing statement.)

Was there anything you think you'd like to improve?

Dion: I don't think so.

Father: Do you think you might try it again and repeat your question, "Who do I talk to?" when you tell Tommy that you want to ask someone anyway, even if it is too late?

Dion: Didn't I do that?

Father: You did in the first sentence, but after Tommy challenges you, it might help to ask the question again.

Dion: Okay. Let's do it again.

(Notice that the suggestion for improvement is phrased as a question: "Do you think it might work better if . . ." or "Would you like to try it again and this time. . . .")

Parents as Teachers of Assertive Social Skills

The trainer in the role-play monitors not only the child's *words* but also the nonverbal components of a message. Thus, if a child lowers his eyes or voice, this action can be called to his attention through a question such as, "Did you notice that you looked away from me when you were telling me the important part of the message?" Only one or two criticisms or suggestions should be made per trial of the role-play.

How many times should one go over a particular situation? The number of rehearsals depends completely on the wishes of the child. In the case of Dion, the father might ask, "How do you feel now about really going out and asking Tommy about Scouts?" If Dion says that he still feels really scared, then it is appropriate to suggest practicing another time. As his feeling of confidence increases, the child will let you know that he doesn't need to rehearse the statement any longer.

Parents and teachers sometimes find it difficult to appreciate the intense anxiety a child may feel over a seemingly unimportant or trite problem. The important thing, therefore, is to ask the child directly how he is feeling about the prospect of the confrontation. It is a very gratifying experience to see children build up confidence to deal with a problem through the use of role-play.

The steps in the role-play which we have described and illustrated are crucial for making the practice successful. Practice, in itself, will not necessarily lead to improved performance. A child learning to hit a baseball may never develop any consistency unless he gets accurate feedback and reinforcement for his attempts. The same is true in helping children to practice assertive social skills. Each of the components that we outlined in the example of Dion is designed to give the child the greatest likelihood of success. Certainly, parents cannot control the lives of their children's friends, but with effective role-play they can at least provide their own children with the best training for successful social interaction.

Parents as Teachers of Assertive Social Skills

Occasionally children may ask their parents for suggestions as to what to do or say in a particular situation. In the case of Dion, the parent was asked the question, "But what if they (my friends) say that it's useless to try (and join Scouts)?" The father then suggested a possible response.

Sometimes a parent may not know exactly what his child should say or do. In that case, it is helpful to suggest that the child watch a classmate or other acquaintance who does seem to know what to do or say in similar situations. After doing so, the child can then discuss the "model's" behavior and decide if he can utilize it himself.

Situations for which observational learning may be helpful include: initiating and maintaining new relationships; doing something instead of fighting when other children are aggressive, and knowing what to do when the teacher is angry at a child.

Sometimes the assertion issue may be between siblings. One child felt that his parents expected him to tolerate his younger brother's tagging along wherever he went. He became very irritable around the house and it took some discussing to uncover the fact that he resented having to be his brother's keeper. His parents were actually surprised to hear this because they did not expect or want him to take his brother with him when he did not wish to. What they did, therefore, was to help him to refuse his younger brother when he asked to come along, and they of course backed up his refusal when the younger brother complained.

Parents can also help children with certain types of assertion issues related to school behavior.

One 13-year-old girl had been talking in class during a lesson and the math teacher overreacted by slapping his ruler very hard on her desk, causing her a great deal of anxiety and embarrassment. From that time on, she was very nervous in his class and was afraid to raise her hand even when she knew the answer to a question. If she was called on, she froze. Her parents helped her overcome this fear by having her repeatedly role-play raising her hand in class until she was comfortable. After doing so, she regained her confidence in the subject, which had dwindled along with her grade.

THE ASSERTIVE FAMILY IN ACTION

In addition to modeling and encouraging assertive behavior, parents can actually set aside time for "family meetings" where requests, refusals, and expressions can be practiced. These meetings are to be called whenever there is a decision to be made which can involve all the members of the family. Deciding where to go for family vacations and weekend outings or planning part or all of the menu for the week are examples of situations where the family meeting can help children learn to express their opinions.

There are some important ground rules to ensure parental sanity in regard to a family meeting.

1. The parents should state at the outset that they want everyone to participate in making suggestions (requests) and expressing his opinion (positive and negative expressions). It should be clearly pointed out, however, that the final decision is to be made by the parent or parents.

2. It is helpful for the parent to take notes on the suggested ideas; at the end of the meeting, participants should be thanked for their contributions.

3. Following the meeting, the parents should attempt to

Parents as Teachers of Assertive Social Skills

incorporate at least one suggestion from each family member into the decisions made. For example, one family plans a monthly menu by gathering suggestions from each member on his favorite foods. The final menu includes at least one of the favorite foods of each person. Another family allows each member to plan the entire menu for an evening meal; those who are capable actually cook the meal for that evening.

Vacation planning is an area in which the entire family can be polled about the types of places they would like to visit. In one family, one child preferred the mountains, another the ocean, and still a third preferred the big city. The task for the family was to figure out how to visit all of these places, given the length of time of the vacation and the amount of money which could be spent. Everyone was then involved in a part of the project. One child worked out the driving route and figured out how much time it would take to go from place to place. Another child computed the cost of driving, motels, meals, and so on. It certainly would have been easier for the parents to do all of the decision making and problem solving. A great deal of time was taken up answering their children's questions. In this way, however, their children were learning the skills of question asking and problem solving. They were also being rewarded for making requests, since some portion of their suggestions were incorporated into the trip. Thus, a family outing became a family project. Such activities are invaluable in preparing one for the decision making and information gathering so necessary for survival in the adult world.

The "Chores" Game
Family meetings can also be employed to deal with some of the painful family issues such as chores. In the following "game," family members are able to participate in deciding what chores they are to do and are also encouraged to make requests and

positive and negative expressions. Parents begin the "game" by writing each of the chores on a 2 × 4 index card and spreading the cards *face up* on a table. Each child, in turn, then chooses the chore he wishes to do by picking up the appropriate card. (This game is played once a month and the order of the children is rotated.) After all of the cards are selected, the children are allowed to try to convince one another to trade chores. One child may say, "I don't want to have to clean the swimming pool, but I'll walk the dog every day." If the child who has to walk the dog agrees, then they can trade cards. In this way, children are learning to express negatives (I don't want to clean the pool), and to make requests (will you trade me?). Younger children can also participate by asking for someone to help them with the difficult chores.

THE ASSERTIVE ADOLESCENT

"What? Encourage my teenager to be assertive? You've got to be kidding! If he gets any more assertive, he'll be running the place!" It is not uncommon to hear such comments from parents of adolescents. Of course, by now the reader should realize that parents who might make such a statement are confusing aggression with assertion. The fact is that parents' best prescription for survival during the teen years is to support and encourage the assertive behavior of their child, because, as we pointed out earlier, the only alternatives to assertive behavior are aggression or passivity.

It is easy to see why parents would want to avoid having an aggressive child in the home. But what about passivity? Isn't it ideal to have a child who doesn't often challenge, who doesn't seem to want to go out and socialize that much, who never

Parents as Teachers of Assertive Social Skills

disagrees, who makes few requests? The answer to that question depends on the parents' goal. If the goal is to raise a child who throughout his life will be dependent on the family for problem solving, decision making, and the other tasks of adulthood, then passivity training is indeed ideal and would make coping with the teen years much easier. The long-run cost of such a child-rearing approach would be devastating, however.

To appreciate fully the necessity for encouraging assertive behavior during adolescence, it is important to recognize that the high school years are the final rehearsal period for independence. The goal for parents, then, is twofold: one, to get through these years with a degree of sanity, and two, to prepare the child for the unpredictable and difficult road ahead. Once again, the person who does well on that "road" both personally and professionally is one who has had experience in making requests, refusals, and expressions of a positive or negative nature.

Requests

It is the child's task during adolescence to begin to move away from his parents, both physically and emotionally. To help him do this, the parents can support and encourage the child's request making. This does not mean that, for the sake of independence, all requests should be granted. On the contrary, part of independence training is to help the child develop a sense of what is reasonable and unreasonable to expect from others. Therefore, the parents' refusals are often as important as the granting of requests.

In addition, request making enables the child to develop another important skill: learning to negotiate a compromise assertively. There are numerous situations in which parents may find it possible to meet their child halfway. For instance, one family had a tradition that the whole family would always be present for Christmas dinner. One year, one of the teenagers was invited to Christmas dinner at a girlfriend's house. The parents were faced with the dilemma of either refusing their child and incurring his disfavor or giving in and feeling bad. Many parents will sacrifice their own desires and let the child have his way, only to play "martyr" later, making the child feel guilty for gaining the edge. One way to avoid all of this is to think "compromise." Parents can offer solutions which might be satisfactory to both parties. No one totally wins or loses, and each gets some satisfaction. In this case, the parents might suggest that their son eat dinner with his girlfriend and then bring her back for dessert. There is never any one correct solution to such problems. What is important is that the accepted suggestion meets the needs of the parties involved in the problem.

In families where there is no compromising and most requests are refused, the children are likely to engage secretly in forbidden activities. On the other hand, children who see their parents as being reasonable and open to discussing requests are much more likely to adhere to their parents' values and decisions.

Expressions of Disagreement or Dislike

Part of the path toward independence entails an investigation of the opinions, philosophies, and beliefs which people outside the family hold. Parents need not panic when their teenager espouses ideas foreign to what is valued in the family. Most of the time, the adolescent simply wishes to show that he is learning about the world and that he has new and valuable information to share with his parents. It does not mean that he is going to adopt all of these attitudes in the long run. His behavior should not be seen as "rebellious" or "anti-authority." It is rather the expression of his own quest for adulthood; that quest involves gathering information from all sides and then making as objective a decision as possible. Parents who see this process as healthy rather than defiant are more likely to maintain a positive relationship with their teenager. Far too often, parents needlessly challenge and are outraged at every statement of opinion that their child makes which runs counter to their own. This reaction usually results in an argument in which the child vigorously defends his position while the parents steadfastly warn him that such ideas are dangerous, ill-advised, and immature. The adolescent soon learns that it is better to keep his opinions to himself, that his parents do not like the idea of his growing up and learning more about the world.

Some teenagers react to their parents' intolerance by simply passively accepting all of their parents' ideas and never bothering to investigate the world beyond their parents' doorstep. Frequently, adolescents who have not had opportunities to think for themselves or to express themselves develop acute anxiety at the prospect of growing up and leaving the family. Many such teenagers maintain that they will wait until they marry before they move away from home because they know they could never take care of themselves. Even sharing an apartment with a friend is too threatening an idea for such a child.

One of the key issues confronting the parents of adolescents is dealing with their children's increased interest in the other sex. Parents who wish to help children at this stage should have the following goal:

To communicate to the child that his or her contact with the other sex is an approved and expected behavior.

All too often, when children make a request to attend a social function, parents initially respond in a negative way. There is an underlying sense that the parents wish the child would remain home and participate solely in family activities. The child who senses this attitude may stop requesting and become homebound or even roombound. It is painful for a child to upset his parents every time he wishes to do something; it is simply easier to be passive and do little socializing. This is true even in cases where the parents finally give in and allow the child to go out. If it is a continual battle for the child to take part in social activities, he may give up because his parents are sending a message that there is something bad about such behavior.

It is certainly appropriate for parents to check with the child regarding the nature and whereabouts of the party and what adults will be there. It is important also for parents to communicate, not just that they are concerned about appropriate behavior, but that they are delighted the child is developing friends of both sexes. This message is rarely communicated to children. The message more commonly expressed (either verbally or nonverbally) is, "Well, okay, go if you must, but stay out of any trouble." Because of this, adolescents often develop a similar attitude, namely: "My parents don't think it's good that I go to parties. They seem to be bothered about all the possible negative things that might happen and don't mention anything at all about the good that comes from such experiences."

Parents who are concerned about their child developing effective social skills will take an interest in the child's social experiences. They will not probe and attempt to dig out personal information, but they will convey that they are interested in their child's sharing of his experiences in relating to new friends of either sex. Parents who wish to give advice need first of all to be well informed about what their child is doing. This can only come about when children sense that their behavior is of interest to their parents.

Parents as Teachers of Assertive Social Skills

If a child seems to be particularly enthusiastic about a romantic relationship, parents can display their interest and support by inviting the friend to a family function. The purpose of this is not to scrutinize the child's choice but simply to convey the idea that the family looks forward to meeting friends they have heard about.

Another important attitude parents can help their children develop is that interactions with the other sex need not occur solely in a party context. We have the term "the opposite sex" largely because the worlds of the two sexes are often so segregated that their only shared interests are romantic or sexual. It is imperative that parents help children to see the "other sex" as people, not just "objects." This can be accomplished through family get-togethers, where the parents can help to bring out the personal qualities and interests of both children so that a fuller picture of their personalities emerges. The parents can then talk to their own child about the positive qualities that they have observed (it is of course not helpful to emphasize negative attributes).

This whole process is of great benefit to the adolescent. Frequently, counselors will talk to teenagers who ask. "But what do you talk about to a girl (or boy)?" It takes experience and parental support for adolescents to learn that boys and girls have much more in common than they might have thought and that the term "opposite sex" might imply.

4.

ASSERTIVE SOCIAL SKILLS TRAINING IN THE CLASSROOM

In this chapter many activities for self-confidence development are suggested for use in the classroom. With modification, most of these activities can also be adapted for use at home. It is of great benefit to offer students assertive social skills training in school in that the learning of a new skill is greatly enhanced when many members of one's peer group are involved in similar training.

The authors have directed several training projects with elementary and high school students and have seen firsthand the powerful effect of group training in assertive skills. The children who participated in these projects showed dramatic improvement, not only in the social skills but also in their grades, in measures of self-esteem, in teacher ratings of popularity, and even in classroom behavior.

The assertive child is a more popular child. So not only does social skills training increase the likelihood of one getting what one wants, thereby allowing one to spend time in more enjoyable ways, but as an added dividend, the child who acts assertively is found to be more appealing.

Why is this so? One might tend to think that because such children ask for what they want, attempt to refuse what they don't wish, and express honest positive and negative sentiments, they would not be highly sought after. The fact is that children who are straightforward and yet also aware of the effect of their behavior on others are viewed as honest and dependable, children whose words can be trusted. They don't merely say or do things because it sounds like the right or popular thing; they are being themselves and thereby allowing their own uniqueness to express itself.

In this chapter, three alternative strategies for teaching social skills in the classroom are presented. They may be used independently or in conjunction with one another.

I. SELF-CONFIDENCE GAME

Of the three strategies, the Self-Confidence Game requires the least amount of classroom time. The game is based on the old "College Bowl" television show. Following are the steps for setting up and playing the game:

1. Have students make up questions based on any classroom material to which all students have been exposed. The students should be instructed to put their questions on the front of a half-sheet of notebook paper and to write the answers on the

back. In addition, the student writes his name on the top of the question side of the paper. Generally, the class should be allowed five minutes twice a week to make up new questions so that recent material and new questions are in use. This assignment should be voluntary and no student should ever be forced to make up questions or to perform in the game against his will.

2. A game involves two teams of three playing against one another. Two games may be run simultaneously in different parts of the room. In addition to the six team members in a game, the following students are involved in running each game:

    a. Moderator
    b. Hand-Raising Judge
    c. Blackboard Scorer
    d. Timer
    e. Scorekeeper

3. The two teams sit in front of the class and the Moderator reads aloud a question from the question box. The first person on either team who raises his hand gets the first opportunity to answer the question. The Hand-Raising Judge decides whose hand was first, and his decision is final. The Moderator announces whether the answer is right or wrong. If it is right, the Blackboard Scorer scores a point for that team. If the question is answered incorrectly, the first person on the opposing team to raise his hand gets an opportunity to answer the question. The Timer calls time if twenty seconds elapses between the reading of a question and a student answering it. The Timer does not interrupt an answer in progress, though. If time is called, the next question is read. The Scorekeeper's job is to note on the scoresheet (see sample scoresheet) each time a student attempts to answer a question.

Assertive Social Skills Training in the Classroom

SAMPLE SCORESHEET

	Attempts
Team A	
Curt	9
John	6
Roger	6
Team B	
Karla	8
Bruce	4
Victoria	5

4. At the end of the game, the scorers turn in their scoresheets to the teacher. The teacher transfers the scores from the Attemps column of each sheet to the Phase One Master List, which contains the names of every student participating (see sample).

PHASE ONE MASTER LIST OF STUDENTS

	Attempts Game 1	*Attempts Game 2*	*Attempts Game 3*	*Total*
Anderson, Ruth	7	5	9	21
Brody, William	3	1	0	4
Carlson, Ned	6	6	8	20
Christianson, Mary	10	12	15	37
Fredricks, Marlene	4	1	5	10
Haugen, Keith	6	7	4	17
Ziff, Janet	5	9	6	20

The self-confidence game is played in three phases. The first is used as a means of determining which students have low levels of self-confidence and which have high degrees of confidence. For the second phase the teacher constructs teams of low-confidence children and has them play one another; the same is done with the high-confidence children. The third phase entails randomly mixing up the teams, as in the first phase.

Phase One To choose teams for this phase, the teacher randomly assigns the students to groups of three. Names can be picked from a hat. If the last team picked has fewer than three members, they can be assigned as alternates to other teams. The teams compete against one another until each student has played three times. The game can be played twice a week with two games run simultaneously in different parts of the room, i.e. eight teams can play per week. Thus, it would take a class of 36 one and a half weeks in order for each student to play once (twelve total teams with eight teams playing each week).

After each student has played three times, the teacher determines which are the low- and which are the high-confidence students. To do this, the teacher refers to the Phase One Master List, which is tallied after each game, and totals the three scores next to each student's name (see sample). The teacher identifies the eighteen lowest scores and *randomly* assigns these students to teams of three. The remainder of the class is then *randomly* assigned to new teams, with any leftovers used as alternates.

Phase Two The teams have now been reorganized so that low-confidence students are playing low-confidence students and high-confidence students are playing high-confidence students.

The game is played exactly as described for the first phase. (Scorekeeping in Phase II is not necessary.) This phase also lasts until every student has played three times.

Phase Three Once again the teams are reorganized, all students being randomly assigned to groups of three. This can be accomplished through the hat selection process. The score-keeping procedure described in Phase One is resumed, the teacher once again transferring each student's score from the Attempts column of the scoresheets to a master list of all students (see Phase Three Master List).

After the third game, the teacher totals each student's score from the three games and compares the increase or decrease from the scores in Phase One. Generally, low-confidence children (those with low attempts in Phase One) will increase their responses in Phase Three. High-confidence-children's scores will drop slightly because of the increased participation of the low-confidence children. As an example, Keith's total after the third game in Phase One was 17; he scored 6 in the first game, 7 in the second, and 4 in the third. In Phase Three, the sample master list shows he no longer scored at the bottom of his group: his scores were now 10 in the first game, 12 in the second, and 11 in the third, for a total of 33.

The authors found that over 80 per cent of the students who were low self-confidence children initially (minimal hand raising in Phase One), significantly raised their hand-raising scores in Phase Three. Interestingly, as their self-confidence grew they made fewer mistakes in answering the questions. The increase in participation was apparent in other classroom activities as well. They asked questions more frequently in class and by the end of the semester their grades had improved.

The success of the self-confidence game in helping children become more assertive due to the fact that in the second phase of the game, low-confidence students are forced to raise their hands because there are no high-confidence children in their groups. It becomes apparent to the players that they don't have the usual dominant children to depend on and they in fact must depend on themselves.

PHASE THREE MASTER LIST OF STUDENTS

	Attempts Game1	Attempts Game 2	Attempts Game 3	Total
Anderson, Ruth	8	9	4	21
Brody, William	6	7	5	18
Carlson, Ned	7	4	5	15
Christianson, Mary	9	8	10	27
Fredricks, Marlene	4	6	8	18
Haugen, Keith	10	12	11	33
Ziff, Janet	7	5	8	20

II. LESSON PLANS

The second strategy for teaching special skills in the classroom consists of classroom presentations and role-plays. This section is comprised of outlines for a series of lessons. The first two lessons are aimed at increasing the students' awareness of positive and negative communications, and in the subsequent lessons the entire curriculum of assertive social skills is presented.

Each classroom presentation can be adequately completed in twenty to thirty minutes. Thus, by employing one session per week, the entire curriculum can be covered in one semester.

Each lesson play is divided into three parts:

1. To the Teacher
   In this section the main purpose of the lesson is discussed.
2. Social Skills Vocabulary

3. Classroom Presentation
   a. *Teacher presents* two or three new ideas dealing with assertive social skills behavior.
   b. *Classroom activity*
      Each session concludes with an activity which helps children practice concepts which have been discussed.

LESSON 1 INTRODUCTION TO COMMUNICATION

To the Teacher

The first lesson has as its objectives: (1) to demonstrate the fact that communication can be of a positive or negative nature, (2) to show that essentially the same thing can be said in either a positive or negative way.

Social Skills Vocabulary

Teacher writes the following words on the board and states, "These are the words which we will discuss today. They are not new words to you but we will be talking about them in a different way." This procedure is followed for all the lessons.

Never	Can't	Not	Should	Don't
Positive			Negative	

Classroom Presentation

Teacher: Sometimes, when people talk to us the words they use make us feel good. These kinds of statements are positive. Sometimes people say things to us and we feel bad. These are negative statements.

I'm going to read some statements to you. Tell me which are positive, good-feeling statements and which are negative or bad-feeling statements.

You never help me with my homework. (negative)
I would really like you to help me with my homework. (positive)

You don't play fair. (negative)
I would like it if you played by the rules. (positive)

You *should* be on time when you visit. (negative)
Will you please come over at the time we agree on from now on? (positive)

I won't go with you. (negative)
I would rather do something else today. (positive)

I can't understand this! (negative)
Can you help me with this problem? (positive)

Teacher: As you heard from listening to these sentences, there are certain words that are often negative-sounding. These are the words on the board: *never, can't, not, should, don't.*

What's wrong with negative words? They often lead to the other person being negative also. Pretty soon both people feel bad and neither gets what he wants.

This time I'm going to read the same statements and I want you to give me a negative response to the negative statements.

You never help me with my homework. (Examples children may give include argumentative statements like, "I do so!" or counterattacking statements such as "You never ask me!"

You don't play fair.

You *should* be on time when you visit.

I won't go with you. (Again children may argue, "You will" or "I won't be your friend if you don't.")

I can't understand this!

Classroom Activity
Divide children into groups of five. Each of the groups has a stack of ten index cards in the middle of the table. On each card is printed one of the words that is on the blackboard (except for the words positive and negative); since there are five words on the blackboard and ten index cards, each word appears on two cards. Each child in turn picks a card and makes up a negative sentence containing the word; he then tries to state in a more positive way the thought expressed in the sentence.

LESSON 2   POSITIVE AND NEGATIVE COMMUNICATION

To the Teacher
This lesson extends the idea that the same statement can be communicated in a positive or negative manner.

Social Skills Vocabulary

Positive   Neutral   Negative

Classroom Presentation

Teacher: Last time, we saw that some statements can sound either positive or negative, depending on the words you use.

Today, we're going to see that the *way* you say things is just as important as the *words* you use in sending a positive or negative message.

I am going to say the same sentence three times, only I'm going to make it sound either positive, neutral, or negative. You tell me which way you think it sounds.

It's nice outside today. (say it positively)
It's nice outside today. (say it neutrally)
It's nice outside today. (say it negatively)

So you see, the same sentence can sound completely different, depending on how you say it.

Classroom Activity

Divide the students into groups of five, each group having a stack of ten index cards on the table. The children in turn select a card and read the sentence on it. The card will instruct the child to read it as a positive, neutral, or negative message. The other students try to guess which emotion is being acted out. The ten statements which are to be printed on the cards are:

What time is it? (negative)
What time is it? (neutral)

How's school? (negative)
How's school? (neutral)

What's on TV tonight? (positive)
What's on TV tonight? (negative)

Will you help me with this problem? (positive)
Will you help me with this problem? (negative)

I'm John's friend. (positive)
I'm John's friend. (negative)

LESSON 3
ALTERNATIVE RESPONSES

To the Teacher

The third lesson introduces children to the three alternative behaviors one can choose from in any given situation: passive, aggressive, or assertive behaviors. The impact and consequences of each type of behavior are discussed.

Social Skills Vocabulary

Passive   Aggressive   Assertive

Classroom Presentation

Teacher: What can you do if another student is bothering you by kicking your chair? Teacher writes children's responses on board, organizing the responses under the words *passive, aggressive* or *assertive*.

Possible Responses

Passive
Ignore it.
Tell child, "I don't like that."
Move to a new seat.

Aggressive
Call child a name.
Kick his chair.

Assertive
Ask child to stop, saying "I don't like it when you kick my chair, will you stop?"

Teacher: In this class you will be learning to make assertive statements. They are useful because they more often get you what you want. They also make you feel better because you stand up for yourself.

When you're passive, you don't do much of anything (point to examples on board). Because you don't do anything, usually you won't get what you want.

When you are aggressive (point to examples on board), what happens? (Ask class.) That's right, you either get in trouble for fighting or calling someone a name, or the person who was bothering you gets very mad at you, which is not what you wanted—what you wanted was that he stop kicking the chair.

When you're assertive (point to example), you clearly state what you want and then if you don't get it you state it a little harder by saying, "Hey Johnny, stop it," or even, "Johnny, stop it or I'll get the teacher." In this way, you've shown that you meant what you said.

Classroom Activity
Divide students into groups of five. There is a stack of fifteen index cards on the table in front of each group. Each student in turn selects a card and reads the phrase on the front. He then decides whether the statement refers to passive, aggressive, or assertive behavior. If his answer is correct (the correct answer is printed on the back), he keeps the card; if not, the card is put in the middle of the deck.
Sample situations are:

Assertive Social Skills Training in the Classroom

Passive
Doing nothing when someone cuts ahead of you in line.

Letting someone copy from your paper when you don't want him to.

Looking upset when someone has done something to bother you, but not saying anything.

Agreeing to go somewhere with a friend when you did not really want to go.

Aggressive
Saying, "If you don't play with me I won't be your friend."

Saying, "You are being a baby."

A child stealing money from a student's desk.

A child hitting another child who cut ahead in line.

Telling other children not to play with a child who did something to upset you.

Assertive:
Saying, "I really would like to play with you, can I?"

Saying, "It really bothers me when you do that, will you stop?"

Saying, "I really don't want to do that today, thanks for asking."

Saying, "I don't like cheating, please don't copy from my paper."

Saying, "Will you help me understand this problem?"

Teacher: As you can see, assertive responses sound a lot like the positive or good-feeling statements that we learned about earlier. That is why they help us get what we want. Assertive statements tell others how we feel in a way that is not aggressive yet makes us feel that we have stood up for ourselves.

LESSON 4
GIVING COMPLIMENTS

To the Teacher
The first social skills area that children should be taught is the one which is the easiest, least threatening, and most pleasant to experience. In this way, the student's first experience with social skills will be a pleasant one. Learning to give compliments is just such an experience. Teachers who have been trained to begin their social skills programs with compliment giving have found it is a good way to get the program off to a positive start and have students look forward to subsequent sessions.

Social Skills Vocabulary
Positive Expressions

Classroom Presentation

Teacher: Can any of you tell of a time when someone did something really nice for you? Do you remember what you said to that person?

It certainly is nice to show appreciation when people do nice things for you by saying, "Thanks, that was really nice of you to do that for me."

What we're going to learn today is that you don't always have to wait for someone to do something for you in order to say something appreciative to them.

Assertive Social Skills Training in the Classroom

Let's say that the teacher has been talking about a story in class and one of the students asks a very good question about the story. What could the teacher say about his question?

That's right, she could say something like, "Hey, that's a really good question."

Let's take another example. What if during art time you notice that a classmate has drawn a very nice picture. What could you say about that?

That's right, you could mention to the person, "That's a super picture you drew."

When we say those kinds of things to people, we are making a positive expression of appreciation. They make us and other people feel good.

Classroom Activity

Teacher: Sometimes we forget to give people positive expressions because we're too busy. Sometimes, unfortunately, all we notice are the negative things that people do.

To help us get used to saying positive things, we are going to get into groups of five students each, and we will go around the group and each person will say something positive to the person on his left. Then each person will say something positive to the person on his right.

Also today, there is a homework assignment which will be fun. Each of you will give three positive expressions to a parent, friend, or teacher by next week. Write down what you said and we can share them in class next time.

LESSON 5   RECEIVING POSITIVE EXPRESSIONS

To the Teacher
Children learn at a very early age that one has to be very careful about receiving compliments. Often they have been taught that if they look as if they enjoy the compliment too much then it might be interpreted that they are too full of self-pride. The result is that people often feel uncomfortable about being complimented, and instead of enjoying the compliment and sharing their appreciation with the person who sent the message, they block or discount the positive statement.

Social Skills Vocabulary

Receiving Positive Expressions

Classroom Presentation

Teacher: Last time, you were asked to bring examples of positive expressions which you made to a friend, teacher, or relative. Who would like to tell about what he said?

Use several examples or as many as are offered. The teacher could share two or three personal examples such as: "I told a student, 'It's really nice to have you back in class after your being sick last week.' Another time, I told a friend, 'I'm certainly glad you called me—it was really great talking to you.' "

Teacher: This week, the words on the blackboard show that we're talking about receiving positive expressions.

Assertive Social Skills Training in the Classroom

Now why in the world would we have to learn about that? What could be easier than saying something like, "Thank you, that was nice of you to tell me," or "I'm glad you like my dress; I made it."

What do people say or do instead of just accepting a compliment or statement of appreciation?

That's right, sometimes they say things like, "Oh, it isn't really very good," or "I should have done better." Those kinds of statements are devaluations of the compliment.

If you devalue the compliments you get, pretty soon people stop giving them to you because no one likes to be regularly disagreed with.

Classroom Activity
Students are arranged in groups of five. Each student describes a recent time when he was given a compliment and responded to it with a devaluation or other nonassertive response. He then practices an assertive response in place of the original statement.

LESSON 6   REFUSALS

To the Teacher
Children need to learn that in their dealings with classmates and friends they have the right not to want to do things that others might want them to do, that they have the right to determine how to use their time and space. An integral part of structuring one's own life in this way is the response of *refusing* other people's requests. Note: Teachers should not imply that children should use these refusal techniques with their parents.

Social Skills Vocabulary
Refusals

Classroom Presentation

Teacher: We all do things that we'd rather not do. Parents and teachers have lots of rules we must follow. Sometimes we forget that there is a word "no" which we are allowed to use with friends and other kids.

When we are asked to do something and we say "no," that is called making a refusal.

When are some of the times it's okay to make refusals? What if someone wants to copy your answers on a test and you don't want to let him do that? What can you do?

Sure, you can refuse by saying, "No, I won't let you use my answers." If they don't stop you can even cover your answers so they can't be seen.

Here's another example. A friend wants to borrow a very expensive skateboard that you haven't even had a chance to try out yet. What can you say?

Right, you can say, "No, I don't want to lend it out."

Classroom Activity

Teacher: Now, here are some examples of times when it's okay to say "No." We will go around the room and, after I tell you one situation, you can try to think of how to make a refusal.

You're in a grocery store and a friend asks you to steal some gum for him. What do you do? What else could you do?

Assertive Social Skills Training in the Classroom

You're on your way home from school and a friend wants you to come by his/her house to see his/her new model bike and listen to records. You're supposed to go straight home. It's now 3:30 and you are supposed to be home in five minutes. It takes that long from where you are now. What do you do? What else could you do?

A friend asks for 10 cents to buy a package of corn nuts. He/she did the same last week and didn't repay you. You don't want to loan the money. What do you do? What else can you do?

A boy/girl asks to crowd in front of you in the cafeteria line. You don't want to let them crowd. What do you do? What else can you do?

Your brother/sister wants to watch television and you are already watching a program and would like to see the end of it. He/she starts to change the channel. What do you do? What else can you do?

You're baby-sitting your brother/sister; your parents have instructed you that you're not to have a friend over. A friend wants to come over and watch TV. What do you do? What else can you do?

You're at the grocery store getting some bread for your mother. They don't have the kind your mother wanted but the clerk gives you something like it. You don't want this kind of bread. What do you do? What else can you do?

A friend of yours is planning to play a trick on another classmate. He/she is going to (trip them, make fun of how they talk, walk, etc.) at recess. You don't want to be a part of this. What do you do? What else can you do?

The teacher accuses you of hitting a fellow student and you don't want to take the blame. What do you do? What else can you do?

You have a substitute teacher today. A friend of yours wants you to play around and sit in a seat that isn't yours. You don't want to. What do you do? What else can you do?

You're at recess. A number of friends want you to play hopscotch, but you don't want to. What do you do? What else can you do?

You've taken some returnable bottles back to the liquor store and the clerk says they don't take them. You have returned bottles there before and don't want to pull your wagon all the way home again. What do you do? What else can you do?

A friend of yours asks to borrow your brand-new skateboard that you got for Christmas. You don't want to lend it. What do you do? What else can you do?

You've gone to the library to get a book on prehistoric animals. There is a particular book that you know is good. The librarian wants to give you one you don't want. What do you do? What can you do?

Your parents want you to play in the band/sing in the choir, and you don't like doing this. What do you do? What else can you do?

The teacher wants you to stay after school and practice your spelling/addition/subtraction. You would rather not. What do you do? What else can you do?

A classmate of yours wants to look at your answers to a test. You don't want to give him/her the answers. What do you do? What else can you do?

You asked the teacher two questions about fractions, which you're having difficulty understanding. You have more questions to ask about them, but when the teacher calls on you he/she says why don't you try to figure it out. What do you do? What else can you do?

Assertive Social Skills Training in the Classroom

The teacher wants you to put your head on your desk. It hurts when you do. What do you do? What else can you do?

You're at recess and teams are being chosen for a game. You arrive when they are just finishing choosing teams, which are now even. One of the team captains says you can't play because you'd make the teams uneven. You want to play very badly. What do you do? What else can you do?

Have the children think of a time when they said "yes" when they would rather have said "no." In groups of five, have them one at a time (1) describe what they really said, and (2) practice making a refusal in that same situation.

LESSON 7   REFUSALS (continued)

To the teacher
The objective of this lesson is to help children discriminate between giving excuses and giving reasons for making a refusal.

Social Skills Vocabulary

Excuses   Reasons

Classroom Presentation

Teacher: Last time, we talked about how it's okay to say "no" to a request. Sometimes people add "excuses" to the end of the refusals. They do this so that the "no" doesn't sound so bad.

Unfortunately, these excuses just lead to further asking:

What happens when a classmate asks to borrow a quarter and you don't want to lend it to him?

You could say, "No, I don't want to lend money." No excuses. Or you could say, "I don't have change." That's an excuse that could get you in trouble if the classmate had change or went and got some.

Of course, if the real reason that you won't loan the money is that you don't have change, then it is not an excuse—it is a reason.

The difference between an excuse and a reason is that an excuse is an attempt to get out of a request; a reason is a real problem that, once solved, will make it okay to grant the request.

Classroom Activity
The students are arranged in groups of five. Each student in turn tells of a time when he used an excuse as a way out of making a refusal. Then the student practices making the refusal without the excuse (adding reasons only when really desired).

LESSON 8   REQUESTS

To the Teacher
The objective of this lesson is to help children differentiate between passive, aggressive, and assertive ways of attempting to get what one wants. Obviously, the assertive approach is the alternative that is to be encouraged as the most effective way of attaining one's desires without the negative side effects of aggression.

Social Skills Vocabulary

Passive	Aggressive (physical–verbal)	Assertive
	Shy Puppy Dog King Kong	

Assertive Social Skills Training in the Classroom

Classroom Presentation

Teacher: Let's say you are reading in the library, trying to get some work done. The person next to you is making all kinds of noise and you cannot concentrate on what you are doing. What could you do about this?

Teacher calls on students and records answers on board.

Teacher: What we are going to practice today is asking for what we want. This is called making a request. It is okay to ask for things. Sometimes you will be pleased to find that people will do what you ask. Other times, people will say "no."

The important thing is that you ask.

The shy puppy dog never asks for anything. He sits around hoping somebody will notice him and take pity on him. That is called being "passive." It hardly ever pays off because people just don't know how to read minds. (Teacher points out passive solutions offered by class)

There's another way to try to get what you want. It's called the King Kong approach.

Teacher points out the solutions offered by the class which fall into the "King Kong" category.

Basically, the King Kong approach means getting what one wants through force, either physically or verbally.

Sometimes this will work and the person will do what you want. *But what might be bad about this approach, class?*

That's right, you might get what you want, but you also might get into trouble or people might think you are not too nice a person.

There is a way to try to get what you want that works a lot of the time, though not always, which also does not tend to make people dislike you.

That is to simply ask, or make a request, that someone do something.

So, in the case of another student bothering you while in the library, what kind of request could you make?

That's right, you could simply say something like, "I can't concentrate with all the noise; will you please talk more quietly?"

Remember, a request . . .

(point to word on the board—the "quest" part)

always ends in a *question.*

Just saying, "I can't concentrate because of all the noise" is not a request.

Let's try some other examples.

What could you do if you're in a reading group in class that is too slow and you want to be in a faster one?

What can you do when you have gone to the store for your parents and you start to leave when you notice that you gave the clerk a five-dollar bill and he gave you change for a dollar?

You're playing basketball at lunch and the score is tied as the playground teacher calls you over to collect the playground equipment. What can you do?

Classroom Activity
Divide the students into groups of five. Ask each child to share an occasion when he made a request in the form of a clear

Assertive Social Skills Training in the Classroom

question. Have the child talk about what happened after making the request.

LESSON 9   REQUESTS *(continued)*

To the Teacher

The first objective of this lesson is to help children realize that requests may not always be successful, but that request making pays off more frequently than passive or aggressive behavior. In addition, this lesson discusses the importance of self-reinforcing statements when requests are not successful.

Social Skills Vocabulary

Self-Reinforcement

Information   Objects   Time

Classroom Presentation

Teacher: Last time, in our groups, we talked about the different times we had made requests. As you found out, sometimes requests get you what you want, and other times they do not. That's because we cannot control what other people do. We can give our best effort to try to get what we want.

What can you do when you make a request and, no matter how hard you ask, the person will not do what you want?

On the board is a phrase—*self-reinforcement*. This means that we reinforce or praise ourselves.

Unfortunately, we are used to waiting for other people to tell us good things instead of regularly giving ourselves compliments.

One very important time to use self-reinforcement is after we have made a request and the person of whom we have made the request turns us down.

How do you self-reinforce?

By saying something like, "At least I tried, and next time maybe it will work to ask."

It's important to keep reminding yourself that nobody bats 1,000 percent. In baseball, if you get a hit one out of every three times, you are considered to be an excellent player.

Teacher begins new topic:

On the board you see the words *information, objects,* and *time.* These are the three types of requests that we can make.

We can ask people to give us information about something, as when we ask for the time of day. We can ask people to supply us with objects of various sorts, as when we request that someone loan us a book. And we can ask that people spend their time in a particular way, as when we request that they come over to play.

Classroom Activity

Now we are going to go around the room and each of you will try to think of an example of each of these types of requests. The person who starts thinks of a situation like wanting to borrow a book. The next person then tries to make the request as if he were really in the situation.

To the Teacher

If students cannot think of a request that fits one of the categories, the teacher can suggest an example from the list:

You see a child on the playground who is running, falls, and scrapes his leg. What can you do? What else?

You see two classmates arguing about a spot in the lunch line. They look like they might start a fight. What can you do?

You are standing with a group of your classmates. One child removes the chair of another child. That child is about to sit down but the chair won't be there. What can you do?

You took a permission slip home to your parents so you can participate in a special program at school. Your parents have not signed it. What can you say to them?

You missed school yesterday because you were sick. There was a homework assignment due then and you want to turn it in now. What can you say to the teacher?

You came back to school after being sick and you have forgotten your absence slip. Your father works at night and you don't want the office to call him during the day because he'll get angry. What can you say to the teacher?

You're really interested in a subject you are studying in history and would like to learn more about it by doing extra-credit assignment. What can you do? What else can you do?

You're doing a group project and not all the group members are doing their part on it. You are carrying the load. What do you do about it? What else could you do?

You're in a reading group that is going too fast and you're getting behind. You want to be in a slower group. What can you say to the teacher?

You're having trouble in math and would like your parents to help you with your multiplication tables. What can you say to them?

You're having trouble with your math and would like your teacher to help you. You ask if he/she would stay after school to help but the teacher says he/she has to go to a meeting. What do you say?

You're ready for your teacher to check your workbook and he/she keeps helping another student. What do you do? What else could you do?

It's time for school, and you want to get into the administration building, but the door is locked. What do you do?

You wish to borrow a child's notes to study for a test. He is afraid you might lose them. What can you say to him?

You wish to use your parent's expensive tools for something you wish to build. How can you request this?

You want to wear a special sweater of an older brother or sister. How can you request this?

You wish to change your program at school and don't know who to talk to about this. What do you do?

LESSON 10   MAKING NEGATIVE EXPRESSIONS

To the Teacher
Helping children to deliver negative expressions is one of the most difficult tasks of social skills training. There is often much prior learning in this area which mitigates against the learning of assertive statements. This previous learning, of course, often comes from the child's observations of significant people and of how they deliver expressions of disfavor.

Because children themselves can be extremely sensitive

Assertive Social Skills Training in the Classroom

to negative expressions, they often feel very uncomfortable giving them, or they have learned to deliver aggressive negative expressions as a means of defense against other people's criticism. Learning new styles of response to bothersome behavior therefore requires much practice, and initially, such practice should involve expressions of low-intensity dislike before proceeding to more emotional issues.

Social Skills Vocabulary

Negative Expressions

General Negatives   Specific Negatives

Classroom Presentation

Teacher: Glenn is a good friend of Rick's. But there's one thing Glenn does that Rick really hates. Every time that Glenn sees him he always says "Hi" by going up to him and socking him hard in the arm.

By now Rick's arm is black and blue and he wants to get Glenn to stop doing this, but he doesn't know how. What could he do?

Teacher writes children's responses on board.

As you can see, there are many ways to deal with this problem. Today we are going to learn about a way to tell people that we don't like what they are doing that is often very effective in stopping them from doing it again.

The rule for making a negative expression is to tell the person straight out, "I don't like . . ." whatever it is he is doing.

In the case of Rick, he might say, "I don't like it when you hit me every time you see me. I wish you wouldn't do that."

There are lots of ways to say "I don't like it." Another is, "It really bothers me"; still another way is, "It really bugs me."

Can you think of even other ways to say, "I don't like it"?

Because Glenn is Rick's friend, Rick didn't want to insult him, he just wanted to get him to stop pounding on his arm.

That's why an "I don't like it" statement is a better alternative than some of those on the board.

Some comments that people make are called "general negatives." They are called "general" because they don't talk about any particular behavior, they simply put down the person doing the behavior. Statements like "You're a jerk" or "Grow up" are general negatives and they don't help friendships very much.

When you say "I don't like it when . . ." you are still being a good friend because you are not putting your friend down, you are simply commenting about your friend's behavior.

Classroom Activity
Go over the list on the board and decide which behavior King Kong would do and which ones the shy puppy dog would most likely engage in.

Here are some possibilities for dealing with Glenn's arm-hitting which may not have been suggested.

King Kong: Raise voice and shout.
                     Threaten to hurt.
                     Call Glenn names.
                     Beat on his chest.
                     Hit him back.

Shy Puppy Dog: Hide from Glenn from then on.
                     Do nothing.
                     Yell "ouch" a lot.

Assertive Social Skills Training in the Classroom

LESSON 11 MAKING NEGATIVE EXPRESSIONS (continued)

To the Teacher
This lesson extends the learning objectives of the preceding lesson by discussing various assertive responses to situations where negative expressions are appropriate.

Social Skills Vocabulary

Disagree

Don't Appreciate   It Bothers Me

Classroom Presentation

Teacher: Would someone like to tell the class about a time when someone did something which really bothered you and you wanted to make sure he/she wouldn't do it again?

Using child's example, ask class how this situation could have been handled with an "I don't like it when . . ." statement.

The teacher can ask the class to suggest assertive responses for the following situations:

Tommy is tired of his friend Keith asking to borrow money at lunch time.

Alice does not like it when her friends tease her about her braces.

Kate resents it when Gail continually interrupts her conversations with her friends.

Classroom Activity
In groups of five, the children relate a time when someone had done something to upset them. They conclude by telling what

they did in response to this behavior. The group then decides if the behavior was passive, assertive or aggressive. If the behavior was not assertive the child role-plays an assertive response.

LESSON 12   SOFTENING NEGATIVE EXPRESSIONS

To the Teacher
One of the reasons that children are afraid to make negative expressions is that they do not wish to hurt their friends' feelings. This fear is often compounded by the belief that if they hurt a friend's feelings they risk either losing that friend or being retaliated against.

The objective of this lesson is to discuss the possible effects of making negative expressions and to help children learn a method of softening the negative expression through the use of a reinforcement sandwich.

Social Skills Vocabulary
Positive Shield

Classroom Presentation

Teacher: Sometimes, no matter how hard we try, when we make a negative statement we may hurt the feelings of our friend.

There is no way totally to prevent this from occurring.

But we can do something to reduce the "sting" of criticizing or disagreeing with someone else.

The technique for doing this is called using a "positive shield."

A shield protects someone from an attack. And when we criticize someone, we can shield them from the attack by saying something positive about the person before making the negative expression.

For instance, remember Rick and his friend Glenn who punched arms?

Rick could initially say something positive like, "You know, Glenn, I really enjoy being your friend and messing around with you," and then he could add, "but I really don't like it when you punch me every time you see me."

Get the idea? First you say something complimentary and then you add the negative expression.

As another example, we talked about Alice, who didn't like being teased about wearing braces.

She could say something like, "I know you're just teasing, but it really bothers me when you joke about my braces."

In groups of five, the children discuss a time when they disliked the behavior of a friend. Each child role-plays an assertive negative message and tries to soften it with a "positive shield."

LESSON 13 ACCEPTING NEGATIVE EXPRESSIONS

To the Teacher
The objectives of this lesson are to get students to understand (1) that it is inevitable that they will occasionally offend others with their behavior and that others may be upset with them; and (2) that when one is in the wrong, the best thing one can do is to accept that fact instead of counterattacking or falling to pieces.

Incorporated in the ability to accept a criticism without fighting back or crying is an understanding that everyone makes mistakes, that it isn't the end of the world, and that people appreciate you more if you simply accept the criticism if you deserve it.

Social Skills Vocabulary

Accepting Negative Expressions   Counterattack

Classroom Presentation

Teacher: Let's say that the teacher comes up to you and says, "You didn't hand your homework in on time." What can you do?

Teacher writes answers on blackboard.

What we're going to learn about today is that everybody makes mistakes and you don't have to come up with fancy stories when you are wrong.

In fact, the "assertive" thing to do in the case of not doing the homework is simply to accept the criticism.

You can do that by saying something like, "Yes, I just didn't get to it."

It's important to let the person know that this is something you will try not to let happen again.

What does King Kong do when someone criticizes him?

That's right, he finds something to criticize the other person about. Does this help people feel good about each other?

No, of course not, it usually ends up in a big fight.

What does the shy puppy dog do when someone criticizes him?

That's right, he is so hurt he usually can't say anything at all, or maybe he cries.

This happens when we forget that nobody is perfect and that we can try harder next time not to make the same mistake.

So the idea is to accept someone's criticism when you are wrong and not to make up excuses or fight back or feel so bad that you just stand there.

In the following example, who can think of what King Kong, the shy puppy dog, and an assertive person might say or do?

Parent says: You didn't take the trash out last night when you were supposed to.
(*Assertive response,* "I forgot. I need to make sure I remember next time.")
Friend says: You were really late coming over to my house to play.
(*Assertive response,* "You're right. I need to allow myself more time next time.")
Teacher says: I don't like it when you talk out without raising your hand.
(*Assertive response,* "I'll remember next time I have something to say.")
In groups of five, the children discuss a time when they were criticized for a behavior which they realize they should not have engaged in. Each child role-plays the assertive response for that situation.

LESSON 14   BROKEN RECORD

To the Teacher
The objective of this lesson is to teach a technique which children can use to keep the other person on the topic at hand,

whether it be a request, refusal, or negative expression. The broken record helps ensure that the asserter will get his point across without getting sidetracked by attacks or evasiveness on the part of the responder.

Social Skills Vocabulary

Broken Record   But the Point Is

Classroom Presentation

Teacher: Let's say a friend wants to borrow your records and you have decided that because records often get ruined at parties you will not loan them out.

You tell your friend this, but then he says, "But we need them; you have the best records."

To help you stand your ground, you can use the "broken record."

What does a broken record sound like?

Right, it keeps coming back to the same place.

So when you want to say "no" but someone keeps trying to pressure you into a "yes," you use the broken record.

The key words are, *"But the point is,"* and no matter what the other person says to try to get you to change your mind, if your mind is made up you can say, "But the point is, I don't want to loan my records."

Do you remember how to use a positive shield?

You can use the positive shield and the broken record together by saying, "I know it would make you feel good if you could borrow the records, *but the point is,* I just don't want to loan my records out."

Assertive Social Skills Training in the Classroom

Classroom Activity

The class is divided into groups of two. The teacher writes the following four situations on the board:

You don't want to play a trick on another friend (pull out his chair as he sits down) and Johnny tries to talk you into it.

You don't want to let another child copy your homework.

You don't want to loan a friend money for lunch because you need your allowance to last the whole week.

You don't want to steal something from another student's desk and your friend wants you to help.

Each child chooses a partner to use the broken record with. The partner tries to talk the child out of saying "no" (the partners should be instructed to give up after four or five tries).

After each situation is dramatized, the children switch roles.

LESSON 15   NONVERBAL COMPONENTS OF COMMUNICATION

To the Teacher

The objectives of this lesson are: (1) to delineate the various nonverbal components of communication, and (2) to emphasize their importance in making assertive responses.

Social Skills Vocabulary

Eye Contact   Facial Expression   Touching

Classroom Presentation

Teacher: We have been talking about the importance of asking for what you want, refusing when you don't want to do something, and giving and receiving positive and negative statements.

But so far, all we have been talking about are the *words* you use to make a request, refusal, or expression.

There is more to getting your message across than just the words you use.

It is also important to *look* and *sound* as though you mean what you say. This gives your statement much more power and increases your chances of getting the reaction you desire.

One way of increasing the power of your communications is to use *eye contact*.

The shy puppy dog never looks anyone in the eye and doesn't have any friends. King Kong doesn't have any friends either, because he stares so hard at people he scares them away. But assertive people look their friends in the eye when they are trying to make a point, as when they are making a request or a refusal.

(Point to blackboard.) The next nonverbal part of communicating is our *facial expression*. If we smile when we are trying to make a negative expression, we confuse the listener. Smiles are for happy times and should be used when we give or receive positive expressions.

The next word on the board is *touching*.

The shy puppy dog is afraid ever to touch anyone. King Kong is always poking and shoving and even hitting people, which scares them away. Assertive people pat their friends on the shoulder once in a while.

Touching can help you really make the point that you liked what someone did. It can also make a person feel better when you have something negative to say if you lightly touch them.

Now we can practice the nonverbal parts of communicating.

Classroom Activity

Students are divided into groups of five. Each takes a turn making a request or a positive or negative expression to one of the group members. The other members of the group are instructed first to make a positive statement about the role-play. (Then, only *one* student mentions whether the eye contact seemed appropriate.)

After everyone in the group has made an assertive statement and the eye contact has been evaluated, the group next practices facial expression, following the same procedure.

III. DRAMA SIMULATION ACTIVITY

Throughout the book we have emphasized the importance of practicing social skills in a safe environment before testing them in the real world. Research has shown that classroom presentations such as the ones we have just described will change attitudes, but behavior will not change unless there is ample opportunity for role-playing.

The Drama Simulation Activity, the third strategy for teaching social skills, can be interwoven into the school program as a thirty-minute activity once or twice a week. The procedure is easy for the students to understand and consists of the following steps:

1. The teacher divides the class into groups of eight. (If the last group is smaller than eight, those children can be alternates in other groups.)

2. The teacher writes the following "role titles" on the board:

Actor
Responder
Moderator
Eye-Contact Observer
Facial-Expression and Gesture Observer
Voice Observer
Content Observer
Token Coach

3. The teacher explains that after each role-play the class engages in, the participants will rotate roles. The Actor becomes the Responder, the Responder becomes the Moderator, the Moderator the Eye-Contact Observer, and so on.

4. The teacher then describes the function of each role.

Actor This is the student who will actually act out a request, refusal, or expression situation.

Responder The function of this role is to try to portray accurately the person who the actor wishes to communicate with. If, for example, the Actor is asking his parents' permission to go somewhere, the Responder attempts to "look" parent-like. The Responder should ask the Actor, before the role-play, how his parents tend to act in such situations.

The Responder should give the response the Actor wants, not the response the Responder thinks the parents would give.

Moderator The Moderator is given a list of assertive problems (see Assertion Inventory at end of chapter) and starts with the first situation. The Actor may choose to bring up an assertive problem from his own life. The Moderator then follows these steps:

a. He asks the Actor to tell him what he will say to the Responder.

b. He then asks the Actor to try the role-play with the Responder. (Only the first line.)

c. After the first line, the Moderator asks the actor what he liked about his role play. The moderator then asks each of the observers for feedback. In asking for feedback, the Moderator always starts by asking the observer, "What was good about the actor's eye contact (facial expression, etc.)?" After this the Moderator can ask for *one* suggestion per observer.

Since the Moderator's role is the most complex, the teacher may wish to mimeograph a check list of the steps which he is to follow.

Eye-Contact Observer This student notes whether the amount of eye contact seems appropriate during the communication. Also to be observed is whether the Actor looks away at the crucial point in the statement.

Facial-Expression and Gesture Observer This student notes whether the facial expression is in agreement with the content of the message being sent. Behaviors such as smiling while delivering negatives or nodding the head "yes" when trying to refuse should be mentioned.

Voice Observer This student notes whether the actor is loud enough, clear enough, and sounds as though he means what he is saying.

Content Observer This student has the more difficult job of noting whether the message itself is worded assertively. For example, does the Actor actually make a request or does he just hint; does he actually say "no" or does he make excuses?

Token Coach This student dispenses a *green* token if he perceives the overall performance as having been assertive; a *blue* token if he perceives it as passive; and *red* if it was aggressive (overly loud, staring in the eyes of the Responder, etc.). (Tokens can be cut from construction paper.)

Research has shown that giving these tokens is an effective means of increasing assertive responses in role-playing situations. They become a subtle yet powerful reward for the children in their groups.

The teacher should instruct the groups that, the first time through, the Actors should rehearse the assertive situations which are read to them by the Moderator. After each student has rehearsed these less threatening situations, then the Actors can be invited to share their own assertion problems.

All of the suggestions in this chapter for an assertion curriculum not only have proved beneficial but, in addition, have been the highlight of the week's activities for many students. The social skills curricula have provided many children their first opportunities to make requests, refusals, and positive and negative expressions. Teachers will find that the personal rewards of viewing the changes in such children are worth the time, patience, and energy necessary to initiate such a program in the classroom.

ASSERTION INVENTORY

A classmate sitting behind you is kicking your desk while you are trying to read. What do you say?

You are going out for lunch recess. You forgot your milk money. What do you say?

You come back from recess and one of your classmates has taken a book of yours without asking. You need the book. What do you say?

A girls asks to cut in front of you in the cafeteria line. You don't want to let her cut. What do you say?

You're at recess and a number of friends want you to play; you don't want to. What do you say?

Your brother wants to watch television, but you already are watching a program and would like to watch the end of it. He starts to change the channel. What do you say?

A friend of yours asks to borrow your brand-new skateboard. You don't want to lend it. What do you say?

A classmate wants to look at your answers to a test. You don't want to give her the answers. What do you say?

A friend of yours is planning to play a trick on another classmate at recess. He is going to make fun of the way he talks. You don't want to be a part of this. What do you say?

You missed school yesterday because you were sick. There was a homework assignment due then and you want to turn it in. What can you say to the teacher?

You are walking home from school and a lady in a car drives up and asks you for directions. You give them to her and she asks you if you'll ride along with her because she doesn't know the area. What can you say?

You're having trouble with math and would like your teacher to help you. You ask if he would stay after school to help but he says he has to go to a meeting. What do you say?

You're at the grocery store getting some bread for your mother. They don't have the kind your mother wanted, but the clerk gives you something like it. You don't want this kind of bread. What would you say?

A friend asks for ten cents to buy a package of corn nuts. He did the same last week and didn't repay you. You don't want to lose the money. What do you say?

AFTERWORD: A WORLD OF ASSERTIVE PEOPLE

A reasonable question to ask at this point might be: "What would it be like if everyone were assertive? Wouldn't people drive each other crazy asking for things they want, refusing what they don't want, and so on?" We might point out first that in an assertive world people would more likely be successful at getting what they want without acting aggressively or passively. The benefits to society of a decrease in aggression and passivity would be enormous. Violence would be restricted to sporting events and would be limited to the participants and not the spectators. The disappearance of passivity would be missed only by a few die-hard fans of pouting, depression, loneliness, and withdrawal.

The fact that must be kept in mind when considering the effects of assertive behavior is that people will always attempt to

Afterword: A World of Assertive People

get their needs met one way or another. This will not change. What *can* change is the way in which they are taught to meet these needs. Societies which have told people to stay in their place have never succeeded in the long run (unless "their place" was very comfortable). The very best one can hope for is to educate people to attend assertively to their desires so that negative attempts at meeting desires are minimized.

To all of this one might ask: "Well, all of this concern about meeting one's own needs is fine, but isn't it a bit self-centered? Where in self-confidence training does regard for one's fellow man come in?" The answer to this question involves another fact of life. That is: until one's own needs are met, true concern for the well-being of others cannot develop. In other words, if we feel empty inside, how much can we afford to give away?

Only when one is not intimidated by the world can one meet one's needs, and only then can one turn his attention to his neighbors and offer them help in attaining their goals. The assertive person therefore can more easily afford the time and energy to assist those who are in need. In addition to merely being concerned, he can actually do something to help others by teaching and modeling the skills which have led to his own success. The assertive person doesn't necessarily feel more deeply for his fellow man; he is just more able to express his caring.

There is good evidence that man may have a natural concern for others. This has been demonstrated in many studies, including one of school-aged children. Throughout a semester the children were observed on the playground. It was noted that when fights broke out between two children, a third child would intervene when one child, in spite of making signs of submission such as running away or turning his back, was still being hit. This and other such studies imply that there is an instinctual tendency to act when others are in need.

Afterword: A World of Assertive People

What happens to this natural desire to be helpful as people get older? Often people don't want to get involved because they fear that once they help someone they will be expected by that person to continue to do favors of one sort or another. However, the assertive person is not afraid to help because he knows how to say "no" when he wants to; he does not fear being taken advantage of. He is more willing to get involved, because he knows he can give as much as he wants, no more, no less.

In his relationships with others, the assertive person behaves quite differently than the "self-centered" person. Because he knows that he has the right to say "no" to someone else, the assertive individual more easily accepts other people's refusals to him. He learns to respect the requests and refusals of others because he expects his to be respected.

The self-centered person, on the other hand, finds it very difficult to understand how anyone could have the audacity not to bend to his desires. He flies into a rage, pouts, or withdraws affection as a reaction to such behavior. In his world, people are not allowed to express their own desires when they interfere with the pursuit of his goals.

The world peopled by assertive individuals would not be the lonely place that it has become for so many in this century. One of the principles of social skills training is that "You don't have to be alone if you don't want to." There are techniques for meeting people, requesting interaction and relationships. In earlier times, these skills were not so important. One grew up in a safe, predictable environment which would not change much in the course of a lifetime. There would be a continuity of friends, neighbors, and relatives. In this era, however, the people we interact with one year may have moved away by next year. In such an environment one must gain the self-confidence to make new friends, new acquaintances.

Somehow, even though we live better today than kings

Afterword: A World of Assertive People

did a few centuries ago, there is a consensus that this is an age of loneliness and alienation. What this boils down to essentially is the lack of ability to meet people and define the types of relationships that we wish to have with them. A recent study noted that over 40 percent of college students stated that they were "shy" individuals who felt they did not have adequate social skills. No wonder, in an age when the need for such skills is so demanding and the opportunities to develop them are so lacking. Children who have been encouraged to request, refuse, and express themselves are in a much better position when they become adults to meet their needs for interpersonal contact.

ASSERTION IN THE HOME

Parents might wonder about the quality of the parent-child relationship in a home where the family members are assertive. In effect, the home is a microcosm of society. The same problems which hamper society at large also affect the family, namely, aggression and passivity.

By definition, a family whose members are assertive behaves with a minimum of aggression or passivity. Family members will not attempt to get what they want through threatening or intimidating one another. Nor will whining, pouting, or sulking be a common mode of interaction.

Parents of children who have learned to make positive and negative expressions will be more aware of what is happening in their child's world. A child who doesn't think he has the right to complain or comment about his friends, teachers, or neighbors will remain silent about such matters. His parents may think everything is just fine in his life when in reality there may be issues bothering him which he is uncomfortable bringing up.

One often hears, "It's important to have good communication with one's children." Putting these words into action, however, requires more than good intentions. It requires parents who care enough to ask children specific questions about their life, and it also requires parents who share positive and negative comments with one another about their daily pursuits.

The way in which the negative expressions are modeled to children is crucial. If the parents model hopelessness or helplessness, then a child learns that there is little that one can do about the problems one encounters in life and so there is, in fact, no good reason for even talking about such matters. Assertive parents do not just freely talk about negative concerns; they go one step further and think through different methods of problem solving so that they are better equipped to handle similar situations should they arise again. This type of modeling conveys a powerful message to the child: out of sharing one's problems comes action which can help one deal with the world.

The assertive family is not just bent on sharing its woes and problems, it is also a place where the positive is stressed. The child in such a family learns that his parents are interested in hearing about what is right, as much as they are concerned about things that are wrong. Sadly enough, many parents only interact with their children when something is wrong, such as when the parents are upset with the child or when the child is bothered by something.

This type of behavior is typified by the parent who comes to school and asks the teacher only one question: "Is my child behaving?" The parent's only concern is that the child is not getting into trouble. Whether the child ever raises his hand to answer a question, has any friends, or seems interested in a particular subject is simply "unimportant" to such parents.

Afterword: A World of Assertive People

Children who are not encouraged to share their good experiences as well as their bad ones learn to emphasize the negative in life, making home life an environment of complaints, insults, and negativity. On the other hand, the home of the assertive family is a much more enjoyable place to be. There are problems which are discussed, to be sure, but there are also reports of many positive happenings. In addition, complimentary statements are frequently made to family members, increasing the enjoyment of home life.

There is still another factor which makes life more pleasurable in an environment where people have learned to make requests, refusals, and expressions: people in such an environment will be more likely to get their needs met, and such people feel good about themselves and others. As we stated earlier, when one feels capable of meeting his own needs he is more likely to be aware of and attend to the needs of others. Obviously, interacting with people who feel good about themselves and are helpful to others is a very pleasurable experience. It is just plain enjoyable to be around such people, whose positive mood is seemingly contagious.

Of course, even the assertive child will find that not every problem will work out to his satisfaction, not every request will be granted, not every positive experience will be received with interest and praise. However, the self-confident child knows that other people have rights and interests also. He does not need to live in a dream world in order to be happy.

From all that we have been saying about the improved quality of society and the family environment as a result of training children to be self-confident, one would wonder if there are any drawbacks to such training. The disadvantage is that to teach children these skills requires even more time and energy than parents are already called upon to invest with their children. But parents' efforts will be reinforced frequently when they see their child's successes in solving problems; his enjoyment of positive friendships; his honesty in saying what he means, both positive and negative; his confidence which allows him to work and play independently; and his respect for the rights of others. Such rewards will ease the burden of providing the environment necessary for the development of such qualities.

For those who are interested in furthering their knowledge of social skills training, we have provided a list of the important works in the field. We hope that they provide a useful supplement to our guide.

BIBLIOGRAPHY

Alberti, R. E., and M. L. Emmons. *Your Perfect Right* (2nd ed.). San Luis Obispo, Calif.: Impact, 1974.

Arnold, B. R., W. W. Winrich, and H. H. Dawley. Assertive training employing anxiety relief and behavioral rehearsal. *Newsletter for Research in Mental Health and Behavioral Sciences*, 1973, *15*(4), 20–22.

Barnard, G. W., C. K. Flesher, and R. M. Steinbook. The treatment of urinary retention by aversive stimulus cessation and assertive training. *Behavior Research and Therapy*, 1966, *4*, 232–236.

Bates, H. D., and S. F. Zimmerman. Toward the development of a screening scale for assertion training. *Psychological Reports*, 1971, *28*, 99–107.

Bloomfield, H. H. Assertive training in an outpatient group of chronic schizophrenics:A preliminary report. *Behavior Therapy*, 1973, *4*, 227–281.

Booraem, C. D., and J. V. Flowers. Reduction of anxiety and personal space as a function of assertion training with severly disturbed neuropsychiatric inpatients. *Psychological Reports*, 1972, *30*, 923–929.

Chittenden, G. E. An experimental study in measuring and modifying assertive behavior in young children. *Monographs of the Society for Research in Child Development*, 1944, *8*(1, Serial No. 31).

Christensen, A., and H. Arkowitz. Preliminary report on practice dating and feedback for college dating problems. *Journal of Counseling Psychology*, 1974, *21*(2), 92–95.

Cotler, S. B., and J. Guerra, *Assertion Training*. Champaign, Ill.: Research Press, 1976.

Davidson, G. C. Self-control through "Imaginal Aversive Contingency" and "One Downsmanship": Enabling the powerless to accommodate unreasonableness. In J. D. Krumbotz and C.

E. Thoresen (Eds.), *Behavioral Counseling: Cases and Techniques.* New York: Holt, Rinehart & Winston, 1969, pp. 319–328.

Doering, M., et al. The use of training to increase intensity of angry verbalization. *Psychological Monographs,* 1967, *76*(37, Whole No. 556).

Dorman, L. Assertive behavior and cognitive performance in pre-school children. *The Journal of Genetic Psychology,* 1973, *123,* 155–162.

Edwards, N. B. Case conference: Assertive training in a case of homosexual pedophilia. *Behavior Research and Therapy,* 1972, *3,* 55–63.

Eisler, R. M., and M. Hersen. Behavioral techniques in family-oriented crisis intervention. *Archives of General Psychiatry,* 1973, *28,* 111–116.

———, M. Hersen, and P. M. Miller. Effects of modeling on components of assertive behavior. *Journal of Behavior Therapy and Experimental Psychiatry,* 1973, *4,* 1–6.

———, M. Hersen, P. M. Miller, and E. B. Blanchard. Situational determinants of assertive behavior. *Journal of Consulting and Clinical Psychology,* 1975, *43,* 330–340.

———, P. M. Miller, and M. Hersen. Components of assertive behavior. *Journal of Clinical Psychology,* 1973, *29*(3), 295–299.

———, P. M. Miller, M. Hersen, and H. Alford. Effects of assertive training on marital interaction. *Archives of General Psychiatry,* 1974, *30,* 643–649.

Fensterheim, H. Assertive methods and marital problems. In R. D. Rubin, H. Fensterheim, J. D. Henderson, and L. P. Ullman (Eds.), *Advances in Behavior Therapy.* New York: Academic Press, 1972, pp. 13–18.

———. Behavior therapy: Assertive training in groups. In C. J. Sager and H. S. Kaplan (Eds.), *Progress in Group and Family Therapy.* New York: Brunner/Mazel, 1972, pp. 156–169.

——— and J. Baer. *Don't Say Yes When You Want to Say No.* New York: David McCay Co., 1975.

Fish, B., and K. J. Kaplan. Does a "foot in the door" get you in or out. *Psychological Reports,* 1974, *34,* 35–42.

Flowers, J. V. Modification of elementary school children's low self-confident behavior by reinforcement and modeling treatment methods. *Dissertation Abstracts International*, 1973, *33*, 3935–3936.

———. Simulation and role-playing methods. In F. H. Kanfer and A. P. Goldstein (Eds.), *Helping People Change.* New York: Pergamon Press, 1975, pp. 159–193.

——— and R. D. Goldman. Assertion training for mental health paraprofessionals. *Journal of Counseling Psychology*, 1976, *23*, 147–150.

——— and J. Guerra. The use of client-coaching in assertion training with large groups. *Journal of Community Mental Health*, 1974, *10*(4), 414–417.

——— and A. R. Marston. Modification of low self-confidence in elementary school children. *Journal of Educational Research*, 1972, *66*(1), 30–34.

Friedman, P. H. The effects of modeling and role playing on assertive behavior. In R. D. Rubin, H. Fensterheim, A. A. Lazarus, and C. M. Franks (Eds.), *Advances in Behavior Therapy.* New York: Academic Press, 1971, pp. 149–169.

———. The effects of modeling, role playing and participation on behavior change. In B. A. Maher (Ed.), *Progress in Experimental Personality Research*, vol. 6. New York: Academic Press, 1972, pp. 42–81.

Galassi, J. P., J. S. DeLo, M. D. Galassi, and S. Bastein. The college self-expression scale: A measure of assertiveness. *Behavior Therapy*, 1974, *5*, 165–171.

——— and M. D. Galassi. Validity of a measure of assertiveness. *Journal of Counseling Psychology*, 1974, *21*, 248–250.

———, M. D. Galassi, and M. C. Litz. Assertive training in groups using video feedback. *Journal of Counseling Psychology*, 1974, *21*(5), 390–394.

Gambrill, E. D., and C. A. Richey. An assertion inventory for use in assessment and research. *Behavior Therapy*, 1975, *6*, 550–561.

Gelber, H. The use of psychological learning theory in the development of assertion. *Canadian Psychiatric Association Journal*, 1967, *12*(2), 207–208.

Gentry, W. D., and P. M. Kirwin. Constriction, aggression, and assertive training. *Psychological Reports*, 1972, *30*(1), 297–298.

Gittelman, M. Behavior rehearsal as a technique in child treatment. *Journal of Child Psychology and Psychiatry*, 1965, *6*, 251–255.

Bibliography

Goldstein, A. J., M. Serber, and G. Piaget. Induced anger as a reciprocal inhibition of fear. *Journal of Behavior Therapy and Experimental Psychiatry*, 1970, *1*, 67–70.

Guisinger, D. L. Controlling sexual interpersonal anxieties. In J. D. Krumboltz and C. E. Thoresen (Eds.), *Behavioral Counseling: Cases and Techniques*. New York: Holt, Rinehart & Winston, 1969, pp. 459–460.

Hartsook, J. E., D. R. Olch, and V. A. de Wolf. Personality characteristics of women's assertiveness training group participants. *Journal of Counseling Psychology*, 1976, *23*(4), 322–326.

Hedquist, F. J., and B. K. Weinhold. Behavioral group counseling with socially anxious and unassertive college students. *Journal of Counseling Psychology*, 1970, *17*, 237–242.

Hersen, M., and R. M. Eisler. Social skills training. In W. E. Craighead, A. E. Kazdin, and M. J. Mahoney (Eds.), *Behavior Modification: Principles, Issues and Applications*. Boston: Houghton Mifflin, 1976, 361–375.

———, R. M. Eisler, and P. M. Miller. Development of assertive responses: Clinical, measurement and research considerations. *Behavior Research and Therapy*, 1973, *11*, 505–521.

———, et al. Effects of practice, instructions, and modeling on components of assertive behavior. *Behavior Research and Therapy*, 1973, *11*, 443–451.

Hosford, R. E. Overcoming fear of speaking in a group. In J. D. Krumboltz and C. E. Thoresen (Eds.), *Behavioral Counseling: Cases and Techniques*. New York: Holt, Rinehart & Winston, 1969, pp. 80–83.

Jacobsen, E. *Progressive Relaxation*. Chicago: University of Chicago Press, 19.

Jakubowski, P. A. Assertive behavior and clinical problems in women. In D. Carter and E. Rawlings (Eds.), *Psychotherapy for Women*. Springfield, Ill.: Charles C. Thomas, in press.

Jakubowski-Spector, P. A. Facilitating the growth of women through assertive training. *The Counseling Psychologist*, 1973, *4*(1), 75–86.

Katz, R. Case conference: Rapid development of activity in a case of chronic passivity. *Journal of Behavior Therapy and Experimental Psychiatry*, 1971, *2*(3), 187–193.

Kaufmann, L. M., and B. R. Barb: A systematic treatment technology for temper control disorders. *Behavior Therapy*, 1972, *3*, 84–90.

Kazdin, A. E. Effects of covert modeling and model reinforcement on assertive behavior. *Journal of Abnormal Psychology*, 1974, *83*, 240–252.

————. Covert modeling, imagery assessment, and assertive behavior. *Journal of Consulting and Clinical Psychology*, 1975, *43*, 716–724.

Lange, A. J., and P. Jakubowski. *Responsible Assertive Behavior*. Champaign, Ill.: Research Press, 1976.

Laws, D. R., and M. Serber. Measurement and evaluation of assertive training with sexual offenders. In R. E. Hosford and S. Moss (Eds.), *The Crumbling Walls: Treatment and Counseling of the Youthful Offender*. Champaign, Ill.: University of Illinois Press, in press.

Lazarus, A. A. Behavior therapy in groups. In G. M. Gazda (Ed.), *Basic Approaches to Group Psychotherapy and Group Counseling*. Springfield, Ill.: Charles C. Thomas, 1968, pp. 149–175.

————. *Behavior Therapy and Beyond*. New York: McGraw-Hill, 1971.

————. On assertive behavior: A brief note. *Behavior Therapy*, 1973, *4*, 697–699.

Lewinsohn, P. M., and M. Graf. Pleasant activities and depression. *Journal of Consulting and Clinical Psychology*, 1973, *41*, 261–268.

Liberman, R. P., L. W. King, W. J. DeRisi, and M. McCann. *Personal Effectiveness*. Champaign, Ill.: Research Press, 1975.

Libet, J. M., and P. M. Lewinsohn. Concept of social skill with special reference to the behavior of depressed persons. *Journal of Consulting and Clinical Psychology*, 1973, *41*, 304–312.

Lomont, J. J., F. H. Gilner, N. J. Spector, and K. K. Skinner. Assertion training and group insight therapies. *Psychological Reports*, 1969, *25*, 463–470.

Ludwig, L. D., and A. A. Lazarus. A cognitive and behavioral approach to the treatment of social inhibition. *Psychotherapy: Theory, Research and Practice*, 1972, *9*(3), 204–206.

Macpherson, E. L. R. Selective operant conditioning and deconditioning of assertive modes of behavior. *Journal of Behavior Therapy and Experimental Psychiatry*, 1972, *3*, 99–102.

Marston, A. R. Dealing with low self-confidence. *Educational Research*, 1968, *10*, 134–138.

Martinson, W. D., and J. P. Zerface. Comparison of individual counseling and a social program with nondaters. *Journal of Counseling Psychology*, 1970, *17*(1), 36–40.

Bibliography

McFall, R. M., and D. B. Lillesand. Behavioral rehearsal with modeling and coaching in assertion training. *Journal of Abnormal
Psychology*, 1971, 77, 313–323.
———— and A. R. Marston. An experimental investigation of behavior
rehearsal in assertive training. *Journal of Abnormal Psychology*,
1970, 76, 295–303.
———— and C. T. Twentyman. Four experiments on the contributions
of rehearsal, modeling and coaching to assertion training. *Journal of Abnormal Psychology*, 1973, 81(3), 199–218.
Mehrabian, A. Significance of posture and position in the communication of attitude and status relationships. *Psychological Bulletin*,
1969, 71, 359–372.
Meichenbaum, D., and R. Cameron. The clinical potential of modifying what clients say to themselves. *Psychotherapy: Theory,
Research and Practice*, 1974, 11, 103–117.
———— and D. Turk. Cognitive-behavioral management of anxiety,
anger, and pain. In P. O. Davidson (Ed.), *The Behavioral
Management of Anxiety, Depression, and Pain*. New York:
Brunner/Mazel, 1976, 1–34.
Melnick, J. A. A comparison of replication techniques in the modifica-
tion of minimal dating behavior. *Journal of Abnormal Psychology*, 1973, 81(1), 51–59.
Neuman, D. R. Using assertive training. In J. D. Krumboltz and C. E.
Thoresen (Eds.), *Behavior Counseling: Cases and Techniques*.
New York: Holt, Rinehart & Winston, 1969, pp. 433–442.
Nietzel, M. T., and D. A. Bernstein. Effects of instructionally
mediated demand on the behavioral assessment of assertive-
ness. *Journal of Consulting and Clinical Psychology*, 1976,
44(3), 500.
Nydegger, R. V. The elimination of hallucinatory and delusional behavior by verbal conditioning and assertive training: A case
study. *Journal of Behavior Therapy and Experimental
Psychiatry*, 1972, 3, 225–227.
O'Conner, R. D. Relative efficacy of modeling, shaping, and the
combined procedures for modification of social withdrawal.
Journal of Abnormal Psychology, 1972, 79(3), 327–334.
Palmer, R. D. Desensitization of the fear of expressing one's own
inhibited aggression: Bioenergetic assertive techniques for behavior therapists. *Newsletter for Research in Psychology*, 1972,
14(1), 36–38.

Patterson, R. L. Time-out and assertive training for a dependent child. *Behavior Therapy*, 1972, *3*, 466–468.

Percell, L. P. The effect of assertive training on modifying cognitive and affective variables. *Newsletter for Research in Mental Helath and Behavioral Sciences*, 1973, *15*(4), 20–22.

Piaget, G. W., and A. A. Lazarus. The use of rehearsal-desensitization. *Psychotherapy: Theory, Research and Practice*, 1969, *6*, 264–266.

Prazak, J. A. Learning job-seeking interview skills. In J. D. Krumboltz and C. E. Thoresen (Eds.), *Behavioral Counseling: Cases and Techniques*. New York: Holt, Rinehart & Winston, 1969, pp. 414–428.

Rathus, S. A. An experimental investigation of assertive training in a group setting. *Journal of Behavior Therapy and Experiemntal Psychiatry*, 1972, *3*, 81–86.

————. Instigation of assertive behavior through videotape-mediated models and directed practice. *Behavior Research and Therapy*, 1973, *11*, 57–65.

————. A thirty-item schedule for assessing assertive behavior. *Behavior Therapy*, 1973, *4*, 398–406.

———— and J. S. Nevid. *Behavior Therapy: Strategies for Solving Problems in Living*. Garden City, N. Y.: Doubleday, 1977.

———— and C. Ruppert. Assertion training in the secondary school and the college. *Adolescence*, 1973, *8*, 257–264.

Rehm, L. P., and A. R. Marston. Reduction of social anxiety through modification of self-reinforcement: An instigation therapy technique. *Journal of Consulting and Clinical Psychology*, 1968, *32*, 564–574.

Rimm, D. C. Assertive training used in the treatment of chronic crying spells. *Behavior Research and Therapy*, 1967, *5*, 373–374.

————. Thought stopping and covert assertion. *Journal of Clinical and Consulting Psychology*, 1973, *41*, 466–467.

————, G. A. Hill, N. N. Brown, and J. E. Stuart. Group assertive training in treatment of expression of inappropriate anger. *Psychological Reports*, 1974, *34*, 791–798.

———— and J. C. Masters. *Behavior Therapy: Techniques and Empirical Findings*. New York: Academic Press, 1974.

Ross, D. M., and S. A. Ross. The modification of extreme social withdrawal by modeling with guided participation. *Behavior Research and Therapy*, 1971, *2*, 272–279.

Bibliography

Roszwell, B. L. Pretraining, awareness, and behavior group therapy approaches to assertive behavior training. *Dissertation Abstracts International*, 1971, 32, 3649–3650.

Salter, A. *Conditioned Reflex Therapy*. New York: Creative Age Press, 1949.

Sarason, I. G. Verbal learning, modeling and juvenile delinquency. *American Psychologist*, 1968, 23, 254–266.

———— and V. J. Ganzer. Developing appropriate social behaviors of juvenile delinquents. In J. D. Krumboltz and C. E. Thoresen (Eds.), *Behavioral Counseling: Cases and Techniques*. New York: Holt, Rinehart & Winston, 1969, pp. 178–192.

Schinke, S. P., and S. D. Rose. Interpersonal skill training in groups. *Journal of Counseling Psychology*, 1976, 23, 442–448.

Serber, M. Teaching the nonverbal components of assertive training. *Journal of Behavior Therapy and Experimental Psychiatry*, 1972, 3, 179–183.

———— and P. Nelson. The ineffectiveness of systematic desensitization and assertion training in hospitalized schizophrenics. *Journal of Behavioral Therapy and Experimental Psychiatry*, 1971, 2(2), 107–109.

Shapiro, D. The reinforcement of disagreement in a small group. *Behavior Research and Therapy*, 193, 1, 267–272.

Topoff, M. Massed practice, relaxation and assertion training in the treatment of Gilles de la Tourette's syndrome. *Journal of Behavior Therapy and Experimental Psychiatry*, 1973, 4(1), 71–73.

Varenhourst, B. B. Helping a client to speak up in class. In J. D. Krumboltz and C. E. Thoresen (Eds.), *Behavior Counseling: Cases and Techniques*. New York: Holt, Rinehart & Winston, 1969, pp. 83–86.

Wagner, M. K. Reinforcement of the expression of anger through role-playing. *Behavior Research and Therapy*, 1968, 6, 91–95.

————. Comparative effectiveness of behavioral rehearsal and verbal reinforcement for effecting anger expressiveness. *Psychological Reports*, 1968, 22, 1079–1080.

Weinman, B., P. Gelbart, M. Wallace, and M. Post. Inducing assertive behavior in chronic schizophrenics: A comparison of socioenvironmental, desensitization, and realization therapies. *Journal of Consulting and Clinical Psychology*, 1972, 39(2), 246–252.

Wolpe, J. The instigation of assertive behavior: Transcript from two cases. *Journal of Behavior Therapy and Experimental Psychiatry*, 1969, *1*, 145–151.

———. *The Practice of Behavior Therapy*. Oxford: Pergamon Press, 1969.

———. Supervision transcript: V—mainly about assertive training. *Journal of Behavior Therapy and Experimental Psychiatry*, 1973, *1*, 141–148.

——— and A. A. Lazarus. *Behavior Therapy Techniques*. Oxford: Pergamon Press, 1966.

Yarnell, J. Symbolic assertive training through guided affective imagery in hypnosis. *American Journal of Clinical Hypnosis*, 1972, *14*(3), 194–196.

Young, E. R., D. C. Rimm, and T. D. Kennedy. An experimental investigation of modeling and verbal reinforcement in the modification of assertive behavior. *Behavior Research and Therapy*, 1973, *11*(3), 317–319.